D1107987

TOWARD A

UNIFIED THEORY

OF

HUMAN BEHAVIOR

TOWARD A

Unified Theory OF Human Behavior

Edited by

ROY R. GRINKER, M.D.

With the Assistance of

HELEN MACGILL HUGHES, Ph.D.

Basic Books, Inc. · Publishers

B
B

First printing, May, 1956
Second printing, June, 1957
Third printing, June, 1958

Manufactured in the United States of America
Library of Congress Catalog Card Number: 56-9098
Designed by Albert Margolies

PREFACE

IN 1950 Jurgen Ruesch and I became dissatisfied with the repetitive and stereotyped nature of the many post-war conferences on research problems in the behavioral sciences. We decided to establish a different type of discussion group composed of scientists from several disciplines for the purpose of approaching a unified theory of behavior or, as we sometimes grandiously stated, of human nature. We communicated with a few kindred spirits: John Spiegel, Lawrence Frank and David Shakow who quickly became enthusiastic for the project. Soon the membership of the group was established to about its present number of fifteen, most of whom have attended regularly. For one reason or another some individuals have dropped out and been replaced, and scientists representing disciplines necessary for new areas of discussion were added as the occasion demanded.

We began our bi-annual weekend conferences in October 1951 and are now preparing for the tenth session. No thought of publication was entertained at the outset, but eventually we concluded that if our discussions were of any value, they should be made public. The verbatim transactions were stenotyped and transcribed in form suitable for editing and abstraction. Because of the large quantity of discussion this volume contains only the first four conferences. We regret that the nature of the contents precluded the preparation of a useful index.

It was decided that the transactions are more important for their contents than as examples or exercises in communications, therefore, unless they clarified significant points or repetitive statements, questions and answers have been deleted and only major presentations and pertinent discussions are included. Actually this volume is an abstraction of about 1600 pages of transcript. Only occasionally is a complete sector of discussion included when rapid movement of constructive thinking splashed over the transcript from several minds. The horrendous task of primary editing would have been impossible without the help of Mrs. Helen Hughes. Even so, each contributor was invited subsequently to edit his own remarks to make, if possible, a more precise or elegant statement of his views.

The first conference, held in October 1951, was called to order with the following preliminary statement of goals:

We gather in conference as representatives of several disciplines of some sciences. The planners considered it advisable to start our discussions with biologists, psychologists, psychiatrists and social scientists, omitting temporarily the physical scientists, but even the fields represented are not fully covered in all of their aspects. Nevertheless, there are enough carefully "chosen ones" to consider this a multi-disciplinary group.

Such a multi-disciplinary group in itself gives no guarantee of significant communications relating to a unified theory of human behavior. Its conferences could easily be of educatory value for its participating members by clarifying concepts and methods of fields strange to workers in other areas, but participants have been selected partially because of experience with more than one discipline and familiarity with several. The group might be tempted to translate concepts from one living or life-derived system to another, as for example biologizing psychology or psychologizing sociology, resulting in tautology rather than unification. We hope rather that communication between disciplines and abstraction from all of them will lead to considerable integration among us and what we represent, so that we may approach even though slightly the goal of unification.

To facilitate this process it was deemed wise to plan an agenda to serve as a compass for the direction of initial discussion, but not necessarily restrictive or exclusive. We propose first to examine the fundamental dynamic concepts of several universes or systems of organization—environmental gestalten—assuming a logical order without the necessity at first of correlating one system with another. The basic assumptions of these abstractions should hold that each organization's patterned process functions in a field of action in which there is a circular relationship between organization and environment. The next step would be to attempt to identify the organizational structures-in-function which constitute the environments of others. If the dynamics of several of such systems could be subjected to common abstractions, then a unified theory may be approachable.

For the first three conferences topics were designated in advance to which each member contributed from the frame of reference of his science. By that time we had come to grips with terms and with scientific models indigenous to each discipline, trying hard not to analogize but to search for some concepts applicable to all. We finally settled down at the fourth conference to consider a detailed outline devised by Jurgen Ruesch, reproduced on pages 303–4, which facilitated greater progress during the next several meetings.

Although in addition to participating I acted as chairman, since the meetings were arranged for and held within my own environment, the Institute for Psychosomatic and Psychiatric Research and Training of Michael Reese Hospital, this was a gratuitous function. The group seemed to have its leadership miraculously built-in for rarely was interference needed to preserve continuity or to hold to its goal. Discussion seemed to flow naturally in context as first one, then another member contributed his ideas. Throughout the text there appear introductions, summaries and transitional statements, for the benefit of the reader, that have been added by me as final editorial touches and for which I alone, and not the group, am responsible.

A final word about our financial support: The first meeting was subsidized by local friends of the Institute. Contributions were made by Messrs. Jack Pritzker, Edward Weiss, Sam Lustgarten, Spiegel and myself. After the first meeting, through the cooperation of Dr. John Gardner we were able to obtain a grant-in-aid from the Carnegie Corporation. This was renewed with sufficient funds to pay for the cost of preparing the material for publication. We are deeply grateful for this support.

ROY R. GRINKER

INTRODUCTION

Since time immemorial it has been man's prerogative to strive for integration of knowledge, although in each historical period he sought a somewhat different solution to the age-old problem. When, in the eighteenth and nineteenth centuries, the frontiers of science were laid wide open, scientists began to map unknown territory by means of simple observation and experiment. Inevitably, special theories evolved which had been constructed to fit particular disciplines and operations. During this era of progressive specialization, the scientists's personal need for integration of knowledge was satisfied through exploration of many diversified fields and through articulate communication with equally universal minds. Thus the striving for unification of knowledge was left to the individual, and no explicit attempt was made to accumulate knowledge concerned with the integration of diversified fields. Today, with the ever-increasing scientific and technological body of information, the individual solution used by our predecessors is no longer applicable. Instead, various attempts at establishing a universal scientific language, at agreeing upon basic scientific assumptions, at developing generally acceptable theoretical systems and at constructing giant electronic brains can be interpreted as moves to build the foundations upon which a body of knowledge which deals with the integration of specialized scientific information can rest.

To past generations, the attempt to make explicit these processes of integration may appear bold. But relying upon the advances made in the fields of language, symbolic representation and communication, we can begin to construct external models for some of the processes that take place inside the individual. Undoubtedly the men and women working in physics, chemistry and engineering have shown us how to construct and apply modern scientific models. But unfortunately their systems, which are concerned exclusively with mass effects and not with identified and living entities, cannot without extended modification be applied to those disciplines that deal with individuals. In these latter fields the greatest handicap to theoretical advance is related to the facts that the human observer is significantly influencing the phenomena which he purports to investigate and that the persons he studies are somewhat unique and cannot be replaced by other similar individuals. But we can call ourselves fortunate indeed that we possess this knowledge and that we are capable of explicitly formulating this very difficulty.

At approximately this stage of scientific development, World War II profoundly changed the scientific atmosphere. All of a sudden, the scientist was called upon to contribute his knowledge and to partake in decision-making previously reserved for politicians and the military. The psychiatrist was called upon to screen personnel, to eliminate the unfit and to rehabilitate those who become psychological casualties; the psychologist was asked to consult on matters of morale and emotional climate and to select those most likely to succeed; the physicist and engineer were asked to build weapons, which turned out to be dangerous to friend and foe alike and which by now threaten the very existence of our lives. Science distinctly had become involved in the manipulative aspects of social organization. The result, of course, was that institutions were created to distribute and utilize existing knowledge, buildings were erected to house staffs and provide service facilities, and countless thousands got directly or indirectly onto the payroll of science. With the growth of the institutional-managerial-political aspects of scientific exploration and with the unavoidable increase in red tape, science became detracted from its original goal: to search for truth and to gather information.

In such a climate of opinion, where the application of knowledge is favored over basic research, there seems to evolve on the part of those who wish to explore the unknown a need to meet with kindred spirits. The present publication is the result of the discussions of an interdisciplinary group that convened to exchange information. The members were not policy-makers or decision-makers; they were not empire builders; nor did they wish to search for an immediate practical application of their labors. Instead, they aimed at exploring the possibilities of establishing some kind of theoretical foundations upon which the study of the individual could fruitfully proceed.

Today we conceive of the individual as a living organism whose social relations are combined into complex organizations, whose inner world of experience is closely related to his social operations and whose soma materially makes possible his varied activities. We also have come to recognize that such a view necessitates a more unitary approach to man, and that what we need is a first approximation to a scheme which will enable us to represent physical, psychological, and social events within one system of denotation. If such an undertaking were to be successful, it would provide for an entirely new perspective of the intricate relations between mind, body, and socio-economic events and would furnish a framework which would consider simultaneously the individual and his surroundings, both in health and in disease. But only a concerted effort of many minds can be expected to yield results. A transcript of the discussion of some fifteen scientists, dedicated to this task, may help others to continue our efforts.

JURGEN RUESCH

TABLE OF CONTENTS

SECOND CONFERENCE

THIRD CONFERENCE

FOURTH CONFERENCE

Conference Members

ROY R. GRINKER, CHAIRMAN
Director, Institute for Psychosomatic and Psychiatric Research and Training of Michael Reese Hospital

KARL DEUTSCH
Professor of History and Political Science, Massachusetts Institute of Technology

ALFRED E. EMERSON
Professor of Zoology, University of Chicago

GEORGE L. ENGEL
Associate Professor of Psychiatry and Medicine, University of Rochester Medical School

LAWRENCE K. FRANK
Formerly Director, Caroline Zachry Institute Human Development

JULES HENRY
Professor of Sociology and Anthropology, Washington University

FLORENCE KLUCKHOHN
Lecturer on Sociology and Research Associate in the Laboratory of Social Relations, Harvard University

HOWARD LIDDEL
Professor of Psychology, Cornell University

CHARLES MORRIS
Lecturer on Philosophy, University of Chicago

TALCOTT PARSONS
Professor and Chairman, Department of Social Relations, Harvard University

ANATOL RAPOPORT
Mental Health Research Institute, Ann Arbor, Michigan

DAVID RAPAPORT
Research Associate, Austen Riggs Foundation, Inc.

JURGEN RUESCH
Associate Professor of Psychiatry, University of California School of Medicine

DAVID SHAKOW
Chief, Clinical and Experimental Psychology, National Institute of Mental Health, Bethesda, Maryland

ALFONSO SHIMBEL
Assistant Professor, Committee on Mathematical Biology, University of Chicago

JOHN P. SPIEGEL
Lecturer on Social Relations and Research Associate in the Laboratory of Social Relations, Harvard University

LAURA THOMPSON
Professor, Department of Sociology and Anthropology, City College of New York

JAMES E. P. TOMAN
Assistant Professor of Anatomy, Chicago Medical School

PAUL A. WEISS
Director, Laboratory of Developmental Biology, Rockefeller Institute for Medical Research

FIRST CONFERENCE

The Intrapersonal Organization

A Model for Relationships Among Systems

The Psychological System

The Observer and the Observed: Human Communication Theory

The Social System: A General Theory of Action

The Societal System, Culture and the Community

Value Orientations

A System of Socio-Psychiatric Invariants

General Discussion Terminating the First Conference

CHAPTER ONE

THE INTRAPERSONAL ORGANIZATION

Presentation by Roy R. Grinker

OUR deliberations are aimed at developing concepts from each field and attempting to derive from them abstractions applicable to all fields. But there is a danger that we might become so much engrossed in the empirical details and methodology of single fields that we lose sight of our goal, which is the discovery of some common concepts. A first question can best be phrased as follows: What does one discipline need and what can it accept and use of the assumptions and concepts of another, and, at the same time how can that discipline communicate its own concepts and assumptions to another? The task of each of us, as a representative of a specific field, is thus two-fold.

I have undertaken the task of dealing with the *intra-organismic* or intrapersonal organization in the most general and succinct terms possible. In such an attempt at any level (cellular, humoral, neurological, or psychological) two difficulties immediately present themselves. The first is semantic and concerns the vocabulary of generalizations or abstractions. Usually, when efforts are made to derive generalizations from the intrapersonal system applicable to others, anthropomorphisms have been utilized as though the parts were endowed consciousness and volition. On the other hand, the forces of the intrapersonal psychological systems are often described in social terms. We speak of boundaries, areas, conflict, compromise and hierarchies as though they were agencies. The phraseology is dynamic enough, but seems always to use figures of speech belonging to the next larger organization. If we consider the actions of one organization in terms of another, the tacit assumption is that the patterns are identical. Yet, logically, identity in language is no proof of reality; in fact, it hinders its testing.

The second and greater difficulty involves the conclusions as to what is basic in the myriad hypotheses and assumptions of any field of inquiry, especially when selection rests on the judgment of an active investigator. He has become highly specialized in the details of structure and function of the organization with which he works, and skilled in special techniques adapted to the detailed questions that he strives to answer. As a result, what is basic to one and perhaps applicable to all living systems is rarely important to him and often is only a peripheral blur to his focus on detailed processes. Furthermore, to find the common factors in biological, interpersonal and social processes, the basic concepts of another organization must be viewed at their point of transaction in order to obtain an abstraction significant for both; in fact, this is the only frame of reference for the scientific observer. In the current stage of our knowledge it may be feasible for the biologist and psychologist to decide what concepts are fundamental to living systems, and if the sociologist and anthropologist agree on which of these are also basic for the social systems we may then reach a level of valid abstraction. Thus it seems to me that we should first determine how much coincidence is hidden behind the varied external technical vocabularies and then grapple with what seems to be unique and incongruous within any system.

To begin with the biological, in contrast to the non-organic systems which are closed and associated with degradation of energy; organic systems more rapidly transform and bind energy within units permeable to permit an exchange of substance across their living boundaries in both directions. Thus, living organisms are open systems communicating and in circular process with their environments. These energy systems are in constant but variable states of activity. They utilize energy to obtain, incorporate and alter substances from the environment. By so doing, they store energy and create new organizations of mass. The intermediate aspects of this change of organization of non-living substances is the liberation internally of utilizable energy which varies in space and time within its parts, characteristic of a mobile system of gradients. Between these are constant circular processes of interaction and communication.

It seems that of these various activities the highest or most intense (chemically, electrically) is most internal or central to the organization and most concerned with the processes of change of internalized substances. On the other hand, the area of lowest activity coincides with the living periphery of the organization which is in process of functional relationship with the environment or the not-individual, whether or not this is another living organism. This area functions in reaching and preparing for incorporation of selected new substances to obtain more sources of energy, and to avoid or destroy interference or danger from the environment.

Studies in embryological physiology indicate that the built-in tensions activate the organism before any sensorial apparatus in communication with the environment is developed or in function. The primary source of action of the living unit arises from an internal energy system which is the stimulus for the first interactions and exchanges of the organism with its environment; only later do perceptive systems evolve and function in this process. Thus, constitutionally derived wound-up activity of the organization facilitates its existence before exteroceptive functions have developed. In other words, organizational functions precede system processes.

It is not my purpose to discuss the intracellular processes in greater detail for these involve a knowledge of the complicated fields of enzymatic bio-chemistry. In the multi-cellular organism many enzymes are liberated by cells in various tissues for extra-cellular, humeral diffusion. They comprise a complicated system of activators with multiple precursors, co-enzymes and complicated chains of checking and reversing antagonistic enzymes, all of which in health seemingly balance each other to facilitate the conversion of substances for utilizable energy, to store energy, and to mobilize metabolic processes under specific circumstances. Study of these energy systems has disclosed strange and intricate complexities to which there seems no end or beginning. Instead, the biologist must assume basic circularity of process.

In many organizations hormonal activities are liberated through the function of more specialized organs. They seemingly add no new functions but facilitate the intra- and extra-cellular enzymatic systems particularly during periods of stress and development, growth and decline.

In even more complicated organisms a nervous system and faster, more variable types of integration and reaction with the environment have evolved. The specialized properties of these highly differentiated nervous structures are their greater degree of irritability and speed of conductivity. The nervous system rapidly conducts internally those environmental stimuli which act on the body through special sensory end-organs and cells. Large groups of body cells far distant from the source of stimulation are set into action from the same environmental stimulus. Other portions of the nervous system conduct impulses through effector fibers and excite large groups of muscular structures and secretory cells into activity. Interposed between the sensory and effector functions are integrating and correlating centers with multiple complex inter-communications concomitant with a corresponding organismal evolution. With this increasing complexity there develop a great number of possible responses to a single stimulus.

The end-organs on which the environmental stimuli impinge, are adapted to respond to specific types of stimuli such as touch, pain, temperature, etc. within a limited quantitative range. Although each organism has a basic property or irritability it is to a selective sensitivity. Furthermore, external stimuli do not influence the intensity of nerve response. The quantity of energy firing and extending along the nerve fiber is constant to its capacity. No matter how strong the stimulus may be, if the nerve fiber responds at all, it will respond in the same quantity to its maximum; this is the all-or-none law. We can conclude that the organism not only selects the energy (stimulation) it accepts from the environment, but it also maintains its own rate of responsiveness. This constitutes the biological and effective rudimentary defense against disintegration. Turning to the central and effector aspects of conduction, various muscular or glandular activities are discharged through a final common nerve pathway which is fired by stimuli from the central nerve net. In this net, depending upon the type and degree of external stimulation, activity mirrors a central quantitative summation or impedance of subliminal charges. Innumerable gradations of effects are possible depending upon the time of discharge and the number of discharging motor units. The end result is thus dependent upon timing and quantity of summation rather than on any special quality of nerve response.

The autonomic or visceral nervous system is more directly concerned with storage and mobilization of energy to and from the large body reservoirs. One portion mobilizes the resources of the body for emergency mass discharge under varying conditions of stress. The other is more conservative and synthetic in its activities and mobilizes in more discrete units. However, these divisions function (like enzymes, co-enzymes and antagonistic enzymes) together, balancing or summating each other, controlling the rapid change of balance subserving thereby a tendency toward a steady state. This autonomic nervous system is closely integrated with higher nervous centers which have evolved later, and participates in many other bodily functions and in response to internal and external sensory stimuli.

The higher autonomic or sympathetic centers were primarily developed with the sense of smell, which projected the animal forward in space and time to permit it to become aware of future danger. Its anatomical position in the 'tween brain or diencephalon places it at the crossroads between the higher cortical centers, with their sensitivity to greater ranges of satisfaction and stress, and the body's machinery for response and adjustment.

At this level of irritability, danger from without (fear), or from within (anxiety), extends the function of organ sensitivity to the highest degree. Here actions, which constitute responses in adjustment to stress, are capable of being set off by symbolic representations of remembered dangers.

The 'tween brain contains relatively discreetly localized centers for the discharge and conservation of energy, acting together in a cooperative fashion. Nor is activity limited to visceral functions when these centers fire, for with increasing needs of severer stress, discharges flow to the somatic division of the nervous system and muscular movements result. If the level of excitation reaches a certain threshold, responses occur in the form of violent aggressive striking, or fighting or rhythmic running movements. Also, the need for substance to build up energy reservoirs may necessitate aggressive and grabbing, intaking movements. Thus, in the service of need or of response to danger, in attempting to maintain a steady inner state, aggressive (motor) systems are activated but this in effect is only a quantitative increase within an energy system which functions to maintain itself.

The property of irritability within living protoplasm is magnified and specialized by the nervous system but no new quality is added. The nervous system hastens energy exchange and widens its effects. By virtue of private pathways from end-organs it selects what part of the environment is permitted to act on the organism and thereby tends to keep the environment in a steady state (from the frame of reference of the organism). Its rate of response permits control over the rate of energy exchange and it activates its motor control in varying degrees and rhythms. From the single living cell to the cerebral cortical mantle, energy systems are in a constant state of flux, and apparent differences in directional flow are only indications of an algebraic sum at a given time since all directions are always concurrently present. Anabolism-catabolism, excitation-inhibition, growth-senescence, life and death are not polar opposites of different systems but quantitative variations of a single complex energy exchange within the organism-environment Gestalt.

However, the human nervous system consists of not only correlating and conducting centers with their peripheral receptors and effectors. The cortical mantle has been associated with the intensification of functions which permit the living organization a greater mastery of time and space, involving memory of the past and projection into the future and the capacity for more choice instead of rigidly stimulus-bound action. Many physiological properties have been ascribed to the cerebral cortex as one would expect with its concomitant psychological functions, but it is doubtful that these represent any basic differences in the organic processes. Therefore, we should turn our attention to the psychological processes and see in what way and to what degree they reflect or re-represent the biological organization.

We would like to state that psychological processes are as energy binding as any other organic process. Sherrington's remarks negate this hope when he says, "The mental is not examinable as a form of energy. As followers of natural science we know nothing of any relation between thoughts and the brain except as a gross correlation in time and space." [1] On the other hand Adrian states, "Mental interaction systems are but higher forms of intra-cellular enzymatic systems." [2] Coghill hypothesized: "In the organic sphere the total pattern has three constituent components, structure, function and mentation. These three components of the living organism undergo varying degrees of individuation. Structure is fundamentally spatial. Function is primarily temporal. Mentation in its highest degree of individuation conforms to neither space nor time." [3] It is at this point of the "more-than-organic function" that the space-time continuum in the organism-environmental Gestalt becomes less clear and a new language had to be devised. Because of the lack of perceptive systems by which we can observe the mental clearly, analogical terms have been used and concepts have been manipulated by "it is as if."

The most earnest attempt to fit the psychological into a biological conceptual scheme has been made by Freud and his followers. They attempt a transition from the internal biological organization of "instincts," or built-in energy systems, to the psychological "drives," attributing to the latter a borderline status between the physical and the mental. According to Freudian concepts, the drives are more flexible, mobile and capable of delay. Their aims or objects are interchangeable and are capable of quantitative variation, or inhibition of aim, of turning to the opposite, etc.

The Freudian psychological model demonstrates considerable congruence with biological concepts. The organism has specific needs which when satisfied release tension and afford pleasure; the sum of excitation or so-called psychic energy is quantitatively fixed; there is a tendency for the organism to maintain a state of constancy; there are gradients of energy or tension and hierarchies of organs or zones used for its discharge; there is an orderly system of development of part-functions, and in maturity the integration of these functions into a new organic whole, with stress producing disintegration and the revival of old part-functions. The classification of drives as belonging to id or ego, self or race preservation, libidinal

[1] C. Sherrington, *Man on His Nature* (New York: Macmillan, 1941).

[2] E. C. Adrian, "Conduction in Peripheral Nerve and in the Central Nervous System," *Brain*, XLI (1918), 23.

[3] C. J. Herrick, *George E. Coghill, Naturalist and Philosopher* (Chicago: University of Chicago Press, 1949).

or aggressive are dependent upon frames of reference and indicate less a distinction of forms of energy than variations of direction perceived from changing positions of the observer. The Freudian psychology conceives of a constitutionally derived inner organization which functions without stimuli from the external environment, the so-called id. The development of later more complicated reactivity with the environment, as in the total organism after its perceptive systems have developed, is a function of the ego which is sensitive to both internal and external stimuli and develops its capacities from a learning, self-corrective process in interaction with the living and physical world about it. It then becomes the functioning organization which perceives inner tension, outer stress and has the power of permitting or inhibiting action and synthesizing conflictual tendencies.

I have not gone into the psychodynamic details of Freudian or other psychologies because they are of less importance than the general principles, contending only that our psychological knowledge today gives indication that the basic conceptual scheme is compatible with our fundamental biological concepts of the living organism.

I would like to discuss one more general concept which relates to the unitary nature of organism-environment in space and time as an action system, particularly emphasized by Dewey,[4] Dewey and Bentley,[5] and more recently by Bentley in his so-called kennetic inquiry.[6] "This is a name proposed for organized investigation into the problem of knowings and knowns where this is so conducted that the full range of subject matters all the knowings and knowns form a common field." He divides scientific inquiry into three fields, physical, physiological and behavioral or psychological in which the techniques of appraisal and the language of reports at present are not interchangeable. This goal of interchangeableness is what we are striving to approach today.

As one reads the language of Bentley, the complexity, the unnaturalness of syntax and the number of multi-hyphenated words necessary to maintain the concept of an unfractured field are disconcerting. It is apparent that contemporary man is under the greatest of strains in conceiving himself subjectively in process, as part of and in transaction with his environment, and in losing his selfness, his I-ness, his boundaries even in phantasy. This difficulty has been raised by Scott in a discussion of the body scheme.[7]

[4] J. Dewey, *Problems of Men* (New York: Philosophical Library, 1946).

[5] J. Dewey and A. F. Bentley, *Knowing and the Known* (Boston: Beacon Press, 1949).

[6] A. F. Bentley, "Kennetic Inquiry," *Science*, CXII (1950), 775.

[7] W. C. M. Scott, "The 'Body Scheme' in Psychotherapy," *British Journal of Medical Psychology*, XXII (1949), 139.

Scott started from experience with schizophrenic patients who were concerned with their souls, minds and bodies, and the search for some sort of unity or integration with their environments or reality. On the other hand there were patients with oceanic feelings or a sense of cosmic consciousness located somewhere in space. Some felt that they had been engulfed by the world, others had swallowed the world. In contrast with the elated feeling associated with this cosmic phantasy is the catastrophic chaos of the depressed or paranoid patient who feels himself completely isolated and differentiated from the rest of the human world.

The fundamental work of Coghill [8] showed that embryonic organisms at birth were unfractionated wholes which functioned in total patterns. From this unorganized, undifferentiated behavior the organism matured by developing an individuation of discrete local reflex activities using fragments of the total movement pattern which had preceded them. This total response, although broken down into discrete individual movements, was never lost because under certain circumstances it could be revised.

The human organism at birth has only primitive awareness of differentiation, or selfness or I-ness. With the process of development this total pattern is differentiated into parts with the body integument as the living interface between a process within and one without. As this occurs the I or the self develops and even becomes differentiated into many parts such as the multiple I's of various roles depending upon the external situation and its demands. At any biological or psychological level such structuring or organization is a by-product or, if you will, the cost of a more specialized function. From a whole system in process with the environment there develops a transactional relationship of parts of the self with the whole and with the environment, but not again unless having a psychosis, sometimes in sleep or infrequently in temporary phases of ecstasy or elation, does the boundary of the self diminish (never to disappearance). Hence, one has to become almost psychotic to approach a frame of reference in which the organism-environmental Gestalt can be perceived. In the temporal aspects of the environmental field, the past is structuralized in memory patterns, the future is mysterious, while the present absorbs all our perceptive systems. All are pictorially represented in our mental processes by space dimensions which can only be remembered or anticipated by projecting our present bodies forward or backward. It is no wonder that of the three aspects of the space-time field we as individuals in groups or societies select one to think, dream, phantasy of and to place greater value on.

[8] C. J. Herrick, *op. cit.*

Let us assume that the human organism at some time comprises one undifferentiated functional system in transaction with its environment. Out of this are differentiated many small systems which still remain under the potential dominance of the whole, but which are linked with each other in a circular process of transaction just as the total organism is related to its environment, society and culture. Each system serves as the environment of the other. The *intrapersonal* functions may be classified into many discrete systems, but it seems logical to use five large natural divisions.

1. The enzymatic system including the hormones.
2. The organ system which includes the function of each organ or the larger confluences.
3. The nervous system.
4. The psychological system (id and autonomous ego).
5. The socio-cultural system (learned or introjected as the ego, superego and ego-ideal).

The living boundaries between these are ill-defined, incomplete, variable and dependent upon the transactions occurring at any particular time and place. In fact, one might state that such boundaries correspond to living semipermeable membranes of a single cell. The integration within each system and the defenses against disintegration constitute the forces that tend to maintain a steady state.

Let us set up an example of a hypothetical case of oxygen stress. At once, a change in enzymatic functions increases the uptake and utilization within each cell of the available oxygen. Although this reaction is only observed within one system at a given tension of oxygen, all other systems are alerted. If the integrative capacity of this system is overwhelmed, the hematopoietic system may throw out more red cells to carry the limited amount of oxygen and to increase its turnover, the peripheral vascular system changes in caliber, and the heart pumps the blood cells faster to utilize the limited oxygen tension to its fullest. Greater oxygen deprivation may stimulate the nervous system to effect changes in the rate and rhythm of breathing through the action of carbon dioxide on the medullary respiratory centers. In the meantime the psychological state of the organism is alerted—at first with minor degrees of apprehension, culminating finally in an anxiety state which prepares it for flight. If all of the previous reactions are not sufficient to decrease internal disequilibrium, total coordinated behavior may destroy its containment or move the subject to flight and into an atmosphere where oxygen tension is more suitable for its needs. If we reverse the process and use a symbolic stimulus acting at a psychological level through fear of suffocation or oxygen deprivation, the result will be an intensification of activity from one system to another until the symbolic danger is no longer present or until the organism has reacted physiologically to adjust for its fear.[9]

From a single system, which strain may cause to disintegrate functionally, to all systems and eventually to a total response, activity progressively spreads and increases to enable the organism to keep a steady internal state. The result is a multiplicity of circular and corrective processes between systems which are oriented toward stabilizing the organism and maintaining its integration. A breakdown between boundaries and an intensification of activity of another system occurs only when the strain becomes too severe. Likewise, the pattern of behavior resumes its primitive infantile total functions when the several systems which have been fractionated out of the whole are no longer able to handle the stress. At first, stress facilitates defenses, but when continued and increased it disrupts and produces strain and, ultimately, de-differentiation. If the level of excitation reaches a certain threshold, energy may be discharged as violent, aggressive striking or fighting or as rhythmic running movements. When the differentiated systems are under strain the whole takes over and the old patterns of integration return. Thus in time of need or danger, when a steady inner state must be maintained, aggressiveness may be seen as an increase of activity in a system of energy exchange which is trying to maintain itself.

Whether the organism reacts as a primitive whole before differentiation, or in straining to handle stress, or has been reduced by excessive stress to a de-differentiated whole, the somatic and psychic systems are in a constant state of transaction with each other. Concomitant somatic and psychological action patterns probably occur only as the result either of lasting traumatic impressions made upon a total system before differentiation or of current stress forcing regression to that state.

Now, each level of activity may be discussed as a system in itself: the bio-chemical or cellular, the enzymatic system, the organ system, the nervous system and the psychological system. I have left the relationship with the environment for others to discuss. The organism's systems are in the same kind of relationship with the environment as the parts are with the organism, considering environment as both physical and social.

I conceive of the integration and disintegration of relationships of the systems as processes that differ quantitatively only. In health there is a constant process going on within each system and between systems. The noticeable effects are difficult to observe except by special techniques; mere

[9] Roy R. Grinker, *Psychosomatic Research* (New York: W. W. Norton, 1953); "Some Current Trends and Hypotheses of Psychosomatic Research," in *The Psychosomatic Concept of Psychoanalysis*, ed. F. Deutsch (New York: International Universities Press, 1953).

measurement in itself often alters the system. In illness the stress provokes an intensification or increase in rate of processes within and between systems. If the stress persists to a point at which disintegration is threatened, emergency defense procedures are evoked. Finally, when the quantity gets to a certain point, disintegration occurs. Within this complex of intrapersonal systems change in any one area will affect all the others.

LIDDELL: *Is stress a quantitative concept? Is stress super-maximal?*

GRINKER: Yes. Stimuli are constantly impinging on the organism and it is constantly reaching out for stimuli necessary to keep it in activity. One type of stimulus which approaches the threshold of stress may be an alarm to prepare for future disturbance; another may be associated with failure of the environment itself. Oxygen deprivation may result from actual changes in the environment and act primarily physiologically throughout the organism. But fear of deprivation may act primarily on the psychological system which in turn affects all others.

THOMPSON: *By using the term "steady state" do you mean open and closed states, or just open states?*

GRINKER: Always open; a *tendency* to a steady state or relatively steady state for there is actually no "steady" state. It is said to be "relatively" steady because the organism must act continually to maintain itself within a living semi-permeable boundary through which circular processes occur.

FRANK: *The open system makes possible a dynamic equilibrium because it is constant, equilibriating itself. In the other, the closed or static system, there is nothing to replace it.*

THOMPSON: Are the circular processes *reversible* or *irreversible*, or *both?*

GRINKER: None of the processes are irreversible; they are all constantly active and reversible. This is true of all the systems of which we are speaking.

ENGEL: *I think that depends on the context in which you are speaking. For example, urea is formed as a product of degradation from nitrogen metabolism. Within the organism it is irreversible—is not reconverted into protein. However, seen in the total environment it comes back to the organism through the plant cycle.*

THOMPSON: *But the psychological system is changing, isn't it, in a sort of spiral process? The process does not just come back to the same thing all the time in the psychological system, does it?*

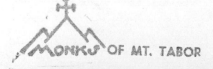

SHAKOW: *It is circular but without returning to the starting point; that is a spiral. Change is going on in one direction but a constant back-and-forth movement is going on all the time. The movement is not on one and the same level.*

THOMPSON: You are describing a total organism here, I take it, and the total organism is constantly changing. As a whole, is the organism changing in a developmental pattern—in a spiral rather than a circle?

RUESCH: *The terms reversible and irreversible refer to changes in time, and "irreversible" indicates a different time unit than "reversible." In other words, all we denote by saying "reversible" and "irreversible" is the speed of the rate of change of processes.*

THOMPSON: *I think we ought to make clear that our whole unit is changing all the time.*

TOMAN: *As a physical model we might take the example of a stream of water from a faucet. This process is not reversible—that is, the water does not go back up into the faucet from the sink. But the form of the stream can be changed reversibly with the force, the shape of the nozzle, etc.*

PARSONS: *The question of reversibility or irreversibility has to be brought in at the very first level. You don't have to say you are dealing with a changing system before you define a system at all. Exactly how relevant it will turn out to be, for what purposes, is an open question.*

GRINKER: We shall leave that question open. To turn to a remaining general statement which I should like to make: because of its sensitivity and responsiveness the organism becomes integrated with its environment to form larger systems, thereby sacrificing some overt autonomy.

HENRY: *It is implied that the interaction of the organism in all its phases with the environment constitutes a circular system, too, so that somehow there is a circular interaction between the psychological system and the environment.*

EDITOR: *In this first presentation of the introductory conference there was an attempt to introduce basic concepts of the intrapersonal or intra-organismic organization which could be called the biological universe. This was not limited to the somatic processes alone but included the psychological without reference to its organic substrate. Concepts of structure-*

function, boundaries and their permeabilities, energy storage and transformations, gradient and equilibrium or homeostasis, all characteristic of open systems, were mentioned briefly. They will be considered in greater detail in subsequent chapters. The relationship among parts or subsystems to the whole sharply accentuated the concept of organismal-environmental Gestalt and the transactional processes among all parts with the field. How stress on one part involves all other parts, within the field under consideration, was briefly mentioned. This led naturally to the next presentation: a model of transactions among several systems or foci.

CHAPTER TWO

A MODEL FOR RELATIONSHIPS AMONG SYSTEMS

Presentation by John P. Spiegel

IT is already obvious that it is impossible to make any statements about relationships among systems without having a model in mind. For instance: even though Grinker reminded us that he was describing circular systems of transaction, nevertheless the word "level" and a notion of hierarchy persistently crept in. We should recognize these unacknowledged analogies or metaphors and specify what our model is. There are habitual traditional ways of assembling data, but we also have newer ways of doing so, and sometimes, because we do not specify how we are organizing our data, we mix one model or one system with another. A very common arrangement of data is a linear hierarchy. Whether the dominant element is at the top or the bottom depends upon one's habit of picturing it. For example, one may start with physical-chemical processes. These then are assembled into what is called the next or higher level of organization. This turns out to be the cell or a biological entity of some sort. Then the cells are assembled into the next and more inclusive level of organization. Let us say this is an organ system, or it is a whole multi-cellular entity. Then the assemblage becomes larger, and one moves on to the next so-called level, which turns out to be a psychological system. These are then assembled into larger groups, culminating at the top in something which is called the "highest level of the culture." One might describe this model as a container-can, chinese box or telescopic system. Everything at lower levels is contained in higher and higher, larger and larger assembly units. Then one may speak of reducing what he has put into the larger assembly units to the original something. It is hard then to know exactly where to ascribe the dominance.

To repeat: the manner of presenting data depends upon one's habit of thought. One who emphasizes conceptual processes would place dominance at the top in a philosophical or conceptual system or a system of culture. But a person who notices concrete phenomenon would put dominance in a specific location from which all subsequent development is derived. It depends on the way we are trained.

However, other notions creep in. For instance, we feel obliged when we get up to a top level of some belief system of the culture to relate it to something outside of this system. The relation may be with Nature, God, or the universe, but a belief system is in contact with something outside man himself. Down at the bottom of the model we also bring in physical-chemical material from the universe, apart from man and the physiological processes he shares with all living things. We try to relate those processes to something that is going on outside the living system—namely, physical-chemical events which exist throughout the universe. Although our implicit belief or way of conceptualizing this is circular, such circularity is usually not stated but kept in the background. Emphasis is placed on description and classification of structure, which has been very useful. Only with difficulty, however, are interactions or functions beween various so-called levels brought out. To introduce the idea of movement into a model of this kind is very difficult.

Another handicap of the linear hierarchy is that if the observer starts out by focusing at one level, then everything else becomes environment. Some of the models described as field systems are of that nature—like Lewin's psychological field.[1] Observation starts at one point in time which then becomes the focus, as for example the psychological system of the individual or group. Then all the rest of the physical, social or cultural systems become peripheral or on the boundary of the field, radiating in or out like lines of force. But if one uses such a conceptual model there is no way of describing interactions except those taking place between the point of focus and the local field surrounding it, thus neglecting those interactions taking place in the extended field itself over time.

Figure 1, below, tentatively represents the principle, presently identifiable, of system foci transacting in the field. The term *Universe* stands for all non-living structural-functional process, from the microscopic to the macroscopic cosmos. *Soma* denotes all living biological process, and *Psyche*

[1] K. Lewin, *Field Theory in Social Science* (New York: Harper & Brothers, 1951).

all symbolic communication process within and between individuals. *Group* signifies small, face-to-face, organized collections of persons and *Society* stands for the system of extended groups characteristic of a locale or state. Finally *Culture* denotes the system of shared values and meanings within a society. All the system foci are seen to be in circular, reciprocal, interdependent transaction with each other.

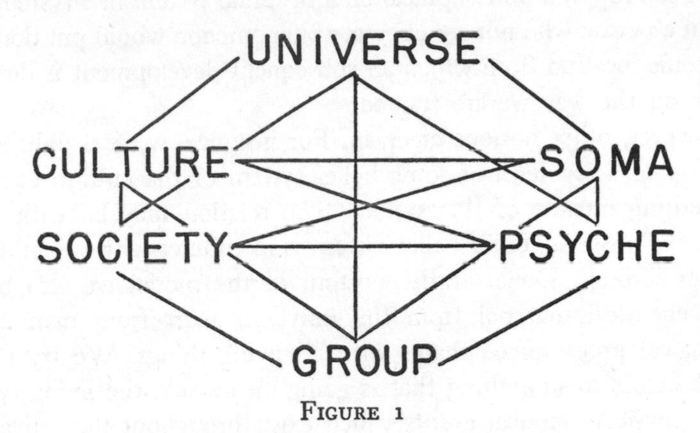

FIGURE 1
THE PRINCIPLE FOCI OF TRANSACTION

Now I propose a conceptual model of my own for analyzing systems and their transactions based on the following assumptions:

1. The field is not a static phenomenon but consists of patterned processes representing systems of organized energy which are in motion relative to one another.

2. In spite of the continual motion and change, the pattern of transactions among the various systems composing the field has a basic stability which can be discerned. If the pattern is observed along a spatial dimension, it appears as a structure. If it is observed along a temporal dimension, it appears as a function. In other words, the distinction between a structure in the field and a function in the field is not absolute but rather is complementary and relative to the position and operations of the observer. The term pattern is inclusive of both structure and function.

3. The field is a four-dimensional continuum. Whether processes are pictured as patterned along a spatial dimension or along a temporal dimension depends on the position and actions of the observer.

4. Since the field is a continuum of patterned, transactional processes, the structure-function of any one part of the field affects the structure-function of all the other parts of the field, and therefore of the whole field. In other words, all parts of the field are in structural-functional relation with each other. This total, diffuse dependence makes it theoretically impossible

to isolate and observe transactions among adjacent parts of the field ignoring the reverberating effect of changes taking place in more remote parts of the field as a result of the very processes being observed. In actual fact, however, such observations can be made on isolated parts of the field if it is stated that the reverberating effects limit the validity of the observations being made.

5. The structural-functional interdependence of all parts of the field makes statements describing dominance or hierarchical relations of one part of the field over another essentially meaningless. For example, if biological, psychological and cultural events are considered to be parts of the field, then such reductive statements as "psychological processes are derived from biological processes" or "personality is the reflection in the individual of the prevailing cultural environment" become irrelevant. Since they are all field phenomena, the particular form that each takes will depend upon the reciprocal relations among all three. One cannot be derived from another but must be considered as having spatial and temporal coexistence.

6. Although the field is a continuum so far as its dimensions are concerned, it is not homogeneous. The patterned energy systems of which it is composed are differentiated from each other as foci or nodes of organization. The differentiation is discerned by the observer on the basis of criteria of integration and maintenance of a "steady state." The identity of the foci of organization is maintained by integrative processes which facilitate energy exchanges among the system foci at rates of exchange or equilibria which preserve the pattern of order within the system. Defense processes also occur and represent partial sacrifices of structure or function within the system of foci designed to control energy exchanges resulting from strain, conflict or incongruence which, if unchecked, would lead to disintegration or loss of order. Insofar as the system foci maintain their integration, they sustain boundaries which distinguish one from another, but the boundaries between the foci are ill-defined, incomplete and variable. The character of the boundary area depends upon the degree of order in the system resulting from transactions occurring at any particular time and place.

ENGEL: *"Transaction" implies process. Dewey and Bentley state, "Essentially the concept is thing in process with thing."* [2] *They called attention to the fact that in the development of knowledge, and in the history of science, there have been three levels. The point of view from which things are regarded as acting under their own power is that of self-action. Interaction refers to the balancing of thing against thing in causal interconnection.*

[2] J. Dewey and A. F. Bentley, *Knowing and the Known* (Boston: Beacon Press, 1949).

This is an outgrowth of classical physics; biology and psychology have tended to lag behind in reaching this phase. Dewey and Bentley suggest the term "process transaction," where thing is in process with thing, particularly as in behavioral phenomena. When organism is in process with environment, knowledge of the organism or environment alone is inadequate. The full system must be observed. One does not talk about transactions between two things, but between whatever number of the things under discussion are in process with each other. Interaction stresses too much the acting of one thing upon another, precisely the bias pointed out in reference to Lewin. You pick one point and tend to think of things impinging on it, or it impinging on other things, instead of seeing the total system.

SPIEGEL: If we assume circular processes to begin with, we avoid the pitfall of "levels." I prefer the term "foci" to "levels" because one is observing and focusing on a part of a system that is continually in transaction or exchange with other systems. Since this is true, every identifiable focus must be somehow interdependent with every other so that no change can occur which does not affect the entire field.

HENRY: *But a conception of complete circularity does not seem to mean only that anything happening in one system will affect the others. It means that the effect will also come back to itself, although modified.*

SPIEGEL: This is correct. Processes then are going on in all directions. You have to assume for the purposes of observation that you can make them stand still, although you cannot do so in reality. Every time you try to stop the processes, you impose a certain artificiality. In order to communicate at all, we have to assume we can stop motion and specify what the relations are at one time. Then we examine the relations at a later time and try to say what changes have taken place in the interim. It is very difficult to observe things as continual processes, so we talk as if we could stop them at a certain point.

HENRY: *Circular systems imply certain mathematical assumptions, that there is a given quantity of something in a system of this kind, and the total distribution of impulses, or whatever they are, could be measured; and if an impulse radiates from one system, having the value of "X," it will come back to it with a similar value, possibly somewhat transformed from "X." This will be a new changed value "X."*

SPIEGEL: At any rate, before we start talking about quantities I think we have to know something about what conveys quantities of what. We notice primarily the rate and quality of change of the processes and to some extent the directions of rate of change.

The foci under observation maintain some observable form. We can assume that the form is of the nature of a steady state which Grinker spoke of before. Changes are proceeding at a certain rate and in a certain direction, so that as one observes, a steady state seems to be maintained. Yet it is only a *relatively* steady state for if observations are made through time, changes can be seen. But even if one observes a focus when it seems to be maintaining one form, it can be noticed that it is being maintained only as a result of processes that are going on all the time. Thus, the structure is a function of function. Structure results from function, and function is an aspect of structure.

FRANK: *The concept of the steady state is taken from thermodynamics. Could we possibly substitute for it the idea of a persistent pattern of the current process? In reality, the steady state is not steady; even minor variations in equilibria are necessary. The steady state within an organization of electrons, as within a lattice framework, is one thing and a steady state in a dynamic open system, like an organism, might be quite different. We force ourselves into difficulties by taking over a figure of speech.*

SPIEGEL: There is another way to understand such a system. When concentrating upon any particular focus, one is confronted with three questions: What are the system's essential components? What are the processes which relate its parts to the whole—the integrative processes? What function in relation to the adjacent or neighboring systems or foci, or the system as a whole, is observable from this particular focus? At any one moment in time there is some function which we could call purpose (although that, perhaps, prejudices the concept a little), which this particular focus is subserving for the entire field. There seem to be three different axes which correspond to the questions of What? How? and Why? They are:

1. The content, substance or basic components of each system. This will be denoted as the *Constitutional Determinants* of the focus of organization.

2. Processes which maintain the structures-in-function or persistent pattern of the focus of organization. These will be denoted as the *Integrative Determinants* of the foci.

3. Traits which characterize the purpose or function of the system as a whole within the field. Such traits or attributes cannot be discovered from observing the basic components of the system, or the patterned relationships of its parts, but only by observing the transactions and interrelations of the system as a whole among other systems. This axis will be denoted as the *System Determinants* of the foci.

If you specify these dimensions or axes for each of the foci—the result is an analytical system which can provide the answers to certain persistent questions. For instance, a study of integrative processes involves the polarities of integration and disintegration at any specified time of observation. If we say that the second dimension is the integrative dimension, then we can examine the focus itself from the point of view of its location in a gradient between integration and disintegration. The processes can be so examined as to show that at any one moment they are tending more toward integration or more toward disintegration. They also may be set up in such a way that disintegration is seen to be stalled off, so to speak, by defensive processes. For biological and psychological processes this method of analysis is valid, but I am not in a position to say whether it is generally applicable; it would be very important to find that out.

Then one can also begin to look at how differences in rates of exchange between various foci affect the balance of integration and disintegration between the foci. That is, if something occurs which speeds up the rate of exchange or transaction—say between Psyche and Group because of something that happened in Soma—it may have the effect of precipitating disintegrative processes or of making it impossible for integrative processes to be maintained in either Psyche or Group.

At that point one would get a change that reverberates around the system. It would cause a change in the basic components as the patterns of their configuration changes. Then we may say that a change between two foci reverberates through three dimensions and on back through the system. Or one can look at the disintegrative effect as the change reverberates around another way.

GRINKER: *From personal experience I know how difficult it is to get lineality out of one's mind. You have talked about "adjacent" or "neighboring," and about something going around in a system, as if in one direction or the other, from one focus to another. That is level, and linear, but not transactional.*

SPIEGEL: It has something to do with the fact that a diagram of the conceptual model is a very crude representation leading us into these kinds of errors.

GRINKER: *In order to avoid polar opposites of integration and disintegration, you put in defense as some kind of middle ground but I think it should be assumed that there are no such isolates as integration or disintegration. Both are going on at the same time. You used the word "de-*

fense" to mean a happy medium, a neutral position, which never occurs because the steady state is never actually steady.

SPIEGEL: No, I use the concept "defense" for active processes which avert disintegration by isolating certain processes which if allowed to permeate throughout the whole system would, because of the increased rate of exchange, result in the disintegration of the system. Examples in the biological focus might be encapsulating processes.

TOMAN: *The discussion has shifted from levels of organization of properties of like material systems to interaction between different material systems. Would you give us an instance of what you mean by "exchange between the foci"? There is clearly some kind of order. You couldn't shuffle them around at random and have them make sense. There is some kind of order of juxtaposition.*

SPIEGEL: There are changes going on all the time. Every change requires a prior change as prerequisite. Let us consider, for example, a change in the function of a group resulting from a change in the Society focus. A change in the role that an individual plays in this group will occur. Strains will develop; he will wish to play one role but will be able to play only another, or he will feel he can't play the newly assigned role because of the way his superego is structured. Now this means a change in the rate of exchange between the individual and the group, a change which reverberates back in a chain system. He may become depressed and withdraw. One has to specify the way the chain, which starts at a certain point, reverberates back through the system. The system is already made up of energies and patterned processes so one has only to specify how the change occurred.

HENRY: *As I understand it, the child as an organism derives its characteristic way of functioning as a human being from certain biochemical processes. Then there are, as Grinker has shown, mechanisms for relating certain integrative functions and mechanisms, too, for relating the system to other units. The issue here of course, as you posit it, is that a child cannot arrive at any way of integrating itself with other foci unless these foci in turn act first upon the child. This is what makes the system circular.*

SPIEGEL: As soon as one tries to apply it in any concrete situation, then one notices that the rates of change at one point are extremely different from rates of change at another. Consequently, strains which hamper the maintenance of integration develop as a result of the differences in the rates of change. Inertia is introduced by reason of the fact that in any concrete item one thing is going on a given rate while another thing is changing faster.

LIDDELL: *Grinker talked about stress and Spiegel talked about strain being set up in this system because of the great diversity of rates of change in these foci, and that leads me to wonder what you conceive to be the relation of stress to strain, as we use the terms in physics. You are getting stress outside of the organism, aren't you—in some kind of interplanetary space in this system?*

SPIEGEL: If an infectious organism gains access to the body, then certainly processes which tend to alter rates of exchange within the body take place in a degrading direction: organizations within the body are being broken down faster than they are being built up. Then one might say that something new has been added which results in strain.

GRINKER: *I do not think stress or strain can be qualified except in terms of the rate and quantity of change, for it is an effect. Strain or stress cannot be isolated or quantified except in terms of its transaction with the system.*

RUESCH: *Do you mean strain or stress indicate stimulation in excess of the capacities of that particular system to cope with a situation?*

GRINKER: *No, not necessarily in excess, because stress or strain may effect a greater speed of integrative processes within various parts in order to maintain the system. The difference is in the quantitative effect. A stimulus is needed and searched for, and stress is avoided. The quantitative effect is on the rate of change.*

FRANK: *In this model is the stress-strain which is found in the soma also to be found in the other systems?*

SPIEGEL: Yes. I would assume that rates of change occur which make the process of holding groups together more difficult—as in a society in process of revolution—so that one then develops increasing stresses and strains, or difficulties in exchange which reverberate all through the system.

TOMAN: *I am troubled by the apparent equivalence of your foci. We have a general idea of what we mean by "soma." "Psyche," however, to my mind is a particular set of properties of the soma. The group is an agglutination of individuals. Also, in your model you have a group of groups, then you have prevalent attitudes among groups, and finally you have the whole physical universe. Between all these sets of things and properties there must be interrelations, but to consider them as equivalent foci is confusing.*

Your proposition started with a description of nature, but you now seem to be dealing with a different level of abstraction.

SPIEGEL: No. I meant it to be a description. It is a model which can describe the processes that we observe in nature. A group is *not* an agglutination of individuals but has these three components: the basic components, namely the individuals and their roles in the group; the integrative processes; and the function and relation of the group to other groups in the system as a whole. These properties may be ascribed to all systems and the description is valid for all systems—including both soma and psyche.

TOMAN: *You find common relationships, on the one hand, between a whole thing and certain special sets of its properties, and then you go on to define properties common to the two areas and to another area which is characterized by being a number of these things.*

GRINKER: *I think this is another instance of the old confusion between structure and function. In each of these foci are properties which are patterns. One of them, the soma, happens to have more irreversible structure. The psychological system, the group and society, exhibit less structure but they are still functional patterns. We are not speaking of them as structures.*

SPIEGEL: One of my assumptions is that structure is only a way of looking at a function and a function is only a way of looking at structure. It depends upon the space-time of the observer.

TOMAN: *Yes, the psyche is a functional pattern but it is a sub-pattern of the soma; there is a difference in level between this pattern and the soma, just as there is a difference in level between quantum properties and statistical properties between individuals and groups.*

SPIEGEL: What Toman is doing is what we have tried to avoid: that is, you take over ways of looking at reality that are congenial to you and try to make them operate in other areas of reality. But that is one of the problems we must examine, namely, are they operative?

FRANK: *Some years ago an English physicist pointed out that classical physics assumed that the nature of the particle could be deduced from observations of mass movements, such as in gas laws. Quantum physics showed that these deductive assumptions about particles were not valid; particles do not act as assumed in classical physics, nor do they possess the properties that had been deduced from statistical arrays.*

Social science today is in much the same position as classical physics. We have many mass observations in social science, and from them we have tried to deduce the nature of the individual person and how he acts. As we have begun to observe and carefully study the identified individual person as contrasted with the aggregate of anonymous data, we discover that individual persons do not conform to the long accepted deductive assumptions about human nature and conduct. With increasing insight into the individual organism-personality, we must now try to reconcile the findings from mass observations and from study of identified individuals if we are to formulate a unified theory.

PARSONS: *That is very well put; but you still have to account for the phenomena involved in backward deduction, that is, from statistical mass behavior on the social level to the individual. But reasoning in the contrary direction has not worked any better; the psychologists have failed to deduce how social systems should operate. These attempts have a long history of frustration and failure.*

SPIEGEL: This model is an attempt to escape from that, and it is only a model. When I said it is a description of nature, I only meant it might turn out to have some use in the observation of nature. These types of behavior of which you speak are already built into the system since all conceivable roles are already there, certainly all the self-perpetuating aspects of behavior. Where new interaction is concerned one would then have to respecify what the field is, to see what new thing is introduced that alters rates of change.

EDITOR: *In this Chapter a big jump was made by introducing a model of system foci in transaction within the extended field of all nature. The dependence of each system upon all others was suggested, obviating linearity, hierarchies, levels and derivations. The properties or functions of each system were designated as constitutional determinants, integrative determinants and system determinants suitable to answering the questions of What? How? and Why? How stress or strain imposed on one system changes all, but at different rates, was exemplified. These concepts were not well assimilated by the group for they seemed to impose a burden on habitual ways of conceiving hierarchies, steady states and circular processes. Thus, from time to time problems of equilibrium within and among systems will repeatedly be brought up for discussion. The usefulness of this model will be exemplified in Chapter Fourteen when the psychological and group foci are compared.*

CHAPTER THREE

THE PSYCHOLOGICAL SYSTEM

Presentation by David Shakow

IN my model (Table 1) I have tried to deal in a limited way with the problem within the focus of psychology; that is, the psyche in Spiegel's diagram.[1] In many places you will see immediately the use of terms equating with those used by others. I have allowed for the stopping of the process which does not imply that it does not go on all the time. All the general principles that we have been discussing are here: open systems, continuous process and circularity of the type that means constant interchange of transactions.

I would like to have you imagine you are looking down a deep alleyway, as if a tube had been sliced at a particular point for us to observe. But at the same time, while certain processes are going on, other processes are ending and some are beginning. What we see depends upon the focus of attention; we are dealing for the present with what we have directly before us, neglecting for the moment the other things. I am not dealing here with structure—and by "structure" I am thinking mainly of the device which maintains these processes and gives some regularity of performance through time. I am presenting here what might perhaps be thought of as the fundamental psychoanalytic model which David Rapaport most recently has brought forth very clearly.[2] It posits the need, the need-satisfying object and the need gratification—the pattern of events in that order of time.

[1] Page 18.
[2] "The Conceptual Model of Psychoanalysis," *in Theoretical Models and Personality Theory*, eds. D. Krech and G. S. Klein (Durham: Duke University Press, 1952).

Table 1

Psychological Model *—Primary Tension Maintenance

(a)	(b)	(c)		(d)		(e)
NEED	TENSION	ATTEMPT TO REDUCE TENSION	NEED OBJECT AVAILABLE	GRATIFICATION		TENSION-REDUCTION (Relatively complete)
			NEED OBJECT UNAVAILABLE	DELAY OF GRATIFICATION: (EGO) IDEATION OF MEANS & ENDS	DISCHARGE OF AFFECT ON INTERMEDIATE & DERIVATIVE MEANS—OBJECTS	TENSION-REDUCTION (varying degrees of completeness)
				SUBSTITUTE GRATIFICATION: 1. SUBLIMATIVE	AFFECT DISCHARGE ON: 1. SUBSTITUTE OBJECT	
				2. HALLUCINATORY (dream, hallucination, obsession, etc.)	2. SUBSTITUTE IMAGE	PARTIAL TENSION REDUCTION (varying degrees of incompleteness)
				3. REACTIVE a. Regression b. Repression c. Reaction-formation	3. SUBSTITUTE BEHAVIOR	
			(or combination of these)	4. OTHER a. Repression (when effective)	Affect-discharge reduced	
	DISEQUILIBRIUM RESTLESSNESS UNPLEASANTNESS ANXIETY	DRIVE TOWARD OBJECT (CATHECTED)	FRUSTRATION	MEMORY; ATTITUDES; FEARS OF REFERENCE; INHIBITIONS; SELF; EXPECTATIONS		EQUILIBRIUM PLEASURE
Cognitive Affective	Affective	Conative/cognitive	Cognitive	Cognitive	Affective/conative	Affective

* Modified from D. Rapaport.

A tension system arises which may be described by such words as "disequilibrium." There follows some attempt on the part of the psychic organism to reduce this tension. If the needed object—that is, the object toward which the need is most fundamentally directed—is present and available, gratification takes place and the tension subsides. That subsidence is relatively complete as compared to other situations of subsidence which I am now going to discuss.

To turn to the second class of gratifications, where these objects of need are unavailable. They are either present and unavailable, or absent; but for one reason or another they are unavailable to the organism at the time.

Under these circumstances there are a variety of possibilities: If the organism is capable of delaying the gratification, there will be an ideation of means and ends around subsequent gratification. We might think about this type of response in analytical terms, as involving primarily function, and the basis perhaps for the development of thought processes. What follows from such a response is some discharge of affect on these intermediate images of the gratification or the substitute images for the gratification and some reduction of tension. Or there may be various kinds of substitute gratification. One of these is the *sublimative* type. Here the affect is discharged on a substitute object of a particular kind, particularly acceptable to society and one's notions of society's needs. It may be complete or it may be only partial, and the tension reduction accordingly would be of different degrees. Or you may have a second type, an *hallucinatory* substitution—where you substitute memory *images* of gratification which do not have to be delayed. Here there is an immediate attempt to achieve tension reduction by way of dreams, hallucinations, obsessions and other mechanisms of this kind.

The third type might be called *reactive*, including such responses as regression, repression, reaction-formation—various types of substitute *behavior*, resulting in tension-reduction. Then there are other types, such as repression when effective. Here no actual symptoms might be established, but merely the affect discharge is reduced. These various forms of response are not separate, they are merely ideally separate ways of behaving. We of course find various combinations of actual gratification with some of the other sorts of substitute gratification, and one has always to consider the problem of their interrelationships.

I think about these levels or different kinds of responsiveness—need, gratification and tension-reduction—as tied up with various aspects of the psychological process. For our present purposes I have not found any better system than the old cognitive, conative and affective aspects. It is very important to recognize them in each of these steps. Although I will isolate them and point out what seem to be the particular predominance and emphases in each of the steps, I do not think that at any one time one can separate the three aspects of the behavioral process and say that one exists purely in isolation.

I would say that at the level of need we are dealing with cognitive processes primarily. The attempt to reduce tension is predominately conative-cognitive, while the gratification, delay of gratification or substitute gratification involves first cognitive and then affective-conative aspects; tension-reduction is primarily affective.

There are successive focusing points for analyzing this kind of situation. Thus, when we are focusing on the need-objects, we look upon the recognition of the objects as primary—the cognitive—and tend to minimize the affective and the conative aspects.

PARSONS: *Where does the evaluative come in, if at all?*

SHAKOW: Evaluative would probably cut across both the conative and the affective, in the sense that it contains both elements and organizes them. It is a kind of organizing process.

PARSONS: *There is not much question of evaluation when dealing with only one need, but when one is dealing with a system, evaluation enters in.*

SHAKOW: Delay of gratification is probably the most complex area for analysis, for then problems of the most complicated symbol systems must be considered. As an example: take a learning situation. I have been interested in recent years in the problem of learning in schizophrenia, and it has impressed upon me a number of factors implicit in learning thinking and learning theory which have not been brought out perhaps as explicitly as they might be. The learning situation is an example of a transactional process in the sense in which Dewey and Bentley use the term; not merely stimulus-response. If I should fall into the error of using the words "stimulus" and "response" in apparently isolated fashion, I hope you will understand the implication; it is sometimes difficult to keep them out of one's vocabulary!

In discussing the natural development of the transactional process in learning, one must keep it in mind that at any one time one may turn to any level and find certain events occurring that are less clear because the whole process has not been under scrutiny.

My own impression is that the primary elements which have to be taken into account in the analysis of learning are three (Figure 2). Take a simple situation such as motor learning. (It is even more complicated but still holds in principle in affective learning.) "SR" is the stimulus situation itself; the background of the particular stimulus-response situation is B-plus. These are the relevant but interfering aspects of a cognitive, affective and conative kind that are factors present in any learning situation. In motor learning, if you are trying to find your way to maintaining contact with a target you must follow the target as it revolves. You may make all kinds of errors in the process of attaining skill at this pursuit task. These are relevant, necessary parts of the learning process which take time.

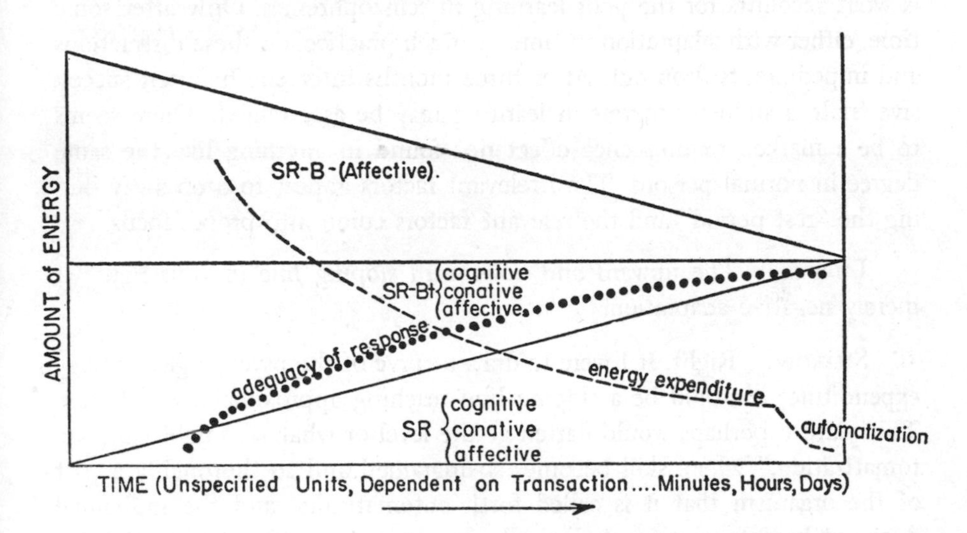

Modifications: changes in proportion of 3 aspects.

Same direction in *normal* situations whether:
- trial and error learning,
- intellectually insightful learning,
- emotionally insightful learning.

Different slopes in *aberrant* personalities (dependent probably on type of abnormality)

Different proportions for:
1. Different people.
2. Different times in same people.
3. Different types of learning activity.

FIGURE 2

NATURAL DEVELOPMENT OF TRANSACTIONAL (STIMULUS-RESPONSE) SITUATION (LEARNING)

There are, however, a whole variety of other background stimuli, which I call B-minus or background minus. These are irrelevant factors in the process of learning. The fears, the insecurities, the special and peculiar significances of the process, the ruminations and whatever else may come in that are not related to the learning process itself but are actually interferences with it—these are largely affective in nature. (The B-minus are largely affective in character; the B-plus involves all three aspects.)

The Figure has time represented on the abcissa but the time units are not specific. I think this general model could be set up for all learning, whether it is trial-and-error, or emotional insight or intellectual learning. I would like to see it tested on all three. The time units may be seconds or months or, in the case of relationship with parents, years.

A study of schizophrenics in these learning situations shows that the irrelevant factors play an important role in learning, in contrast to the normal person. My opinion is that the prominence of the B-minus factors is what accounts for the poor learning in schizophrenics. Only after some time, either with adaptation in time or much practice, do these distractions and impediments drop out. After three months intervene between successive trials, a sudden progress in learning may be ascertained. There seems to be a marked reminiscence effect not found in anything like the same degree in normal persons. The irrelevant factors appear to drop away during the "rest period" and the relevant factors come into proper focus.

LIDDELL: *The upward and downward sloping line in your figure is merely negative adaptation?*

SHAKOW: Right. If I were to draw a curve of the psychological energy expenditure, it would be a sloping line reaching approximately a plateau. This plateau perhaps would flatten at the level of what we might call "automatization," where skill becomes so ingrained and so thoroughly a part of the organism that it is called forth automatically, and the individual does not have to give psychologically, as we say, any attention to the act. This is an important concept because, as has been pointed out by many people, so much depends upon the number of things we can do automatically. It also has great significance for the problem of neuroses and psychoses.

HENRY: *Could you give me an example of normal behavior of these relationships?*

SHAKOW: Let us take the learning of a simple type of motor activity; it might be typewriting or skating. Skating is obviously a process which improves with time; so you have an ordinary learning situation. How do you acquire that skill? You make all kinds of trials and errors. You fall and get up and finally learn to move your feet in the proper way. But also, at the same time, relevant interfering processes come in which call for the reorganization of musculature and the integration of the various physiological and psychological functions so that they work smoothly in, for instance, the attaining of gracefulness. Grace might be thought of as the dropping out of these background interfering factors.

Over and above these relevant factors (which are present for all people) there is a range, of course, in the speed with which one acquires skill. At the level at which I am thinking, probably that range is not as wide as one ordinarily thinks of it.

In addition there are the B-minus factors. Perhaps, while learning to skate, I saw someone I like fall. That makes me feel a little less certain about skating. Or, I know that my father had great difficulty learning to skate, and that makes it a competitive kind of activity. Or, at the deepest psychoanalytical level, skating might have some very special significance for you.

All of these factors may inhibit you and impede you in acquiring a skill that on the surface, at least, is a relatively impersonal skill. You see no reason why it should involve your deepest personal needs (and I am speaking now of "deepest" from an analytical standpoint); or such things as ego status, besides the more obvious social and more public considerations.

In the case of a schizophrenic, you may try to make simple learning as impersonal as possible and still you get what seem to us to be a good many of these distracting factors. Once these factors are overcome, there seems to be relatively little difference in the physiological limit of a schizophrenic and a normal person. The former starts off much more poorly than the normal subject, but if you keep the experiment going for a long time, you will see that difference disappears.

PARSONS: *Whatever may be the organizational schizophrenic personality relative to the outside situation, is it far more regular than the normal? Does it grow from the outside?*

SHAKOW: Yes. There may be reverberating effects too. I must caution you, however, that I have simplified this situation. I do not mean that some facts are clearly of one kind and some clearly of another kind. In the total process, as you start to analyze factors that may be playing a role in the poor performance, you come out with some generalization which, in a sense, is a model because we do not have the data to substantiate it as yet.

THOMPSON: *What would be examples of interfering background? Could you give some examples in learning to skate?*

SHAKOW: Yes. You must learn how to move one foot in front of the other; that is a natural part of the learning process. Then you have to learn how to be able to stand up on the skates.

THOMPSON: *What would be interfering with that?*

SHAKOW: Your particular emotional reactions to the situation; the fact, say, that you see your associates all away ahead of you. The fact that they know how to skate well and you do not, and cannot, freezes you instead of motivating you to greater effort and concentration. Or take a boy who comes home saying he won't go to school any more. The trouble may lie either in current relationships to his peers—the objective situation—or to emotional relationships within himself. By "within himself" I mean his images of past experiences and relationships with others, and the current relationships with his peers merely re-arouse these underlying anxieties.

HENRY: *The SR line, the stimulus-response line, does that represent the attitude: "It's cold now; there's ice; I can go skating?"*

SHAKOW: No. The stimulus-response relationship is your relationship to the environment you skate in, or the typewriter if you are learning to type, and to all the other kinds of stimuli present. There is constant interaction and selection from among the mass of stimuli of those which are responded to as appropriate or relevant to the learning process. In addition some stimuli are relevant but interfering, and others are quite irrelevant and interfering.

The first of these two curves (dashed line) that I have drawn is a curve of energy expenditure—that is, showing how much the organism or the person has to put out at any one time to learn this much. The second curve (dotted line) shows the effectiveness of the response at parallel points. At the point where the skill is automatized, the least energy is demanded. The energy expenditure and the effectiveness of the response run of course in contrary directions.

SPIEGEL: *I was trying to put this into the system I spoke about. In general you are describing the impacts of the integrative processes at the focus of the psyche, and are giving a special case, say, of an integrative process in the nature of self-correction.*

SHAKOW: Yes, as drawn out in time, rather than as a cross-section of time. I think that is what must be involved.

FRANK: *One possible objection to the model under discussion is in the way we look upon tensions. It is frequently asserted that the individual is primarily concerned with reduction of tension and this of course is amply confirmed by clinical study of disturbed personalities. However, in normal living we find that much of the satisfaction and fulfillment in life comes from intentionally building up tensions, deferring consummation and often accepting purely symbolic fulfillments.*

A second objection arises from the notion of purely biological needs and the attempt to interpret human personality expression in terms of gratification of these basic needs. We cannot forget that human personali-

ties do not live as organisms, driven by organic needs and physiological functions. We know that early in life the basic organic needs for air, food, elimination, sleep, and so on are transformed into a variety of goal seeking, purposive strivings for deferred and symbolic goals as the only way in which a child can learn to live in our cultural and social world. The theory of delayed gratification seems to rest on a conception of basic organic needs and simple tension reduction without adequately recognizing these many different kinds of transformation.

EDITOR: *In a model of the psychological system, a modification of the psychoanalytic theory was presented. The pattern of events was: need, need-satisfying object and need gratification into which tension obtrudes. The psychological functions are involved in attempts to reduce tension by dealing vigorously with the need or by using substitute gratifications. Need involves cognitive, and tension the affective aspects. The processes associated with tension systems were exemplified by learning and its interferences in healthy and schizophrenic individuals.*

CHAPTER FOUR

THE OBSERVER AND THE OBSERVED: HUMAN COMMUNICATION THEORY

Presentation by Jurgen Ruesch

WHAT we studied so far was, first of all, how the human observer studies phenomena. I now wish to amplify these observer-bound properties which influence our picture of nature. We are not interested in the way nature is constructed but in how the observer perceives it, and his method of perceiving. The properties of the scientific observer and the processes by which he gathers scientific information seem to me to be best explained by a theory of human communication, the basis of which I have outlined, together with Gregory Bateson [1] and in several other publications.[2] In social science and in psychiatry the observer is always in a personal situation when he gathers information. I emphasize the word *always*. Whether the data be psychological or cultural, they must always be found and gathered, and you cannot

[1] G. Bateson and J. Ruesch, *Communication, the Social Matrix of Psychiatry* (New York: W. W. Norton, 1952).

[2] J. Ruesch, "The Therapeutic Process from the Point of View of Communication," *American Journal of Orthopsychiatry*, XXII (1952), 690; "Synopsis of the Theory of Human Communications," *Psychiatry*, XVI (1953), 215; "Social Factors in Therapy," *Assoc. Res. Nervous and Mental Diseases*, XXXI (1953), 59; "The Interpersonal Communication of Anxiety," in *Symposium on Stress* (Washington, D.C.: Army Medical Service Graduate School, Walter Reed Army Medical Center, 1953); "Psychiatry and the Challenge of Communication," *Psychiatry*, XVII (1954), 1.

obtain information from a crowd—only from individuals. Basically, the sociologist, anthropologist, or psychiatrist will gather data derived from persons. It cannot be otherwise. However, once he has gathered those data, he can interpret them as he pleases, using whatever systems he likes. In other words, first he gathers data from specified individuals and later he can omit the names of those individuals and deal with the information itself.

The information an observer can collect depends upon his location within or without the system and upon his views of the boundaries. In the nineteenth century we viewed things primarily as having only one boundary—namely, the outside. Freud, I think, was the first one who postulated

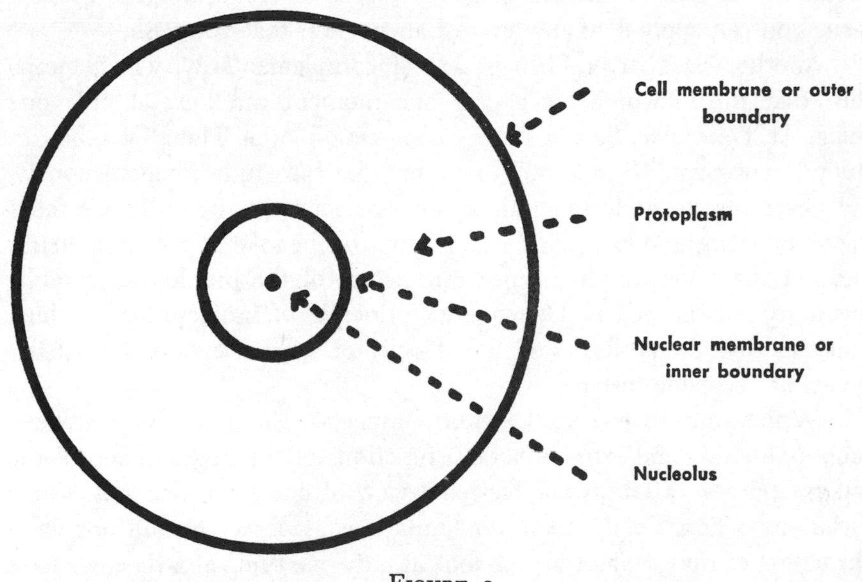

FIGURE 3

SCHEME OF THE CELL STRUCTURE SHOWING INNER AND OUTER BOUNDARIES

that an entity had an inner and an outer boundary, and he arrived at that by translating the then existing neurophysiological concern with cell structure—nucleus, protoplasm, and membranes—into psychology.[3] The ego would be analogous to the cytoplasm, the superego and id analogous to the nuclear structure. Any individual feels the outer and inner boundaries impinge upon him.

In the middle of the twentieth century, the concept is implied that any organization, whether biological or social, has an inner and an outer boundary. One can look at either boundary from two sides, and for successful

[3] Cf. Figure 3.

functioning there must be information that pertains to the structures located beyond the inner or outer boundary.

HENRY: *In a hospital ward what would be the inner and outer boundaries?*

RUESCH: Just as in cell physiology membranes are hypothetical, so they are in psychology. They are revealed by discrepancies of views. In the individual it is the view of himself contrasted with the view of other people. In a hospital ward it is the view held by the participants on that hospital ward as compared to the view obtained by outside observers. In terms of nations, it would be the view of the United States as seen by us as contrasted to the view of the United States as seen by Englishmen or Frenchmen. You can apply it to any level of abstraction that you wish.

Another essential problem is that of complementarity, which means this: that the human being at any one moment can look at only one thing. At Time One, he can study Phenomenon A; at Time Two, he can study Phenomenon B; and at Time Three he can study Phenomenon C; but never can he study them all at any one moment. Basically, we focus upon one thing, and we neglect other views for the sake of obtaining better views at that moment. In essence, the nature of the problem of complementarity is expressed in Heisenberg's principle of indeterminacy, which indicates that the position and the velocity of a particle cannot be determined at the same instant.

Which are such complementary aspects? Emotion and intellect; proprio-function and extero-function; functions of the in-group and of the out-group; view of self as one feels and view of oneself as one sees. These dichotomies bear simply upon our limitations as observers, and not upon the nature of things. Since we can look at only one thing at a time, we have to split it up. The thing we consider now is what we focus upon and label, being well aware of the fact that there are countless things we are ignoring. In human communication, we usually are not able to say what the things are on which we do not focus; but we are at least vaguely aware of the existence of the neglected aspects.

SHAKOW: *Is there another kind of complementarity involved that is much more serious and more difficult to deal with? In emphasizing one aspect, perhaps one brings about a temporary distortion of the situation, endowing one part with a particular prominence.*

There is the complementarity which results from the actual destruction of the process being studied by making the observations. For instance, if you stop in the middle of the learning process to test how well the subject has learned, you have interfered; you have given him additional practice and thus have interfered with the learning process.

RUESCH: Yes, but that is a different event. Complementarity refers, as it is commonly used, to the ability of the observer to gather information at a given moment. Of course, we must assume that there are events which follow each other in time and that information of this kind supplement one another.

TOMAN: *We do not always need to deal with complementarity. Items may be arranged, not in strict polarity but in threes. The observer might be the one in the middle.*

RUESCH: But still the fact remains that you can look at only one thing at one time. With multipolar phenomena, one must consider them in succession. Regardless of how many poles exist, they cannot be seen all at once.

THOMPSON: *The problem of seeing an event or phenomenon from the inside and outside and all around it, simultaneously, is one that modern art tried to solve, beginning with Picasso, following the publication of Einstein's early work. And now we social scientists are facing this problem fifty years later. To use only one focus at one time is, perhaps, just a temporary limitation of approach. When we have made the transition that has already been made by the modern artists and by modern physicists, we will operate with many foci at once, seeing the outside and inside and all around simultaneously.*

RUESCH: You can do that, but then you run into another kind of distortion. Take for example the map projections of the globe. You can choose the projection of the globe that you wish, but if you look at two of them simultaneously they seem to reinforce each other's distortions. For each purpose, there is an optimal map and one which is less optimal.

PARSONS: *You have to be rather careful about attributing too much to this one great transition between the nineteenth and twentieth centuries, because fundamentally what the calculus does, and systems of equations, is to do what language cannot do, namely, look at complementary things at the same time without having to switch perspective back and forth from one to the other. That, I think, is perhaps the greatest single significance of mathematics.*

THOMPSON: *It may be one of our goals in multidisciplinary research that we do not work alone each in our own science, but that perhaps as we continue working together in multidisciplinary teams, we shall be able to observe multiple foci.*

RUESCH: That is what many people hope; but ultimately the information derived from a team of twenty people is to be integrated in one brain. We have no machine as yet that compares to the integrative qualities of man's brain.

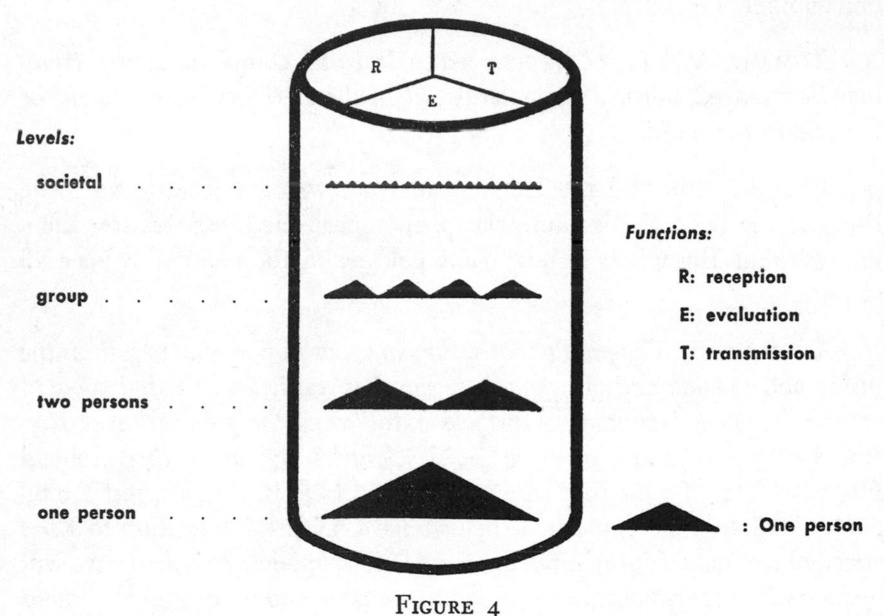

FIGURE 4

THE OBSERVER'S COMMUNICATIVE CAPACITY

FRANK: *Whatever exists actually (as contrasted with such a concept as the point) has a variety of dimensions, and each of our specialized disciplines has concentrated upon observing, measuring and interpreting one set of those dimensions and more or less deliberately ignoring all others. We are struggling to gain a conception of the multidimensionality of human organism-personalities, and to learn how we can deal with multidimensional observations without distorting or neglecting one or more of them or trying to warp all of them into a single dimensional system or framework.*

RUESCH: Let us view the human observer's communicative functions as consisting of reception (R), evaluation (E) and transmission (T). Since the individual's upper capacities are known in terms of numbers of neurons and in terms of his performance, we can schematically represent these biological limitations by a cylinder. If the individual looks at one person, then his perceptual-evaluative capacity is occupied with this person. If he considers two individuals at the same time, the magnification with which he views each person becomes smaller. When he interacts with a group, individuals lose still more detail until by the time he considers, let us say five hundred or fifty thousand people, each person gets to be but a little speck. When you consider 150,000 people, no one single person is distinct, but the patterning of these people may appear more clearly. There is an appropriate type of magnification for looking at the individual or part of the individual, dependent upon the number of people that have to be considered simultaneously.

When we communicate we never consistently talk about any one of these perspectives. For example, we quickly consider one person; and in the second half of the same thought we think about that person in a two-, three-, four-, or five-person situation; then all of a sudden, perhaps in the same breath so to speak, we think about this person as part of a large group. What we do is to think and talk about human processes by employing some sort of oscillation phenomenon; we constantly switch the magnification with which we focus upon the individual. In addition to the magnification, we switch frames of reference. You find multiple frames of reference in any one thought or statement. Confusion, and at the same time lucidity, of communication depends upon these switches, because if you ever think of something in one of these perspectives only, you do not understand what is going on. In order to understand the human being, one needs constant oscillation, which phenomenon is related to perception of differences rather than to perception of the thing *per se*. Thus all information we exchange is transacted in a social situation, the context of which determines to a large extent the nature of this exchange. The field of communication thus concerns itself with the phenomenon of how information that is outside the human being gets to be represented within and how information that is inside gets out. In other words, the science of communication deals with the representation of outside events inside and of inside events outside.

PARSONS: *Would you not say that is what I would call "action level," or that is the analogue of physico-chemical interchange between organism and the other? Physico-chemical interchange is how something gets in and out, but communication is the interchange process of action systems.*

RUESCH: I would say that communication deals with the penetration of boundaries.

PARSONS: *So does the organism-environment interchange.*

RUESCH: Instead of calories, information is exchanged. In order to accomplish this end, three functions are needed, which I have represented longitudinally in the schematic cylinder.

The basic function of reception is devoted to the process of input; the function of transmission is devoted to output; and the function of evaluation is devoted to storage of memory traces, to decision-making and to control. But the functions are interrelated with the levels. At the one-person level, the individual can do with himself what he pleases. In a two-person system, the freedom is already limited because the sorts of things that go on between two people require that at a given time there exist mutual adaptation: for example, one person talks and the other listens. In group systems and particularly in societal systems, people become parts of evaluative, transmitting or receptive bodies. There are news analysts, military observers and scientists; there are decision-making and executive bodies; and there are action bodies that transmit messages: the propagandists and broadcasters.

None of these functions operate with equal intensity all the time. Not only do we receive and also transmit, but by and large we oscillate back and forth between these functions.

When we view communication in any situation, we have to consider the oscillations that take place in the head of the participant-observer between the perspective levels and the various functions. In addition, these oscillations take place in the system that he studies. This complicates matters incredibly, and for convenience's sake it seems profitable to view natural events not in terms of the reality of the matter but through the eyes of the observer, specifying as much as possible the communication system of which he is an integral part.

SHAKOW: *Does "oscillation" carry a special meaning in your vocabulary?*

RUESCH: No. All I wish to indicate is a going back and forth which varies with the mental speed of the individual and the speed of the phenomena that are observed.

SPIEGEL: *Why does it have to be a lineally constructed model?*

RUESCH: It does not. I am not a good designer. It is a little more difficult to design if you put the observer in the center of the globe and have the various functions and levels around it. Let us say you would have the observer in the middle of an onion, and around him you would have the various systems. The calix would be the functions of receiving, transmitting and evaluating.

SPIEGEL: *Is what you are presenting an explanation of the way the individual behaves, or is it an explanation of the way one can explain total behavior?*

RUESCH: If an observer presents something, we can look at what he presents with the help of this system. You can look at whatever he presents, whether he be an anthropologist, a sociologist or an analyst, rather than figure out what the real events looked like that he purports to describe.

SPIEGEL: *It seems to me we are being impaled on one of the horns of the dilemma, because the event is being constructed on the basis of the psychology of the individual.*

RUESCH: You cannot get away from the fact that any scientist, whoever he may be, will be a human being.

THOMPSON: *As I understand it, you said that the human being has a fixed perceptive capacity. How do you arrive at that?*

RUESCH: There are lots of scientific data for that. We know, for example, that the digit span forward or backward is limited. The range of memory for distinctly separate items varies within fairly narrow limits. You have ten fingers. There are twelve months in the year. All practical measures in life are gathered in numbers that can be distinctly kept separate and range between seven and thirteen.

There exist a lot of experimental data covering the limits of the perceptive capacity of human beings. For instance, if you simultaneously stimulate the individual by visual and by auditory means, the acuity for either mode decreases as compared to single visual or auditory stimulation. In other words, we have enough evidence to say that at any one moment the organism can attend to a limited number of stimuli. If the input or output exceeds the capacity of the individual, breakdown occurs.

Let me now give you a practical example of how the concepts of levels and functions are applied to the two-person system. A simplified version of a two-person communication system has been diagrammatically sketched in Figure 5, below.

Starting with the processes of exteroception of person A, we can distinguish three kinds of stimuli. The first set of stimuli derives from objects and events other than persons; the second set of stimuli derives from actions of the other person; and the third set of stimuli derives from the actions of person A which are seen or heard by the exteroceptors of the

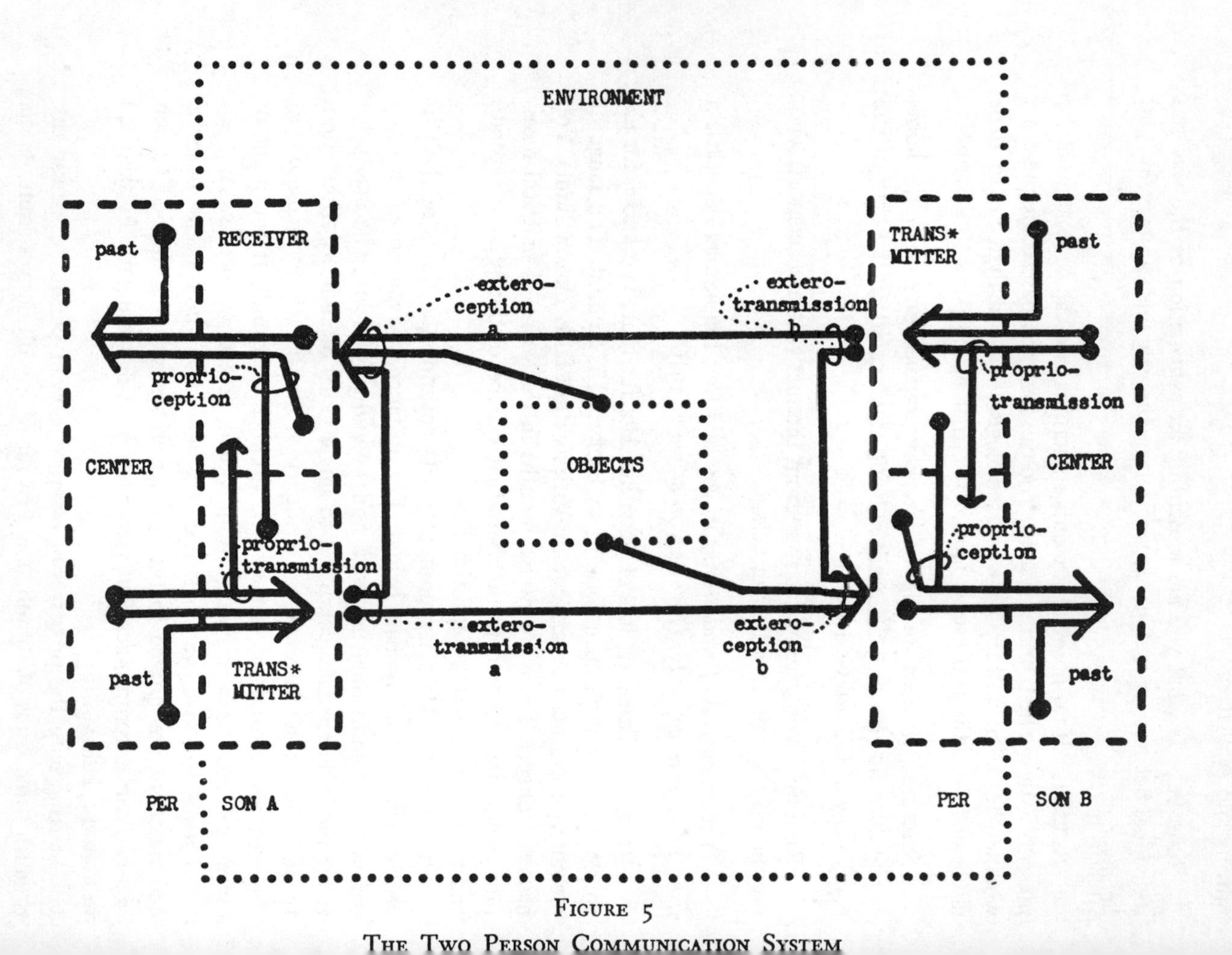

FIGURE 5

THE TWO PERSON COMMUNICATION SYSTEM

same person. These three sets of stimuli reach the sense organs. In the sense organs the acoustic, visual, osmic, gustatory, tactile, temperature, pain and vibratory stimuli are transformed into nervous impulses; at this point some of the external stimuli are perhaps also transformed into some chemical impulses, which then are conveyed by the humoral pathways. After having undergone such transformations within the receiver, the external stimuli which now have become nervous impulses are transmitted to the communication center. There these afferent impulses are joined by other impulses which originate in the organism itself. These derive on the one hand from other peripheral stations of the organism, and on the other hand they derive from impulses which circulate within the communication center and denote past events. The processes of perception, therefore, have three roots: the impulses which derive from exteroception, the impulses which derive from proprioception, and the impulses which denote past events. When these combined afferent impulses reach the communication center, they are subjected to a complicated series of operations which deal with the evaluation of what has been perceived. Essentially one can say that these evaluative processes consist of operations with the available information. At this point one must remember that stimuli which reach the organism are probably not only transformed once but several times before they reach the communication center, and each process of transformation entails a loss of information. The transformation of these nervous and perhaps chemical impulses consists essentially of renewed codification. And codification of information is referred to as that process by which events are represented within the system of communication. Thus a person has information about its receiver and transmitter within the communication center, while at the same time the receiver and transmitter exist in their own right. It is for this reason that the dotted line representing the environment includes these organs because they lie outside of the psychological center of the individual.

Once a message has been evaluated, the communication center emits impulses directed toward the effector organs. These efferent impulses, being the result of complicated operations with information on hand, transmit messages to the outside world (exterotransmission) and to other stations of the body (propriotransmission) so that coordinated action becomes possible. In the transmitter these impulses are transformed into muscular contractions and glandular activities which convey messages to the outside world.

The messages emitted by person A can then be picked up by person B, and after passage through the organism of person B, the transmitter of person B will broadcast the response to person A. These two persons have to be viewed as one system in which messages circulate and oscillate forth and back innumerable times. Communication takes place when person A emits a message which is received by person B, who in turn responds by sending an acknowledgment to person A. Inasmuch as person A knows the context of the message, the interpretation that B gives to this message, when communicated back to A, gives person A a chance to evaluate whether B has understood the message. Thus, through progressive change and corrections, understanding takes place.

The analysis of larger communication systems proceeds very much along similar lines. What we want to know is: Who talks to whom? About what? In which context? With what instructions? In which form, and with what kind of effect? Or, if I put it into a more systematic manner, the *first* question one can ask is the question as to *physical and social reality*. In other words, what are the limitations and the context of this communicative situation as seen by the consensus of observers? It is defined as the limitation of the physical and social reality. If an individual is blind, that imposes a distinct limitation upon his perception. A committee like this, composed of fifteen members, applies the rules of a scientific gathering. Music is not provided for entertainment; neither are beds; therefore, the context limits the activities of the members. The context thus defines what sort of label is given to a situation; what sort of perspective, in terms of the cylinder, is called for; what sort of a division of labor exists; what sort of specialized functions of communication are called for; what sort of rules there are—written or unwritten—and whether we know them implicitly, and whether we all follow them; and what sort of roles are to be assumed, and if they are clearly defined.

HENRY: *I often find myself forgetting that what we are doing here is constructing ideal types.*

RUESCH: This is not an ideal type—this is the analysis of actual situations. This is something you or I can actually do, something that has been done, and something that all of us do all the time. Whenever you start to investigate a communication system, wherever it is, you must define it in some way. You must define the field in which it occurs; you cannot do otherwise. From the label you pin upon the situation depend the interpretations you are going to give to the exchange of messages.

The *second* question inquires into the origin of the message. It may be paraphrased by saying, "*Who is saying it?*" If you deal with a governmental agency, it has a name; if it is an individual, we label him with all traditional means of identification—name, age, sex, role, group membership or whatever other means of identification we possess.

The *third* question inquires into the destination of the message. It may be paraphrased by saying, "To whom is the message addressed?" To the people of the United States? To the citizens of Chicago? To the members of this committee? To one specific person? Or, perhaps, to self?

The *fourth* question raises the problem of content and inquires as to what the message refers to. What is being said will vary as it is interpreted by different participants, and there exists no single way of interpreting the content. Although the term *horse* is well defined, everybody who is going to use the word *horse* will refer to different referential properties. The interpretation of content on the part of a third person, not directly connected with the exchange of messages, will depend upon the following information:

1. What was the intent of the sender?
2. What is the interpretation of the receiver?
3. What is the amount of consensus achieved between the sender and the receiver?

From the degree of agreement or disagreement, conclusions can be drawn about what was talked about.

The *fifth* question inquires into the *codification systems* and media of communication which have been used: perception channels, transmission channels, verbal and non-verbal modes, language. The patterning of the various channels in itself represents a form of codification. Writing a note to a man in the office next door is interpreted differently from just walking over and saying it.

The *sixth* question inquires into the method of *metacommunication*, which indicates the interpretive devices used in the exchange of messages: explicit instructions, implicit instructions contained in role assumption, reference to context of the situation, rules, sequences, patterning. Metacommunication has to be separated into the giving of instructions and the interpretation of instructions. If you enter a store as an automobile buyer, you are treated quite differently from the way you would be treated if you let it be known that you are a seller of an old jallopy. Under the rubric of metacommunication come all the emotional factors. When we talk with someone else, we evaluate the state of his or her organism, his tension, irritability, kindness and patience—all factors that bear upon the interpretation of messages.

PARSONS: *I think you are stating a point that I make in a slightly different way, that is, that no symbol in human communication is ever purely cognitive. It is always both cognitive and expressive at the same time.*

SHAKOW: *But in different degrees. It is very important to keep in mind these different degrees, because I think it has been the source of difficulty to social scientists. For instance, Rapaport*[4] *and others have emphasized the affective in the interpretation of psychometric data on the personality to such a degree that the cognitive aspects have been lost; they seem to assume that all communication is affective, whereas in many situations it is largely cognitive.*

RUESCH: We meet this problem by saying that any message is divided into the content of the message and the instructions about the message. Sometimes, for example, a person may tell you something, and his words are nothing but an interpretation of the content carried by the gesture. Or in another situation the gesture may be used to emphasize what is being said. You do not know ahead of time which is going to be metacommunicative instruction and which is content. It varies as the conversation continues.

THOMPSON: *You have not discussed communication without words through psychomotor tensions. I mean the kind of communication that goes on between people which is non-verbal and not affected by words. It is highly developed in some cultures.*

RUESCH: One person sends; the other person receives. On the part of the receiver there is an interpretation which depends upon the instructions of the sender. If somebody is very tense, then the other person might try to pick up all the other signals that are being transmitted in search for clues that might help him to interpret this tension.

The *seventh* and last question in the analysis of a communication network inquires into the feedback devices and the effects achieved. If a statement made by one person has been received and picked up by somebody else or by some other organization, what is the result? In what way does it influence the actions undertaken upon receipt of the message? What will the reply be? But this subject has been treated extensively elsewhere.

To forestall misunderstandings, I should like to call your attention to two points. In communication theory, action is treated as being controlled by information because there is no action without information. Muscles do not contract by themselves; nor do machines, which can be viewed as extensions of muscles, live in space alone—they are controlled by some sort of evaluative mechanism embodied in the human organism and the nervous system. The second point I should like to make is with

[4] David Rapaport, "The Conceptual Model of Psychoanalysis," in *Theoretical Models and Personality Theory*, eds. D. Krech and G. S. Klein (Durham: Duke University Press, 1952).

regard to emotions. In communication theory, emotions represent evaluations of the state of the organism. Whether registered continuously or discontinuously, the evaluation of the state of the organism at any one moment is necessary for the organism in order to function. Conclusions such as "I am tired," "I am hungry," or "I am bored" are the result of numerous impressions and will dictate the next step.

In communication theory, "conscious" means that anything that has been perceived must have been sent, and "unconscious" means that the person perceives something that he did not perceive before.

FRANK: *Two points should be recognized in this discussion. First, every cultural group establishes in its members a selective perception of what is going on in the world, in other people and in themselves. Secondly, every cultural group also gives priority to some of the many, many to-whom-it-may concern messages, as Norbert Wiener has said.*[5] *Thus, each of us picks out from the "surround" and pays attention to what we selectively perceive. Even when messages are not sent specifically and directly to us, we are receiving and responding to them. Thus we may say that we are continually selecting, evaluating and interpreting what is going on in the surround and in ourselves and shaping our lives accordingly.*

RUESCH: In the theory of human communication, noise has no place. Anything that Wiener, in his machine systems, calls noise, we call metacommunication. Anything that enters, regardless of what it is, will shape the content and will not, as in the telephone system, merely reduce intelligibility.

Now let me turn to the question about the to-whom-it-may-concern messages. Messages may run from one to one, from one to many, from many to one, or from many to many. When the origin of the message and its destination are known, the result is a greater degree of intelligibility and greater security, and consensus can be reached. If, however, the origin of the message or its destination is unknown, and particularly when both are unknown, then frustration sets in.

PARSONS: *I think that is the solution of the problem of behaviorism. The postulate with which Ruesch started out this afternoon is that the difference between the natural and the human sciences—the behavioral sciences, in this sense—is that in the latter the observer communicates with his subject. You cannot communicate behavioristically. In other words, you have to treat as evidence symbols and their meaning.*

That is what the behaviorists in the old days tried to rule out. For

[5] Cybernetics (New York: John Wiley, 1948).

example, observations of verbal behavior were not scientific evidence if accepted as meaning. There are empirical errors of varying degrees of seriousness, but sometimes these really radical errors hold forth for a long time. I think that was one of them. It has turned out to be exactly the contrary. The sciences of this field have advanced by devising techniques of handling symbolic evidence rigorously and technically, and if they had refused to touch it, they would not have advanced significantly.

FRANK: *It is relevant to what Parsons has just said to recall that only recently nearly all of the data used by social scientists were by-products of administrative procedures and recording of political, economic, legal and social activities; that is to say, social scientists never collected their own data but rather took their data from various records and reports, like the Census. Accordingly, they were limited to these records and could handle them only by the quantitative methods then possible. In this situation they were more or less justified with the assumption that the observer was not participating in the observations, and it is indeed interesting to recognize that the social scientists depended upon non-scientific agents to collect their data.*

Today there is more and more field work with interviewing and direct observation of people's activities and growing realization that the concepts and assumptions of social scientists largely govern their observations and the methods they employ to obtain their data.

GRINKER: *I think your model, Ruesch, corresponds very well with the biological model and with the foci model, except that you now fill up the spaces and discriminate as to the nature of the communication between the systems, whether they be biological or interpersonal systems. Would your model involve any contradiction with the concepts that already have been set forth?*

RUESCH: I do not think there are fundamentally any contradictions. I think it depends upon the purpose. My model enables us to study, and, if you want, to relate cultural to social events; it is ideally suited to the purpose. It is not suited for studying pathology, because the question raised in studying pathology is not answered by that sort of model. It is a totally different question.

GRINKER: *I disagree when you say that pathology is something apart.*

RUESCH: No, I do not say pathology is something apart. I say my model is essentially bound to the study of signals, impulses, messages—whatever you want to call them. If you deal with things in which the impulse or message is excluded, this model is no good.

GRINKER: *Why is it not amenable to study by your model?*

SPIEGEL: *If you say that the processes you have described are essential to integrative processes (and I certainly think they are), then there is a pathology whenever disturbances occur in the communication process. It may be any pathology. Think of pathology as a disintegration of process. It must have to do with disturbances of coordination which depend upon communicative processes.*

RUESCH: They have a communicative aspect, I grant you that, but in practice all models have an optimal application, and the optimal application of my model is in studying something that is in transition and achieves certain effects.

FRANK: *Information theory may be used for various purposes. Physicists, it seems, are preoccupied with information theory largely because they are trying to develop a new epistemology for modern physics. As Rothman has said, "The kind of information one gets is simply the kind of measurement one chooses to make." While that may sound like a platitude, it is a very important commentary on information theory and the concern with obtaining specific kinds of data from specified events. For a unified theory of human behavior, we need a communication theory which goes beyond the presently recognized information theory by recognizing the processes which seem to be more or less uniquely involved in all human communication.*

PARSONS: *I would say that the kind of communication that is relevant is a function of the frame of reference and the type of system we are dealing with, and the communication theory alone does not tell you that. It does not tell you what kind of system you are dealing with. I think that is the sort of trouble that the social scientist is put into. He does not specify what kind of system and frame of reference the communication theory is tailored to. Then he starts to make inference about all kinds of systems from his communication theory, without going into this primary question.*

There is one perfectly clear distinction: neural communication is in the organism, symbolic communication is in interpersonal relationships. The mechanisms clearly are not the same, although the neural mechanisms are certainly involved in the latter on some level.

I think it is extremely dangerous to lay down a general communication theory and say: "This explains neural communication; it explains biochemical hormonal communication; it also explains verbal communication in interpersonal relationships." I am sure Wiener's cybernetics has not done that.

RUESCH: We are considering the two-surface or boundary problems that I mentioned before. In any communication system, there must be an observer. The observer has a purpose and a training and an identity, and by that his observations are defined in terms of the bias he uses. Wiener assumes communication almost without human observers. He postulates superhuman observers as all physical scientists do. I start with an identified human observer or several who are at least identified. I believe that in social sciences we must have an identified human observer in an identified position at an identified moment. Social science does not work with a non-identified or superhuman observer.

PARSONS: *Wiener makes the very round assertion that anything beyond the most elementary levels of generalization in social science is impossible because of the problem of noise. It has happened in history more than once that men with high reputations and prestige have asserted that there were certain ultimate limits to the development of knowledge in certain directions; and again and again they have been proved wrong. But when a man of Wiener's stature makes such an assertion then, in the first place, one must take it seriously. After all, you do not want simply to take the cue and resign from your profession because he has made it clear that you are batting against a stone wall. Secondly, one must find some way of understanding where he erred. I think this is the point at which he goes astray.*

TOMAN: *Wiener is essentially trying to deal with prediction of interrelationships in the outside material world, from anti-aircraft sighting to the prediction of the specific intensity and speed of a reflex in a cat. He is able to go a long distance and to evaluate and quantify and insofar as he attempts to give mathematical statements for events that require description, without solving the specific problem of how the observer causes distortion, there is nothing fundamentally wrong with what Wiener has done.*

PARSONS: *Except to draw certain inferences for the study of human behavior.*

RUESCH: And there you have to study the peculiarities of Wiener as an observer.

PARSONS: *If the observer affected the phenomenon it would not distort the kind of system Wiener has been working on; but it does not follow that the kind of system Wiener has been working on is the kind of system the social scientists have been working on.*

THOMPSON: *Does Ruesch have any criterion for the training of observers, or any generalizations to make along the lines of the social sciences? How are the observers that you speak of to be trained?*

RUESCH: The self-observer? We know of no better method for self-observation than psychoanalysis. But it has to be complemented by the observation of outside events. That is the task of training in social science —not only theoretical social science but in field work as well—because the sort of thing you observe in an Indian setting or in a modern American community cannot be observed in psychoanalysis, lying-on-a-couch. The two things have to be complemented. Personally, I don't think there are good social science observers without their being also self-observers; because otherwise they introduce distortions through their own bias and emotions. I don't think we have good psychoanalytically trained people who can observe social science phenomena because they do not have the knowledge of relevant cues and cannot integrate data beyond single individuals.

There is another point: when one works with someone who has been trained in psychiatry, he operates with the basic assumption that the human being is as good a scientific entity as he is a biological entity. But whether the human being is a scientific entity is very much of a question, and in many procedures the human being has turned out not to be a good scientific entity as a unit of study. It takes something like a year of working with somebody to get out of his head that simple assumption that the human being is an entity. On the other hand, if I deal with the opposite sort of person who knows that a man may not necessarily be an entity, then I have to deal with the reverse problem.

EDITOR: *In this Chapter it was emphasized that observations in all sciences are derived by an individual who has a position in relation to his object. He receives and transmits information which is limited by his position. This may be at an inner or an outer boundary but never both at once. Each set of observations may be complementary to another or an oscillation process may facilitate a fusion of separate observations. Not even multiple observers in multidisciplinary research can achieve more, since the data requires integration in the mind of a single scientist. Hence, natural events are viewed, not in terms of the reality of the matter, but through the eyes of an observer who is a part of a communication system. Ruesch gave in lucid detail the basic principles of communication systems*

as applied to human beings, stressing not only their cognitive but also their evaluative aspects. Communication differs with the type of system under discussion, and certainly in the psychological and social sciences there must be an identified human observer in an identified position at an identified moment. This makes for considerable difference from Wiener's cybernetics which are applicable to material systems and not to the behavioral sciences.

CHAPTER FIVE

THE SOCIAL SYSTEM: A GENERAL THEORY OF ACTION

Presentation by Talcott Parsons

I AM going to present a somewhat different viewpoint from that of Spiegel, but I strongly agree with his objection to the hierarchical ordering of systems. On the other hand, I make a distinction between a frame of reference and a class of systems. I think that we have a common frame of reference for several of the systems or classes that have been discussed, differing from that of the physical sciences. I think biology is in a very special sense interstitial between these two fundamental frames of reference.

In two recent books what I am about to say is elaborated in considerable technical detail.[1] The frame of reference involved is what a group of us agreed to call "action." The choice was as between the terms behavior and action. The terms do not matter much, but I believe "behavior" tends to be a somewhat more restricted term and it has become associated with behaviorism. So, we preferred the word "action."

Action is not concerned with the internal structure or processes of the organism, but with the organism as a unit in a set of relationships, the other terms of which we sum up under the concept "situation." We preferred "situation" to "environment" to avoid confusing it with the bio-

[1] T. Parsons, *The Social System* (Glencoe: The Free Press, 1951); T. Parsons and E. A. Shils, *Toward a General Theory of Action* (Cambridge: Harvard University Press, 1951).

logical meaning of environment. From this point of view the system is not the physical organism nor the object of physical perception, but it is a system of behavior or action.

Then behavior, as ordinarily used in psychology, acquires a new quality. A new system comes into being when there is interaction or transaction (we have been using the term "interaction" in this specific meaning) between two or more behaving organisms. The element of contingency is of critical significance in that the dyad has to be treated as a distinct type of system, and not just as, in the older psychological sense, the behavior of two persons. There is a very important difference which Sears has called "double contingency."

What is this double contingency? I shall take a cue from Shakow's diagram.[2] The first contingency comes in at the point of the delay of gratification in any behavioral process, and delayed gratification is always, in some sense and to some degree, uncertain gratification. Certainty of future gratification is the limiting case, but in most situations there is an element of uncertainty. So you can say that the gratification is contingent upon the development of the situation. But when the situation includes another act or an alter to ego (using "ego" and "alter" as conventions to keep our points of reference straight), the contingency includes not merely what might affect ego's gratification in the future situation but also what alter might do as a reaction to what ego does.

The contingency of alter's reaction, which is part of the situation and in interaction the most important part of the situation, is not only contingent on other factors in the situation but on what ego himself does, or on what alter interprets ego as intending to do. So communication enters as a fundamental condition. Double contingency essentially means an order of system that differs from the classic behavior system, where the behavior of the organism is studied in terms of a single contingency situation, as the classical T maze. The rat turns along the right arm, and gets the food; along the left arm he does not get the food.

This is not the time to discuss the difference between a sign or, as Morris calls it, a signal, and a true symbol. For our purposes the kind of interaction system in which we are interested always involves communication in complex symbol systems. I have just begun to take a serious interest in the theory of symbolism since it is one of the critical points of the whole concept. I find it not only convenient but highly illuminating to think of culture as consisting of complex symbol-meaning systems which arise out of social interaction and are embodied in it, and which (an extremely important property) may be transmitted from system of action to

[2] See page 28.

system of action. From this point of view there are two fundamental types or classes of system of action, namely, personalities and social systems.

One phase of learning is the transmission of culture from personality to personality. The corresponding term (a very interesting and well-established term in anthropological usage) is "diffusion," which is learning from social system to social system. Culture is not merely something accessorily added, but is integrally built into personality and social systems as components. For the building-in process in the personality we have to thank Freud's insight into the development of the superego by a process of "internalization." On the social system side, the building-in of culture is called "institutionalization." In one sense it and internalization are two sides of the same thing; and in another sense they are not. There is here exactly the same problem of perspective mentioned before. While it is terribly important to see their equivalence to each other, it is equally important not to confuse them.

Social systems and personalities are not symmetrically related to each other. As two types of system, they are not simply two branches of a tree. Rather, they are related. Two personalities interacting constitute a social system, and each is, for the other, part of the situation. There are non-social aspects of the situation, and from the point of view of the personality they are part of the situation (Figure 6, below).

Let us call the two personalities ego and alter. For an integrated social system I would use the word "collectivity" which may be constituted by two or more persons. Asymmetry lies in the fact that there is no social system without personality, and I would go so far as to say that, although there may be behavior systems or organisms without social systems, there is no personality in the human sense without social system. It is asymmetrical because there is an independent integration of personality within the organism. The collectivity is in a true sense an emergent system. Whenever and however it begins, the child has to be socialized; he has to be integrated into the social system of which the other people surrounding him are parts, and that means he has to internalize the culture.

HENRY: *In your terminology, the collectivity emerges from the interaction between ego and alter?*

PARSONS: I mean only that the collectivity may continue though individual members of it disappear because they are replaced. If all the individuals were separated from interaction with each other, although there would certainly still be living biological organisms the collectivity would disappear. But if they had not been exposed to a process of socializa-

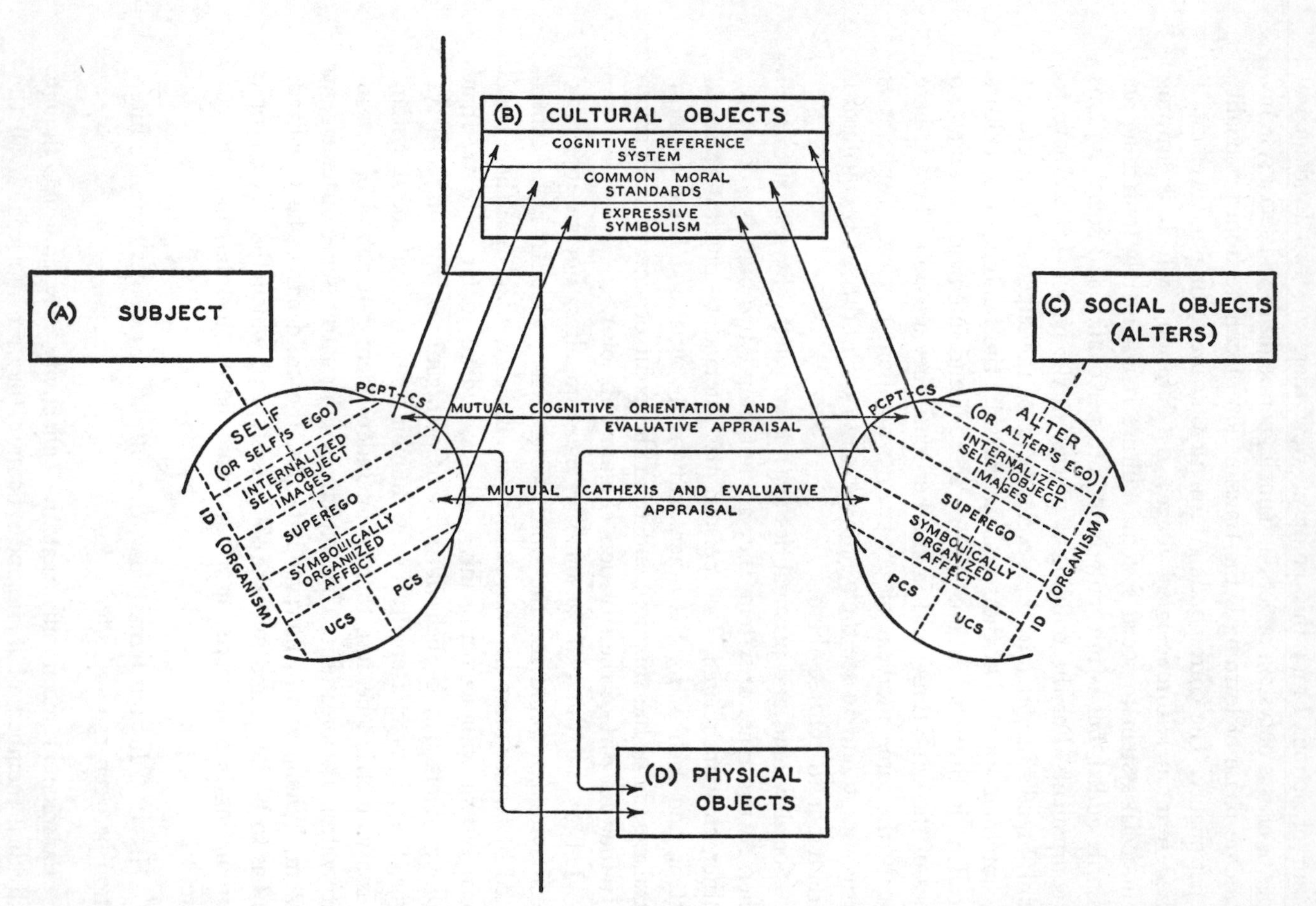

FIGURE 6. THE FUNCTION OF THE EGO IN INTEGRATION OF THE PERSONALITY AS A SYSTEM

From: "The Superego and the Theory of Social Systems," in T. Parsons, R. F. Bales, and E. A. Shils, *Working Papers in the The-*

tion they would not be personalities. Both biological organisms and personalities are always present when a collectivity is present.

SPIEGEL: *How is it necessary to derive one from the other, or make one emerge from the other?*

PARSONS: This relationship explains certain asymmetries in the theoretical structure. A generation ago Durkheim stated that a collectivity is constituted out of the motivational systems of individuals; with the integration of culture into the motivation of its members is perhaps the modern way of putting it. Durkheim used the term "society." There is asymmetry in the relation between personality and social system but it is asymmetry only for certain purposes.

Some things have been developing in the last two days that seem to me to be extremely exciting and fundamental. We have been working for some time with concepts which we call pattern variables. They were first developed by me in connection with analyses of social structure and attempts to classify role types. But I was not clear as to exactly what I was doing theoretically. We began to see that the pattern variables could be derived from the frame of reference of action, and that five dichotomous concepts constituted a system (Figure 7).

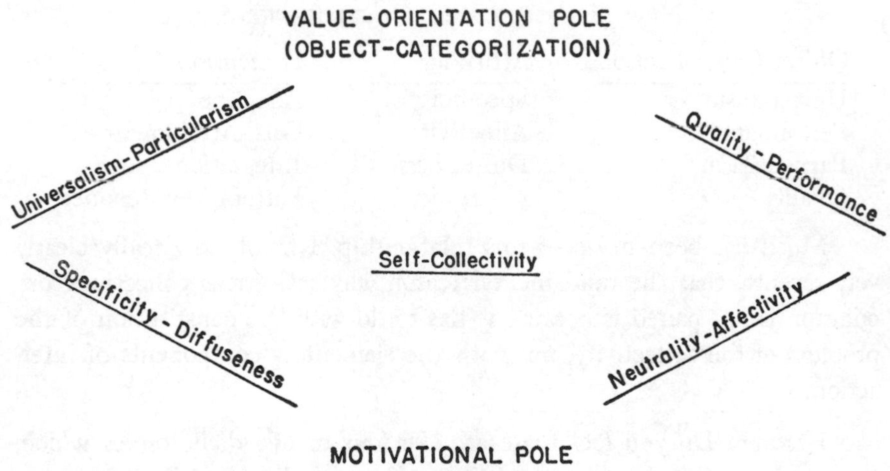

FIGURE 7

GROUPING OF PATTERN VARIABLES

From: T. Parsons and E. A. Shils, *Towards A General Theory of Action* (Cambridge: Harvard University Press, 1952); T. Parsons, R. F. Bales, and E. A. Shils, *Working Papers on the Theory of Action* (Glencoe, Illinois: The Free Press, 1953).

My scheme involves five dichotomies, five pairs of concepts. One of them had to do with the collectivity, as distinguished from what we call self-orientation, which means orientation disregarding the norms of collectivity. Ultimately we saw that the five pairs were not a catalog but had a definite 2-1-2 structure relationship. We put them in a diagram, with the collectivity in the middle and the pairs on each side. It also was clear that of the paired pairs, one was particularly concerned with the motivational side of the frame of reference and the other with the situational side of the system.

At the situation pole the pairs are universalism-particularism, and quality-performance. At the other pole are what are called specificity-diffuseness and affectivity-neutrality. In the middle is self versus collectivity. This pairing has turned out to be of increasing general importance, and an increasing clarification of it has come through quite a long series of steps, the last and in many respects the most important of which were published recently.[3]

Just as an example, very recently it seemed to me that these pairings, combined into a four-fold table, could be used as a basis of classification of the content of expressive symbolism, as distinguished from the meanings of expressive symbolism, as well as of role status in the social structure and of the content of non-social objects in the situation.

TABLE 2

NEW "DIMENSIONAL" CLASSIFICATION[4]

Object Categorization	*Attitude*	*Dimension*
Universalism	Specificity	Adaptive
Performance	Affectivity	Goal-Attainment
Particularism	Diffuseness	Integration
Quality	Neutrality	Pattern-Maintenance

Much has been made of this relationship. I finally saw really clearly very recently that the fundamental reason why self versus collectivity orientation is not paired is because it has to do with the constitution of the problem of the collectivity, not with the elementary components of interaction.

HENRY: *Do you feel these are the four or five dichotomies which, to you, determine the content of expressive symbolism and limit it in any society?*

PARSONS: They can form a basis of classification and understanding of the organization of systems. The question has been asked, "What are

[3] T. Parsons, R. F. Bales and E. A. Shils, *Working Papers on the Theory of Action* (Glencoe: The Free Press, 1953).

[4] Adapted from T. Parsons, "Some Comments on the State of the General Theory of Action," *American Sociological Review*, XVIII (December, 1953), 625.

they?" In concentrating on these pairings, a cross-relationship the other way has been ignored. Only this past week did I really begin to see some importance in that cross-relationship. If you eliminate self versus collectivity, and if the rest of them are paired, four fundamental categories result. What are those four categories? I remember a long session with Fred Mosteller on the problem about a year and a half ago, when he suggested a mathematical solution. Charles Bush thought our model would be suited to a four-dimensional space, in a strict mathematical sense. Recently I considered the idea of space and asked if these were to be treated as the coordinates of a space, what is the location and the change of location in the coordinates? In other words, what is the analogue of motion in space? It is difficult to get all four dimensions in three-dimensional diagrams.

HENRY: *As I redraw the lines here I see what you have in mind. For example, ascribed status is related to neutrality in the sense that where there is an ascribed status we may expect a rather neutral emotional pattern.*

PARSONS: The ascription-achievement distinction of Linton is a special case, and I regretted once using that terminology. I would prefer to use the terminology of quality and performance. I think now I had better try to define my terms in the most generalized sense, before I show you what I think came out of seeing them in a cross-classification which had not been used before (Figure 8).

	Universalism	Particularism
Performance	Achievement values	Appreciative values
Quality	Ascriptive values	Moral-integrative values

	Neutrality	Affectivity
Specificity	Approval attitude	Response attitude
Diffuseness	Esteem attitude	Acceptance attitude

FIGURE 8

TYPES OF PERFORMANCE VALUE APPROPRIATE TO EACH PHASE

Simplified from: T. Parsons, R. F. Bales, and E. A. Shils, *Working Papers on the Theory of Action* (Glencoe, Illinois: The Free Press, 1953).

First, we will take *ascription-achievement* or *quality-performance*. An actor seen as an object, either by himself or by alter, has two aspects. They both must always be there. It is impossible to conceive an actor without both, but in a given context one aspect may be the significant one, and the other not. In one aspect, shall we say, he is a bundle of qualities. He has attributes which are given like those of a physical object, independent of his motivation or his probable performance. On the other hand, unlike a physical object an actor has to be seen as an actual or potential performer, and in his case communication is probably the most important kind of performance. There is a lot of semantic difficulty over the term "achievement," and I found myself using "achievement" in this somewhat unusual way.

The *universalism-particularism* pattern concerns the basis of classifying objects as belonging together. They may belong together, as in a normal cognitive pattern, by virtue of having common properties. I would include relations of interdependence, the commonest being definable by the point of reference of any given observer. This chair, for instance, has green leather, presumably, from the perspective of anyone in this room. But objects may also be classified together, whether they are social objects or not, according to whether they belong in a particular relational system or not. Ruesch's watch and my watch, for example, have certain similarities as mechanisms, but in relational terms there is a very important difference between his watch and my watch, because they belong in two different relational systems. That is what we call the particularistic category.

Turn now to the dichotomy *self-collectivity*. A given orientation or action decision or direction may be specifically oriented to the fact of belonging in a collectivity, to the fact of solidarity. We usually express it in common speech by saying, "This is my obligation."; "It is an obligation to my job."; or "It is an obligation to my family."; and so on. Or it may be in the sphere where the question of solidarity is in abeyance. If I don't get home until 7:30 without notifying my wife that I'm going to be late, I can be said to have violated an obligation to my family; but if I get home between 5:30 and 6:15, which period is in the self-oriented sector, it does not involve obligation to my family. In other words, there are particular solidarity relationships because the same person is involved in many collectivities. A society is one collectivity, but it is also a network of subcollectivities which cut across each other in very complex ways.

Of the other two dichotomies, *specificity-diffuseness* concerns precisely the problem that Lawrence Frank raised concerning the basis of selective significance relative to objects. In diffuseness, the basis of selective significance for emotional meaning is the object *qua* object, which may be a constructed object, but once constructed it is the object by object. The stock example is, "A child loves its mother." The mother is the object, but the mother is a complex object and there are many particular gratifications of which the mother is the primary agent which are organized in a system relative to this total object.

Another way of organizing the significance of objects is by *gratification-interest*. For instance, we class food objects together because they are all potential gratifiers of hunger needs. There are all sorts of such possibilities of cutting across objects to form categories. Thus, in addition to words there may be a lot of other things about the food that are potentially significant. We organize them together into a system by selecting their relevance to a particular interest or class of needs.

Finally, the last pair is *affectivity-neutrality*. There is some doubt as to the semantics of this dichotomy, and I am not sure those are the best terms. It concerns essentially whether, in a given situation, a potential opportunity for gratification is taken, or whether instead the need is inhibited.

We may walk up and down the street and pass several people vending food, and we may feel a certain stirring of hunger but don't buy anything. We think it is not a good idea to eat between meals so we will wait until mealtime and then we will eat. That is acting with respect to hunger need with affective neutrality as far as the opportunity for gratification between meals is concerned, and with affectivity when at the right and permitted time hunger is allowed to go into overt action. Affectivity is satisfaction by means of action.

Now we shall begin *cross-classifying* these dichotomies. We shall first put together affectivity and performance. As I pointed out, using hunger for an example, they belong together. They are part of the same process. The affectivity is from the viewpoint of the inside; the performance is from the point of view of the outside. We now pair neutrality with quality. If neutrality is the inside and quality is the outside, it amounts to saying that when a need is inhibited, the object has only attributes. It isn't performing. If you eat the food, the food does not perform—you perform. But if, in interaction the objects are social objects, then there has to be interaction, that is, communication.

Continuing with cross-classification, the third pair is specificity-universalism. The fundamental point is again the inside and outside perspectives. If the interest is specific, then objects are classed together independently of a solidarity of belonging together in a specific interrelational system; that is, if the interest is in food, then everything edible is classed together. If the interest is in knowledge, then everything with common properties is classed together.

The fourth cross-classification is diffuseness-particularism. I said that the fourth point concerns selectivity relative to an object as a whole—the selectivity of significance. This concerns that object system which is particularly significant to ego. The object system seen in its significance is ultimately the integration of the motivational interest and objects in a system.

Now let us try to define what we mean by motion or change. This is where I think the new insights and ideas appear. If you think of Euclidean space and change of location, you say that a process of motion has a direction which is defined relatively to an arbitrarily selected origin. But you have to describe that process and what has changed in terms of all three coordinates of the space. The values of three variables have changed if the particle has changed its location in the space. That is the logical model. If there is an action change, then you have to be able to specify what has changed in the value of each of the coordinates of a space—that is what it means to say that it has changed. Another way of putting it is to describe a change requiring four statements of fact—a four-dimensional system—which states the difference with respect to each of the four variables. This affectivity-performance variable is pretty close to what psychologists sometimes call "gradient."

Because of this inside-outside structure the change may be described in terms of inside and in terms of outside. In terms of outside, I should say what we mean by a change in performance is an approach toward goal attainment: state B, which is a later state, is closer toward goal attainment than state A. From the point of view of the inside, state B, as a result of the change, contains an increment of gratification which is not to be found in state A.

HENRY: *What would be your objection to substituting the word "motivation" for "affectivity"?*

PARSONS: None. This is just the term that we have been using. We all get set on certain terminological ways. You might run into a semantic difficulty in another direction. I would be inclined to use "affectivity."

ENGEL: *You said internal change would be an increase of gratification. Couldn't it be increase in frustration?*

PARSONS: Yes. It could either approach or get farther away from the goal state.

SHAKOW: *But you are pairing these now? You are talking about an approach toward goal attainment, and therefore you have an increment in gratification.*

PARSONS: Yes. Let's deal only with the positive side. (The logic of it will allow a negative perfectly well.) The category "Shows tension" turned out "Should have a special relation to neutrality." That seemed very strange to me, because one connects neutrality with affectivity, but it gave an idea that I really think fits the case. With respect to the second variable, state B in the positive case differs from state A in that it has produced situational consequences relative to state A which constitute qualities of objects in the situation that are no longer parts of the performance system. They are there; they are finished; they are not performance any more. That is where the outside view is seen. The inside view is that tension has been reduced. In the one state, gratification has been attained and in the other, tension is released. Gratification increment and tension reduction are two different variables. They are not the same, yet many psychologists have assumed them to be the same thing. Realizing that I would get into semantic confusion if I did it, I chose to say that what has happened subjectively from inside is tension reduction and what has happened objectively from outside is achievement. One must distinguish achievement from goal attainment. Be careful of the term "achievement."

Finally, we say that under specificity-universalism, state B differs from state A in that there has been produced an increment internally of specific interest gratification and externally of organization relative to action. It might be called adaptive reinforcement of learning. Internally you have gained rewards in Hull's sense.[5] Externally you have learned an adaptive pattern. That every action process should involve learning or unlearning is the implication of this.

We now come to what is the most interesting point of all, the boundary maintenance area. It is a value maintaining system and not a mechanical system or physical-chemical system in the ordinary sense. Then, you can say this: State B differs from state A in that internally an increment has been added to what we called "the optimization of gratification"; an increment to the total gratification system, not merely the gratification of a particular need. We deliberately chose that term. We wanted to avoid "maximization" because we did not want to be accused of being naive hedonists, and we did not know whether there was an integral that could be integrated in the mathematical sense; so we deliberately chose an unconventional word. From the external point of view, it seems to me that this is the production of an increment to the value realization of the system. This is where evaluation and values come in—value standards. There have to be standards in order to define this variable and give the values of it.

It had struck me that in classical mechanics the three laws of motion somehow seemed to correspond to the three dimensions of Euclidean space. There are three dimensions and three laws. I do not know whether

[5] C. L. Hull, *Principles of Behavior* (New York: Appleton-Century-Crofts, 1943).

with four dimensions there should also be four laws, but I have arrived at a statement of four laws.

Law I: *An action process will continue unchanged in direction and rate unless impeded and deflected by opposing forces.*

Law II: *If, in a system of action, there is a change in the direction of a process—not rate but direction—it will be balanced by complementary change which is equal in force and opposite in direction.*

Law III: *An increase in the rate of an action process is a function of the magnitude of the motivational force involved.*

Law IV: *Any pattern of process in a system of action will tend to be confirmed or eliminated as a function of its place in the integrative balances of the system.*

Drawing on the logical structure of classical mechanics, there is only one thing missing and that is mass. You can ask, "What is the logical equivalent of mass?" First, the counterpart of mass in classical mechanics for action is the "motivational power" of an act. It is the capacity to influence. The word "drive" has been contaminated, from my point of view, by the Hullean usage. We use the word "drive," but my colleague James Olds was responsible for introducing a distinction between "drive" and "drives": [6] "drive" as general motivation potential, as it were, and "drives" as that differentiated relative to particular interest direction. I would say if there is differentiation, it is not part of this system; it is a consequence of the organism.

When Bush pointed out the possibility that our model required a four-dimensional space,[7] obviously the question then arose of what mathematicians call the orthogonal principle. In Euclidean space it is the rectilinearity; that is, there is a 90° angle between two coordinates. There has to be an orthogonal principle in Bales' interaction scheme [8] because he is classifying acts, and I am analyzing dimensions. If you see how the two are related, then you understand it. It must be related to two fundamental facts, that pattern variables are paired and that there is an inside-outside duality. Those two things together must hold the secret of the orthogonal principle. There must be mathematics to cover it.

RUESCH: *If I understand you correctly, you say that these functions are gradients or continuous functions. I think it has to be proven first. Most of the functions we deal with are discontinuous and when we deal with discontinuous functions we have our usual difficulties. Can you deal in this scheme with a discontinuous function?*

[6] J. Olds, *The Growth and Structure of Motives* (Glencoe: The Free Press, 1955).
[7] Cf. T. Parsons, R. F. Bales and E. A. Shils, *op. cit.*
[8] R. F. Bales, *Interaction Process Analysis* (Cambridge: Addison-Wesley, 1950).

PARSONS: I think that is for a mathematician to answer. People are puzzled again and again by the dichotomous character of these concepts. There are various interpretations of what a dichotomy may mean. At one time I thought that a polarity in the sense of a probability may vary between zero and one, and these are the limits of a range of variation. But it became more and more clear that this was not what they were. They could not be interpreted that way although if they represent alternatives, in a statistical population there can be a variation of from zero per cent to one hundred per cent in the way choice has gone, relative to any given situation. But in a logical structure they are not polar variables.

RUESCH: *Polarity usually refers to entirely discontinuous functions. You put one sort of thing here, and another sort of thing there.*

PARSONS: We have no idea of what various possibilities in mathematics would fit this scheme. The critical point is that to locate a body relative to a point of origin in Euclidean space, you must have three independent statements of fact relative to each of three coordinates. There cannot be different ways of saying the same thing. From the coordinate defined by the point of origin it is X units along one coordinate, Y along the second and Z along the third. I have talked with mathematicians and know enough about mathematics myself to understand that "N" dimensional space makes sense, mathematically, and also makes sense to these data. The sole difference between a statement of fact relative to a four-dimensional space and one relative to Euclidean space is that to locate a point you must have four independent statements of fact.

FRANK: *And these four in addition to the three-dimensional space?*

PARSONS: In addition, yes. The three dimensions are not the dimensions of Euclidean space. That is a very important point. It is not Euclidean space plus one more dimension—it is *another* space. I do not mean the fourth is another space. I mean that the four-dimensional space is another space.

RUESCH: *If I understand you correctly you are saying that you are trying to establish a mathematical model for these functions that you have described. Do all the assumptions underlying mathematical models apply to your system and are all of the things you do with your data and your conceptual scheme covered by this mathematical scheme? The mathematical system would be a closed system, would it not?*

PARSONS: Yes, it would.

RUESCH: *But how do you reconcile your closed system with the agreement we arrived at this morning that all social systems are open systems?*

PARSONS: I think it is a system in two different senses or on two different levels. We distinguish between three levels of conceptual system as distinguished from empirical system, and have called them a categorical system, which is one in which you have definition of components, their classifications and certain structural classifications of their combinations relative to a frame of reference. There is, however, no statement of the laws which state the relations of variables. The second state is a theoretical system which is categorical plus a complete set of laws, and the third stage is an empirical theoretical system. You could have a theoretical system and not have empirical closure, because other systems impinge upon it, and there is a certain abstractness in the applicability of this theoretical system. The same is true of the biological system in physiology, where the physical-chemical systems of the organism are investigated. Obviously, the physiologist aims at a complete theoretical system with respect to the particular aspect of the physical-chemical processes of the organism in question. But there may be several such systems on the physical-chemical level, and they may be abstract relative to behavior. I do not see any fundamental theoretical difficulty. I think the fallacy of physical concreteness pretty well took care of that problem.[9]

TOMAN: *We began our conference with a search for entities, but these were intended to be new entities, not those derived immediately from the basic physical sciences, because everyone seemed to realize that we were discussing new phenomena which were not easily predictable from the behavior of atoms and molecules. In physical science one deals with the relationship between dimensions, not the dimensions of the type Parsons was talking about but irreducible quantities such as mass, charge,*

[9] This statement was made as it were "in the heat" of excitement over a theoretical development which had just been worked out. The broad outlines of the scheme which emerged at that time have been retained and built up since. A considered statement of the main scheme in this part will be found in T. Parsons and R. F. Bales, "The Dimensions of Action Space," in T. Parsons, R. F. Bales and E. A. Shils, *op. cit.*, III. Further developments will be found in Chapter V of the same collection: T. Parsons, R. F. Bales and E. A. Shils, "Phase Movement in Relation to Motivation, Symbol Formation and Role Structure," and in T. Parsons, "Some Comments on the State of the General Theory of Action," *American Sociological Review*, XVIII (1953), 618.

In general the interpretation that the pairings of the four pattern-variables across the attitude-object line constituted the definition of the dimensions of a four-dimensional space has held up and been continually used since then. Since it has not yet been possible to work out mathematical models, we are not yet sure of the exact mathematical character of this space, however. That it is a four-dimensional Euclidean space, however, seems unlikely.

dielectric constant, distance, time, temperature, and so on. Such irreducible quantities I am sure we have not found here today, although we have been looking for them. It is the relationships between these irreducible quantities that constitute the theory we are looking for. But even if we all agreed upon certain irreducible quantities, we would not necessarily have a theory. A theory should have implications for practice, for doing something. Any workable theory of human behavior is going to have implications at the psychiatric level for therapy, at the social level for handling juvenile delinquency, wars, family problems, and so on. Further, a theory should also contain implications for its own refutation in practice. I use that last word "refutation" very strongly. It is not a pessimistic term—it is in agreement with what I conceive the scientific method to be. Any amount of compatible information can be compiled, but it does not prove a theory. It is the responsibility of those who propose a theory to look for these places in which it might conceivably not work, make their predictions, and then see whether it does work or not.

EDITOR: *In this Chapter Parsons outlined his famous "General Theory of Action" in a simplified, easily understandable form. His "double contingency" encompasses what others have been discussing as transactional and dependent upon communication of complex symbols. Out of and imbedded in social interaction are symbol meaning systems which may be transmitted between various systems of action. From the pattern variables of action, five concepts were derived, four of which are paired. They may form the basis of classification and understanding of the organization of systems. These are clarified in the text. From these concepts, a four-dimensional system may be described in action and may define a four-dimensional, non-Euclidean "social space" for which four "laws" may be set forth.*

CHAPTER SIX

THE SOCIETAL SYSTEM, CULTURE AND THE COMMUNITY

Presentation by Laura Thompson

I TAKE it that one of our functions is to present the conception of the societal and related systems which we have found fruitful as tools in multiple-disciplinary research. The following discussion is based mainly on the theoretical and methodological findings of research in Indian personality and administration, a ten-year multi-disciplinary project focused on the practical problem of how to improve the welfare of the American Indian scientifically.[1]

In this research we used a number of disciplines, including cultural anthropology, social anthropology, sociology, psychology, neuro-psychiatry, psychiatry, medicine, administration, pedagogy, ecology, linguistics, and others.

By the societal system anthropologists generally mean the entire system of interpersonal relations, both formal and informal, which comprises the interaction pattern of a society. These relationships are expressed in the society's institutions and institutional practices, in its cultural traditions and products, and in its behavioral and symbol systems including its language, art forms, religious ceremonials, literature, values, goals and aspirations.

[1] L. Thompson, *Personality and Government: Findings and Recommendations of the Indian Administration* (Mexico, D.F.: Research Instituto Indigenista Interamericano, 1951).

The societal system is of course man-made. It is essentially the slow, accreting creation of the human organisms who, generation after generation, have made up the human group which, observed at a given moment in space-time, we call the society. The societal system of a particular society has been created in response to need: that is, it has been created in response to the inner and outer needs of a particular group of human organisms in environmental context, viewed in long-range time and space perspective.

In order to understand the societal system as an on-going life process, created by and arising from the needs of its human component, we must view it in its total relevant environment extending backward and forward in time and inward and outward in space. When this is done we discover that any one societal system in relevant environmental context is one facet, so to say, or one part of a multi-dimensional cultural event in space-time.

My point is that to understand any one societal system at a particular point in time and space we must understand the whole multi-dimensional pattern of cultural events in space-time of which it is a part. When I use the term "understand" I mean understand in an explanatory sense rather than merely in a descriptive sense. As Whitehead pointed out, it is only an explanatory type of understanding which will enable us to make predictions about a whole event or its parts to the extent that predictions are possible.[2]

I have now moved from my original focus on a societal system to a broader focus on the multi-dimensional pattern of cultural events in space-time of which the societal system is a part. According to this approach, in order to develop an adequate concept of the societal system we must develop an adequate theory of the whole multi-dimensional pattern of human events in space-time, which is a human culture viewed in broadest perspective. My next task, therefore, will be to present very briefly a concept of culture which has been found fruitful as a tool in multiple-discipline research, having as one of its aims to develop an explanatory understanding of a particular societal system.

As you probably know, the concept of culture, the focal concept of the anthropologist, is undergoing radical revision in line with the struggle of anthropology to emerge out of the primarily descriptive, natural history phase of scientific development to a more mature, postulational phase. The traditional definition of culture as a sum-total or aggregation of elements, traits or patterns has of course become outmoded. But anthropologists have found difficulty in developing a new concept of culture adequate to the needs of modern multi-disciplinary research.

Actually, an adequate theory of culture, accounting satisfactorily for its

[2] A. N. Whitehead, *Essays in Science and Philosophy* (New York: Philosophical Library, 1948).

myriad forms and multiple processes, could not emerge until the following conditions had been fulfilled:

1. Human culture had to be recognized explicitly as the product and process of human organisms and therefore as a biologically-based phenomenon.

2. Having recognized the biological base of culture, it was necessary to have an adequate theory of organism on which to build a biologically-based theory of culture. In other words, the science of biology had to develop beyond the bio-physical, bio-chemical phase to the functional, integrative phase.

3. This theory of organism had to account not only for the activities of single organisms but also for the activities of groups or communities of organisms in environmental setting: e.g., it had to account for natural ecological arrangements and communities. In other words, the science of integrative ecology had to develop beyond the phase of general description to the phase of explanatory description.

4. An adequate theory of personality had to be evolved which would account for the growth, development, organization and integration of personality in total relevant environmental setting and under changing pressures from within the human organism and outside it; which would account for the decisive role of culture in the development of personality; and which would account for the creative, purposive role of personality in the building, integration and regeneration of cultures.

5. The science of linguistics had to develop to the point where the interrelationship between linguistic structure and culture structure emerged.

6. An integrative, interdisciplinary methodology had to be developed which was adequate to describe and analyze not merely social behavior but a whole culture-in-environment in spatial and temporal perspective, including its ecologic, somatic, sociologic, psychologic and symbolic dimensions.

7. And finally, human communities which had been relatively isolated through millennia under extreme environmental pressures had to be analyzed multi-dimensionally so that the processes of culture creation, culture growth, culture adaptation and integration with the environment, culture crisis, culture reintegration and culture disintegration could be understood in geographic setting and in long-range historical perspective.

When these conditions had been fulfilled it became clear that the cultural activities of the human organisms comprising a local community are behavioral activities which, together with complementary physiologic and morphogenetic activities, tend to be directed toward goals normally related to the biological ends of maintenance, reproduction and development of the local community as part of a specific total web-of-life in environmental context. The directive activities of a human community, as well as those of other species in the life-web as a whole, are not primarily a "struggle for existence," but rather they are primarily a creative, cooperative development directed toward the fulfillment of biological ends.

In order that a group of human organisms may live and complete their life cycles successfully generation after generation, certain conditions must be fulfilled. The group must actively maintain its structure-functional wholeness within the range of normality and it must satisfy its essential needs and requirements. To do so it must inhabit an environment which is functionally correlative with its particular needs and requirements for maintenance, reproduction and development. And it must be integrally adapted to its environment or series of environments throughout the life cycles of the succession of generations.

Adaptation to the environment is a necessary condition to the existence of every living creature and every functioning community. And for human groups environmental adaptation necessarily implies, in the course of time, some degree of cultural specialization, as well as complementary physiologic and usually (in the long run) morphogenetic adaptations. For while an isolated human community, like an isolated plant or animal community tends under certain conditions to adapt itself organically with the environment, it also tends to adapt itself environmentally in a *distinctively human* way. That is, a human community-in-environment viewed in long-range space-time perspective tends to integrate itself logically and esthetically. Thus, in contrast to the communities of all other living species, the human community expresses not only a basically organic type of integrating dynamic but also a uniquely human (i.e., symbolic) integrating dynamic.

This logico-esthetic integrating dynamic is the distinctive process in human culture creation and development. It is responsible for the generalization that in every highly integrated culture the basic structures of the culture (i.e., the ecologic, somatic, sociologic, psychic and symbolic structures) tend to express a common structural type, which characterizes both the culture as a whole and its several parts, including its manifestations in individual overt behavior patterns. This common structural type expresses, usually to a large extent implicitly, a set of core values. Due to the nature of the human culture process described above, the core values of a culture tend in the long run to form a system which is both logically and esthetically integrated. As Frank has stated, the core values are the basic assumptions or organizing conceptions of a culture regarding certain key problems of living: i.e., the nature of the universe, of men, of animals, of plants, and the relationships of these to one another. Through the symbolic integrating process, the core values of a deeply integrated culture comprise an emotionally-tinged, logico-esthetic system, rather than a congeries of disparate "themes." Only in a complex, composite culture (like our own) or a relatively simple, composite culture (like that of the Navaho) do these values appear to be an aggregation of unrelated or loosely related "themes."

Once firmly established and embedded in the institutional system, in the symbolic system, and in the group personality structure of a community, an integrated core value system is highly resistant to change. Unless the community is wiped out or severed from its original natural environment or a similar one, and sometimes even then, such a system tends to persist with little structural change for centuries, even millennia (e.g., Hopi, Papago). Indeed, in ancient, relatively integrated communities the indigenous core value system, mirroring the group's age-old basic ideology regarding the nature of the world and its power dynamics, is rarely affected directly by acculturation pressures. Usually it is affected, if at all, only indirectly or partially (e.g., Icelanders, Old Saxons, Basques).

In sum, from the multi-discipline viewpoint, a human local community-in-environment is not *primarily* an inorganic, physio-chemical system, nor is it *primarily* a system of human relations (i.e., a societal system). It is an organic organization or structure-functional web-of-life composed of diverse species or kinds of animals, micro-organisms, plants and human groups, in the context of inorganic nature. Seen all-of-a-piece human community is an integral part of a larger organic whole or complex web-of-life, and its existence and welfare depend on the existence and welfare of the larger whole in environmental context.

Since the ecological environments of the earth are highly diversified, there is and can be no such phenomenon as a generalized cultural community capable of active existence and reproduction generation after generation in all kinds of environments in which human life is at all possible. Existing communities, as we know them, are all of definite kinds, each kind culturally specialized in some degree for a particular mode of life in a more or less restricted environment. They may be quite simple or extremely complex in organization, technology and symbolic development, their structure—whether simple or complex—may be biologically balanced to a greater or lesser degree, etc., but they must all be to some extent integral with their environment, otherwise they cannot continue to exist and reproduce. Indeed, a primary condition to the continuing existence of any local human community, from the simplest to the most complex, is its integration with the environment—its integration with a more or less specialized environment which is correlative with, and capable of satisfying, the essential needs and requirements of the human organisms throughout their life cycles during successive generations.

Each local community, therefore, must be specialized in some degree. A highly specialized ecological environment, such as a desert, an island or an arctic environment, for example, requires highly specialized cultural developments to meet the life needs for maintenance, reproduction and development of a human group through the centuries and also necessitates complementary physiological adjustments and developments, and in the course of centuries, perhaps millennia, morphoplastic adjustments and developments.

It is important also to bear in mind that the conditions of group existence and perpetuation through the centuries must be *actively* established and maintained. A human community, which is an organization of human organisms, actively builds up and maintains in the course of development its structure-functional wholeness or integrity, chiefly by the behavioral, physiologic, and if need be (in the long run) morphogenetic activities of its component human organisms and groups of human organisms (families, clans, castes, etc.). If this integrity or wholeness is disturbed by injury or adverse environmental influences (e.g., decimation by an epidemic, climatic change from warm to cold or from moist to dry, etc.), it tends to be re-created, as far as possible by appropriate physiological, behavioral, and if need be morphogenetic activities on the part of the community as a whole or its components, so that the normal state tends to be re-established or a new adaptive norm of structure and function established. This trend toward self-recovery and self-rehabilitation on the part of the community operates, if possible, in the case of interference with its normal activities from without (e.g., enemy raids, colonial and proselyting pressures, foreign types of leadership, political factionalism) and from within (e.g., over-population in relation to the food supply under existing technology).

If possible the group actively seeks an appropriate environment and strives to maintain itself therein. Its human components actively seek out, select and prepare the substances necessary for their metabolism (edible wild plants, game, salt, etc.) and/or they borrow or invent means of producing or otherwise acquiring them (e.g., technologies for domestication of plants and animals, of mining, trade relations, etc.), and of storing them against future needs (e.g., storage of food and other surpluses, etc.). The group develops ways of rearing its young so that its culture will be transmitted and perpetuated (communal child training patterns). As noted above, it develops a symbol system and a set of core values which tend to integrate it logically and esthetically with the environment. In all these ways and in many others, the human community builds and perpetuates itself and its culture and strives to reach its normal actualization. This striving is only to a limited extent purposive, that is, at the conscious level and accompanied by foresight of a goal. It consists to a large extent of activities and processes at the unconscious level, but nonetheless developmental and directive toward biological ends.

It follows that the activities of external agencies (e.g., administrative bureaucracies, missionary or commercial interests, etc.) will only harm or destroy a community's life-web and injure its human component unless they reinforce with conscious purpose, knowledge and wisdom the primarily unconscious developmental and directive activities of the organism as life-web builders and as culture and personality builders. The role of an external agency (governmental or otherwise), interested in the promotion of community welfare, should be a life-web nurturing role, a role which fosters the development of a whole culture-in-environment as an integrate, by means of permitting, protecting and, if necessary, reinforcing the community's own inherent directive, purposive and creative activities. Great caution should be exercised by such an agency, however, not to interfere with the creative or restorative activities of the organisms (e.g., by supplying the goal or end-state through an external agency and not by the group's own efforts) lest the creative or restorative action likewise come to an end and the development of the organic organization be arrested or crippled.

On the basis of the foregoing briefly stated working assumptions and concepts, the living community, deep-rooted in time and space and relatively integrated culturally, emerges as the significant unit of multidiscipline research which strives toward an explanatory understanding of cultures, societal and psychological processes in broadest perspective. Laboratory conditions for the study of such processes are found, for example, in ancient communities where cultural time is measured not by years or centuries but by millennia. The cultural, social and psychological phenomena of such communities have sufficient space-time depth to allow adequate sampling, relatively precise observations, and relatively adequate generalizations concerning cultural as well as social and psychological processes in broadest context.

In our explorations of such types of communities by means of a multiple-discipline methodology, we have found it fruitful to work simultaneously in six dimensions. These are as follows:

1. The ecologic dimension—the pattern of relations between the community and its natural environment.

2. The somatic dimension—the community viewed as a group of somatic units.

3. The sociologic dimension—the interacting human organisms which comprise the community viewed as a society.

4. The symbolic dimension—the communal symbolic system including language, ceremonials, arts and crafts, mythology, folklore, science, etc.

5. The psychic dimension—the community viewed as a group of transacting personalities in process of formation and self-realization.

6. The core values dimension—the community's system of largely implicit, emotionally-tinged beliefs and attitudes regarding the nature of the world, of man, of animals and plants, and the sources and dynamics of power within that system.

Appropriate procedures for research in each of these dimensions, and for the multiple-discipline analysis and integration of the findings into a meaningful whole, have been developed or are being developed. If any one of these dimensions is overlooked, however, we have found that our results are skewed, so that successful solution of the whole community problem is ruled out. We therefore look upon them, according to our present knowledge and development of methodology, as variable sets relevant to the solution of whole community problems.

Finally, I wish to point out that human cultures are often treated either as if they were inorganic, physico-chemical systems, or as if they were organisms. According to our present knowledge, both analogies are inappropriate. Rather, a human culture may be viewed appropriately as a complex, multi-dimensional pattern of human events in space-time, both product and process of human organic organizations.

RUESCH: *Are your core values moral values?*

THOMPSON: They are beliefs and attitudes regarding these basic problems: the nature of man: the nature of the universe; the nature of the other parts of the organic world which in our society may not seem to be important but in other societies are extremely important. For Paleolithic man the nature of the animal world was paramount because he was dealing with animals.

SPIEGEL: *What is the differentiation between core values and symbolic systems?*

THOMPSON: First we had our scheme with no core values in it, and we tried to see whether it would work out. But it would not work out because the core values are apparently the set of relevant variables subserving integration. They were found as structuring the organization of all the sets.

In a community with a highly integrated culture, you find the core values reflected in the structure of the sociological system and in the structure of the ecological system. We have not proved that they are in the somatic structure but that is our hypothesis, and it looks as though they are—that they are in man's muscular system.

FRANK: *What is in symbols?*

THOMPSON: The language; the whole of the language system. Its structure is its grammar, also arts and crafts, mythology, literature, religion, ceremonials and science if they have any.

RUESCH: *You do not feel the symbolic is part of each one of the others that you have mentioned?*

THOMPSON: Yes, it is a part. I must point out that our hypothesis arose from a wide range of disciplines including the practical disciplines of schoolteaching and administration of these communities. We found that we had to deal with the symbol system separately in our analysis. The variable sets are operational, you see.

We all recognize that multiple-discipline research is extremely difficult, and the more disciplines involved the more difficult it becomes. We find as we go along in this kind of research that it is necessary to formulate explicitly assumptions and working concepts; and if, in the course of the research, you find that they are inadequate, then you must reformulate them before you continue or you cannot solve the problem. Our job, as we look at it, is to solve a problem.

We were given by the Indian Service (our research was conducted under Government contract) the practical problem of improving human welfare in Indian reservations—both the welfare of individuals and the welfare of groups. We were faced with the job of translating that practical problem into a scientific problem, and solving it. I think we succeeded in solving it theoretically, at least, and to a small extent practically.

HENRY: *Sooner or later the anthropologists are going to be very seriously challenged on the matter of integration. The problem is, how do you prove it? An example is the statement in your book that the Hopi language is consistent with a world view that rules out dualities. We find the same view among the Zuni who have a totally different language which belongs to a totally different linguistic family. Over and over again the statement is made: "Such-and-such behavior is congruent with," or "It is not surprising that" but rarely can satisfactory proof be given of congruence.*

Possibly in your practical work, where you can view changes in microcosm and have been able to institute changes and see them work, you have succeeded in establishing certain crucial tests of the integration of one aspect of culture with another. I would think this essential to demonstrate integration. You have postulated, one might say, that one form of behavior was integrated with another and that one form of behavior occurred because another did. Then a crucial test arose. The government did something, and your prediction, lo and behold!, came true—behavior A changed because it was integrated with behavior B.

THOMPSON: A good example of that is that based on Whorf's study of the structure of the Hopi language.[3] The Commissioner of Indian Affairs and his staff were meeting two groupings of Hopi communities. As an experiment they endeavored, as did also the superintendent of the reservation, to phrase their ideas and so structure them that they were nearer the way the Hopi structured their ideas, in order to facilitate communication. We have no satisfactory test of it, but we observed that communication was facilitated through this means.

Another example would be when we returned to the communities with our findings regarding individual children who had been studied by this method. We studied 1,000 children chosen as a representative sample from thirteen selected communities in six selected tribes, and when in a later phase of the research we returned with findings on individual children and communicated those findings to the teachers handling the children, the teachers said that their teaching was facilitated. In fact, they became very enthusiastic about the research; but they had not been so before because they did not believe in these tests, just as most people do not believe in psychological tests. However, when they saw that the tests actually worked and that from the findings of the tests we had discovered things about the children that they did not know and could not have discovered themselves through their own observational and other methods, then they were convinced of the soundness of the test procedure.

FRANK: *We might rephrase Henry's statement: the core values in a culture have somewhat the same role as the postulates of a unified theory. Thus, postulates, as we know, can never be proved or disproved, but their consequences can be subject to an experimental testing, as is shown by the development of relativity.*

We may then say that these core values (postulates) are expressed, communicated, translated operationally into ecological, cultural, social, sym-

[3] B. L. Whorf, "The Punctual and Segmentative Aspects of Verbs in Hopi," *Language*, XII (1936), 127; "Linguistics as an Exact Science," *Technology Review*, XLIII (1940), 2; "Science and Linguistics," *Technology Review*, XLII (1940), 6; "Language and Logic," *Technology Review*, XLIII (1941), 6; "The Relation of Habitual Thought and Behavior to Language," in *Language, Culture and Personality: Essays in Memory of Edward Sapir* (Menasha, Wisconsin: 1941).

bolic and somatic patterns and relationships in and by individual members of the cultural group. To discover whether there is any unification in a culture, we may examine individual personalities to see how each acts and relates himself in these various patterns and relationships where there may be a greater or less degree of unity or congruity. However, we must not forget that the individual bearer of cultural traditions, through the very process of being enculturized and socialized, may more or less seriously distort and neglect some aspects of his cultural traditions and therefore exhibit a highly idiosyncratic lack of unity, as contrasted with the more coherent and highly integrated formulation of cultural traditions around which he and all other members of his group deviate. In their religion, their philosophy, their art and literature or folklore, almost every group expresses a much higher degree of unity and coherence than they exhibit in their actual conduct and relationships. In developing a unified theory, we should recognize both the traditional formulations of the core values and their interpretation and translation in and by individual personalities.

THOMPSON: Another thing relevant to Henry's point: When we reached the final integrating phase, we found that some members of the staff were able to integrate these many sets of variables successfully, others less so; and we isolated what we call "structural insight" as being a necessary part of the personality of the successful top integrator.

In my opinion "structural insight" can be measured through the Rorschach test at least, and perhaps through other tests. We have not had a project on this particular problem, but it is not something transcendental or mystical, or anything like that. It is a personality trait and it may be scientifically described. It is related to what we measure in the part of the Rorschach which tests "mental approach." This type of person, on being tested, comes out with a habitual mental approach to problems which is complex and organizational and abstract. However, I do not believe every person who shows that trait by Rorschach test will be able to integrate these complex variable sets. In addition to having that quality in your personality, you must have developed "structural insight" through experience and need.

I would like to mention one point about the psychosomatic set of variables. We anthropologists do not believe in the separation of "psycho" and "somatic"; we are all committed to the operational viewpoint. When our methods develop greater precision, and when they are free from dualism, we will not have to separate the psychic from the somatic. In the last day or two I think we have fallen far short of putting the "psycho" and "somatic" together. I think there will be some objection in this group to doing it. This entered as a problem in our procedure in the Indian study. We made medical examinations on each child and classified the records under the "somatic" category. If we had recorded constitutional types we would have classified them under "somatic." If we had taken racial measurements, they would have come under "somatic."

We categorized our findings from psychological tests and life histories partly under "psychic." Then we had to bring our findings together. On a single individual we would attempt to find the wholeness, if there was a wholeness. We tried to find the wholeness from the great variety of data on a single unit of research; for example, on a single child.

ENGEL: *This model is not really meant to be comparable to other models?*

THOMPSON: No. This is a research tool growing out of research, to be tested by further research. We are planning to set up a second research project designed to test the generalizations and the tools arising out of this first ten-year project. We have selected our communities on the basis of the criteria that we set up in our first ten-year project.

This is a dynamic system and all aspects are interrelated; but our problem is how we can study the community as a whole in environment. You cannot just study the community without the setting. I have told you what method we used. We could have done a great deal more but we thought we had done quite a lot in the process. In the second project I hope we can consider constitutional types and continue with the racial measurements, or at least make use of what has been done.

EDITOR: *Societal system was defined as all the formal and informal aspects of the entire system of interpersonal relations. These are developed for satisfactions of inner and outer needs of the human components. It should be viewed from all aspects of time and space. To understand or explain societal system, it must be viewed as a multi-dimensional pattern in the space-time of which it is a part. Anthropology has emerged as a science by the development of conditions necessary for an adequate theory. Here Thompson enumerates the seven minimal conditions to be fulfilled. Adaptive transactions between society and its environment tend to create a system of logical-esthetic integration central to which are relatively un-*

changeable "core values." Human ecology can be understood as a living community through multi-disciplinary studies simultaneously in six dimensions, which are listed.

Discussion arose as to the congruence of special data with the integrative process and its testability. It was stated that core values, basic to integration, should be treated like a unifying theory and its various consequences subjected to experimental testing.

CHAPTER SEVEN

VALUE ORIENTATIONS

Presentation by Florence Kluckhohn

GREGORY BATESON says, "The human individual is endlessly simplifying, organizing and generalizing his own view of the total environment, and constantly imposing his own constructions and meanings, and these constructions and meanings are characteristic of one culture as over against another." [1] He is talking about the core values. Clyde Kluckhohn says it this way: "There is a philosophy behind the way of life of every individual and every relatively homogeneous group at any given point in their history." [2]

My own interest has been largely within the fields of sociology and anthropology, and more recently in the fields of culture and personality and the relation between the two. Because of the way in which some of the cultural material has been generalized and because, too, of the lack of theory (this is a fair statement which comes out also from Thompson's presentation), the cultural anthropologist up to the present time has depended too much upon mere empirical generalization. This has made interrelation with the other fields difficult. What would we say about the relation of one set of core values to another? I, for one, think that anthropological theory is not systematized sufficiently to allow a systematic comparison of the core values of two cultures.

[1] "National Character and Morale," in *Civilian Morale Second Yearbook*, ed. G. Watson (Boston: Houghton-Mifflin, 1942).
[2] *Mirror for Man* (New York: McGraw Hill, 1949).

A more serious problem is that the comparative anthropologist who, having discarded to the great advantage of science some of the evolutionary theories of the development of culture, became too much concerned with comparative values and hence has tended too much to regard each system as a unitary and unique one. Whether it has been the work of Ruth Benedict in Japan, or many other people in various cultures around the world, there has seemed always to be an assumption that these core values are a single unitary integrated system. This I challenge. Often the situation is not simple. It may be an integrated system but not the unitary kind that some of the anthropologists have led us to expect. A good deal of the criticism of work such as Benedict's has been due to the fact that she was looking at the culture too much as a unitary system and did not treat the variation within it.

Partly in order to treat this variation, I have constructed a classification of what I call value orientations or cultural orientations. Relative to the classification, some first steps have been taken for the development of a theory of variation. I hope the scheme will allow one to compare cultures systematically better than has been done before, and also to relate better the concepts at this level of cultural analysis with the concepts at proper levels of abstraction in other disciplines.

First, let me give you a definition which appears in a paper by Clyde Kluckhohn on value orientation which in some part was taken out of the paper that I wrote on culture orientation. He says, somewhat formally, "A value orientation is a generalized and organized conception *influencing* behavior of nature, of man's place in nature, of man's relation to man, and of the desirable and non-desirable as they relate to man-environment and interhuman relations." [3]

Or, to put it a little less formally, the term "value orientation" is used to refer to those value notions which are (a) general, (b) organized and (c) which include definitely existential judgments.

The basic assumption for the classification of value orientations derives partly from a study of cultures, partly from a study of the work of anthropologists, and partly from philosophy. It is: *There is a limited number of basic human problems for which all peoples at all times and in all places must find the solution.*

The second assumption is that *while variability is certainly to be noted in the solutions which are found, it is within limits,* that is, within a range of possible variations.

To return to the first assumption: I have singled out five common

[3] *Ibid.*

human problems of key importance. They can be phrased in the form of questions:

1. What are the innate predispositions of man? In other words, what is the definition that a people will give of basic human nature?
2. What is the relation of man to nature?
3. What is the significant time dimension?
4. What modality of activity is to be most valued?
5. What is the dominant modality of man's relations to other men?

We have been using shortened names for the five: the first one, the human-nature orientation; the second, the man-nature orientation; third, the time orientation; fourth, the activity orientation; and fifth, the relation orientation.

The limits of variability and solutions found for these common human problems I have tentatively conceptualized. I hold no brief for trichotomies as such, but the breakdown in each case into the three-point range has an empirical as well as a logical grounding.

The range for the first one is actually not three but six positions. Is the definition of human nature that it is fundamentally evil, but perfectable, or evil and immutable? Is the definition of human nature that it is a mixture of the good and evil, which is viewed as either mutable or immutable? Or is human nature conceived to be either good and mutable or good and unalterable?

Turning to the second orientation, the man-nature relationship: Is the view of the relation of man to nature that men is subjugated-to-nature, that is, the victim of it and helpless in front of it? Is it that he lives in harmony with nature? Or is his relationship to nature exploitative, a conquering of nature?

The third orientation, labeled the time orientation, has been treated by a number of writers, but usually only two of the three positions have been treated by a single author. Frank is one person who has treated all three positions—the past, the present and the future.

The three point range of the activity orientation—the Being, the Being-in-Becoming, and the Doing, was derived for the most part from the distinction made long ago by philosophers between Being and Becoming. Moreover, to some degree the three-way distinction is in accord with the classification of personality components made by the contemporary philosopher, Charles Morris—the Dionysian, the Buddhist and the Promethean.[4]

The abstract component which Morris labels the Dionysian—the

[4] *The Open Shelf* (New York: Prentice-Hall, 1948).

component which releases and indulges existing desires—is very roughly the equivalent of the Being orientation. His Buddhist component—the component that is self-contained and controls itself through meditation and detachment that bring understanding—is somewhat similar to the Being-in-Becoming orientation. His active, striving Promethean component is also similar to the Doing orientation.

The correspondence, however, is far from complete. As used in this scheme, the terms Being and Becoming, now made into the three-point range of Being, Being-in-Becoming and Doing, are much more narrowly defined than has been the custom of philosophers. Furthermore, we hold that these three orientations vary in relation to those which deal with the relation of man to nature, to time and to innate predispositions. The tendency of the philosophers, writing with different aims, has been to treat these orientations as relatively undifferentiated clusters.

The essence of the Being orientation is the spontaneous expression of what is conceived to be "given" in the personality. The Being orientation. as compared with either the Being-in-Becoming or Doing ones, is essentially nondevelopmental. It might even be phrased as a spontaneous expression of impulses and desires; yet care must be taken not to make this interpretation too literal. In no society, as Clyde Kluckhohn has commented, does one ever find a one-to-one relationship between the desired and the desirable. The concrete behavior of individuals in complex situations, and the moral codes governing that behavior, usually reflect all the orientations simultaneously.

A stress upon the "isness" of the personality and spontaneous expression of that "isness" is not pure license as we can easily see if we turn our attention to a society or a segment of one where the Being orientation is dominant. Mexican society, for example, is clearly one in which the Being orientation is dominant. Their wide-range patterning of the *fiesta* alone shows this. Yet never in the fiesta or other patterns of spontaneity is there pure, unhampered gratification of impulse. The demands of the other orientations—the relational orientation, the conception of human nature as being good and evil and in need of control, and others—all make for codes which restrain individuals in definite ways.

The Being-in-Becoming orientation shares with the Being a great concern with what the human being is, rather than what he can accomplish. But here the similarity ends; in the former the idea of development, so little stressed in the latter, is paramount.

Erich Fromm's conception of "the spontaneous activity of the total integrated personality" is close to the Being-in-Becoming type. "By activity," he states, "we do not mean 'doing something,' but rather the quality of the creative activity which can operate in one's emotional, intellectual and sensuous experiences, and in one's will as well. One premise of this spontaneity is the acceptance of the total personality and the elimination of the split between reason and nature."[5]

A less favorably prejudiced and, for our purposes, a more accurately limited statement would be: The Being-in-Becoming orientation emphasizes self-realization or self-development of all aspects of the self as an integrated whole. Examples of Being-in-Becoming (this is simply prediction on my part) might be found in Zuni culture, in the very esthetically intellectual people in our own culture and to some extent in French culture. It seems to be an orientation that is difficult to maintain as dominant in a given society unless there is a narrowly-defined aristocracy.

The Doing orientation is, characteristically, so much stressed in American society that there is little need for an extensive definition. Its most distinguishing feature is the demand for accomplishment in accord with standards which are conceived to be external to the acting individual. Self-judgment, as well as the judgment of others, is largely based on measurable accomplishment through action. What the individual does, what he can or will accomplish, are almost always primary questions in our scale of appraisal of persons. "Getting things done" and finding ways "to do something" about any and all situations are stock American phrases.

Erich Fromm also recognizes this orientation as separable from his concept of spontaneity (which is close to the Being-in-Becoming), but he seems to view it as mainly compulsive. With this I cannot agree. Many persons in our society who follow patterns in accord with the Doing orientation are compulsive; many are not. Conformity, which is essential to all societies, whatever the arrangement of their orientations, should not be so much and so often confounded with compulsiveness.

RUESCH: *What is the pure being?*

KLUCKHOHN: That is the one where the emphasis is upon "isness" and spontaneity. It is non-developmental. The Mexican is a good example.

The fifth and last of the common human problems treated in the conceptual schema is the definition of man's relation to other men. This orientation, the relational, has three subdivisions—the lineal, the collateral and the individualistic.

Sociologists have long used various types of dichotomies to differentiate homogeneous folk societies from the more complex urban societies. Gemeinschaft-Gesellschaft, traditionalistic—rational-legal, mechanical-organic solidarity or simply rural-urban are the most familiar of the several

[5] *Escape From Freedom* (New York: Rinehart, 1941).

paired terms. Anthropologists, who for the most part have studied Gemeinschaft among folk peoples, have frequently in their analyses of kinship structure or social organization made much of the difference between lineage and a lateral extension of relationships.

The distinctions I am making here obviously owe much to the concepts used in both of these fields but are not identical with those of either field. The lineal, collateral and individualistic relational principles are analytical elements in total relational systems and are not to be confused with categories descriptive of concrete systems.

It is in the nature of the case that all societies, all groups, must give some attention to all three principles. Individual autonomy cannot be and is not ignored by the most extreme type of Gemeinschaft. Collaterality is found in all societies. The individual is not a human being outside a group, and one kind of group emphasis is that put upon laterally extended relationships. These are the immediate relationships in time and place. All societies also must pay some attention to the fact that individuals are biologically and culturally related to each other through time. There is always a lineal principle in relationships which is derived from age, generational differences and cultural tradition. The fundamental question is always that of emphasis.

For some types of problems it may be sufficient to differentiate only between the individual and the collectivity. In most cases, however, it is important to know what kind of collectivist principle is being stressed.

"Individualistic" as used in the schema does not mean an individual apart from the group. However, in an individualistic society individual goals have primacy over group goals whereas in both lineal and collateral societies group goals have primacy. In the lineal case there is the added factor that ordered positional succession through time is a man's goal.

One of the best mechanisms for maintaining a lineal principle is primogeniture. The Zunis have mechanisms for maintaining a certain kind of lineality at least in one part of the system. The Navahoes are a group-oriented people, but without any of those mechanisms, and our evidence seems to be that they are dominantly collateral.

RUESCH: *Could you give us a type among white people? I am not familiar with the Indians.*

KLUCKHOHN: I think we would find that certainly in large areas of Italy collaterality would be the dominant principle. Also, it was our prediction in our work this summer that the Mormon Americans, in contrast to the Texan Americans, were a fundamentally collateral group who are now moving toward individualism. And they proved to be a much more collateral group than the Texans.

I would like to make one general qualifying remark. No society ever emphasizes any onc of three principles to the exclusion of the other. It is a matter of emphasis. The possibilities for any one society are shown when you work out the logical combinations of the three. For instance, in the dominant American pattern individualism is first order. The second order is collateral, and the third is the lineal position. Or first order may be individual, the second lineal and the third collateral. There may be any combination of the three principles with varying combinations of weakness or strength for each order.

However, I do not think it is possible for any society or any individual in a society to behave always consistently according to one orientation. For instance, in American culture, in the occupational system which is our major prestige system, one would expect to find individualism first and collaterality second, but in other spheres of activity—the recreational area, for example—I would expect the collateral to be dominant. In other words, in no society is there a single dominant emphasis which is found consistently in all areas of life.

HENRY: *In mentioning the fact that in a given society more than one principle might be stressed, you immediately answered one of my criticisms. For example, in France in the Middle Ages where men struggled for prestige and waged war to that end, the society appears individualistic because of the importance of the magnates. But if you consider the organization of agriculture, then there is possible a combination of emphasis, lineal and collateral.*

KLUCKHOHN: Certainly. I would add that there is a dynamic interplay between the two. In this first pattern, which I think is the American in time of crisis, collaterality moves up and individuality falls back. At that point, Americans become much more conscious of group goals and sacrifice their customary preference for their own individualistic goals. There are temporary swings. There are also sometimes dynamic shifts from one of the principles to another. Heavy pressure, either internal or external, can in time force a shift from one of these to the other.

There is a difference between people who look to the past as something that is the best order to be maintained and those who prefer present situations and who consider it neither possible nor desirable to maintain the past. The latter do not feel that the "golden age" lies in the future, whereas a future-oriented people are constantly projecting and believing that change is a good thing. Then there is a question of the meaning of change. Some say that change is bad and that as change comes, things get worse. Others say change happens for better at times, for worse at other times—it depends on the circumstances. Still others look upon change as a positive improvement, even though there may be setbacks.

To test the theory of value orientation variation, we went to the Southwest where we had a cultural laboratory. There we have five groups with different cultures within a radius of sixty miles. The natural environment of each is much the same. There is more water in one particular area than in another, but the whole area is in the southwestern desert. The groups were the Zuni Indians, the Navaho Indians, the Spanish-Americans (Mexicans), a group of Texan American homesteaders, and a group of Mormons.

We aimed to develop a series of questions for each of the ranges of orientations. The battery of questions on each range related to several different kinds of life activities. The questionnaire was translated into the Spanish and Zuni languages. For questioning the Navaho an interpreter was used. The material is now complete on three of the cultures—the Mexican, the Mormon and the Texan. The Zuni and Navaho material is now being collected.

By way of experiment we made prior predictions about the findings. There were five of us who had been in the field and who had studied different cultures; I studied the Mexican, my husband the Navaho, Jack Roberts the Zuni, and so on. On the basis of ethnographic data and personal knowledge, we ventured to predict what the data would show. We proved to be quite accurate in the three cases thus far analyzed. There are dramatic differences between the three.

HENRY: *I would like to raise one question here that is relevant to a problem of methodology. There is always the danger in the administration of a questionnaire that you tap not actual behavior but the ideal pattern.*

PARSONS: *But even if that happened it would be all right for this purpose.*

KLUCKHOHN: We had a set of twenty or twenty-five questions. Because we first wished to know what the subjects considered the "best," we deliberately questioned on the "ideal pattern." We also asked another question relative to half of the life situations, particularly those that had to do with the difference between the Being and the Doing. This was: "What would you actually do in this case, in contrast to what is best?" Some interesting variations came out. A third question was, "What do you think the majority of other people in your community would think was best?" We asked this in order to see if there was any difference between what the person himself says and how he sees himself vis-a-vis the rest of the group.

THOMPSON: *Were you not in danger of excluding, by the formulation of the question, orientations that are other than these three? For instance, taking an over-all view of cultures throughout the world and through history, it seems to me that the orientation of time in the present tense is quite rare. Our language has three tenses—past, present and future. The present is quite idiomatic in our language and our grammar, but is rather rare if you look at the languages that we have studied. However the orientation of a past-future would be very common, but it would be excluded through your questionnaire.*

KLUCKHOHN: You are raising a very real objection. This was only one way of going at it. I think there will have to be other ways in order to reinforce the scheme itself.

HENRY: *You think of the language of the Araucanians, for instance; they have fourteen tenses. The Inca have twelve. Actually, these tenses are not formed and are not stated in Kechua as pure time units, but rather in terms, you might say, of emotionally-drenched aspects of time, so that the future becomes something very dubious and surrounded by many contingencies while the past has another emotional quality.*

KLUCKHOHN: These objections would be true if you made the analysis by language only but you should be able to establish value orientation variation in other ways. Obviously there are limitations to this method, in spite of the amount of time and energy we put into trying to cross the culture lines. One thing we now aim to do is to take the questionnaire material and check it against the ethnographic data which is extensive.

We predicted that the Texans, of course, would be predominantly individualistic, and second order collateral. Of the Mexicans I asked a fourth question on the relational questions, "How would this have been thirty years ago? What would have been the right answer or the best answer thirty years ago?" because we anticipated that these people, formerly strongly lineal, are now moving in the direction of the individualistic orientation in many areas of behavior.

We predicted that the particular Texan group tested would be predominantly oriented to the future with a fair amount of present-time orientation. For the Mexicans we predicted a strong orientation to present time. On the Doing-Being distinction, it was predicted Mexicans were Being and the Texans Doing; on the Man-Nature, that the Texans would be predominantly versus nature and the Mexicans subjugated to nature.

There were so few Mexicans that the sample used was the whole population. Of all the other cultures a random sample was taken. Twenty persons were chosen in each of the groups, for these are small groups. There were 287 Texans, the Mormons numbered roughly 300, and the Navahoes roughly 500. The Zuni population of approximately 3,000 was the largest, and it is doubtful the sample size was adequate in their case.

Our hope is that the orientation schema will provide a method of systematizing "value" material which will make possible a treatment of values in interaction processes. Moreover, this kind of systematization of values reveals more of the dynamics of personality than does an itemizing of culture content which is then given a psychoanalytic interpretation. Many of the students of national character structure have had trouble when using the latter method for they have taken specific items of culture content out of context. Those items may be critically important, but out of context their meaning is lost and there is then no way of saying that the same item in another culture should have a different effect.

TOMAN: *I would like to make a three-fold statement on methodology. Are not many of these populations, particularly if they are taken from a large area, multi-model? I certainly would expect so where there is caste system of classes and where work is not homogeneous. The method would have to be such as to indicate the multi-modality; not just the number in each mode but also the relation of those modes to the ability to enforce a type of opinion.*

It is also important, in order not to attribute these differences in values to particular ethnic groups, to make sure that there are some kinds of controls in occupational groups selected from the same ethnic group.

A third point concerns the time value and predictive value of an experiment set up in this manner. It would be a good idea to secure data at reasonably well separated times, and not just to imagine what the data would have been, say a generation ago.

KLUCKHOHN: I agree entirely. The only check I got that satisfies your requirements is from the Mexican group I studied intensively sixteen years ago. I made some of these statements about them sixteen years ago, and it gave me great satisfaction to find that I had been right.

SPIEGEL: *I believe these two presentations may be linked with the conceptual inclusive model. In both Thompson's presentation of community and Kluckhohn's presentation of the analysis of culture orientations as a more detailed examination of the core values, if the question comes up, "Where would one look for these?" or "How would one look for them?" it seems to me that the point could be made that you would look for them everywhere—in the individual, in the group, in the social system, in the somatic structure and so on. Again one would think of it with reference to my system foci, which is a more comprehensive scheme. If you put the cultural orientations into a system, and if the system is an interdependent one, their influence must appear everywhere.*

EDITOR: *Kluckhohn, following logically on Thompson's discussion, stated that core values of one culture should be compared to those of others and within cultures which are not uniform systems. She classifies value orientations or cultural orientations as value concepts or notions held by man. There are a limited number of basic human problems that man tries to solve and a limited variability of solutions. Her scheme envisages five major questions, each answerable in a three-point range: What is the innate predisposition of man (what is human nature)? What is man's relation to nature? What is the significance of time? What modality of activity is to be most valued? and, What is the dominant relation of man to other men? Each category and each range was discussed and exemplified. Combinations and changes can be observed. Such core values may be found by examination of all systems: the somatic, individual, group and societal, and influence them all.*

CHAPTER EIGHT

A SYSTEM OF SOCIO-PSYCHIATRIC INVARIANTS

Presentation by Jules Henry

THE presentation which I am about to make is an expression of my continued interest in the closer collaboration of the social sciences and psychiatry. Erich Lindemann recently stated the following as one of the major obstacles to good mutual cooperation between the psychiatrist and the social scientist:

"The psychiatrist is likely to remain patient-centered and focused on intrapsychic phenomena even if he wishes to contribute to social science. The social-science-centered statements of the social scientist are likely to appear to the psychiatrist as being 'superficial' and lacking in pertinence for the individual case requiring care."

As Lindemann sees it, when the psychiatrist perceives a social dimension in the problems of his patient, the perception may not help him because his clinical problem is to manipulate the patient and not the society. The purpose of this discussion is to help toward the dissolution of the patient-society dualism.

But in science dualisms can be dissolved only by theoretical formulations of such character as to bring both members of the dualism within reach of one set of invariants. As long as we think about patients in one way, and about society in another, Lindemann's thoughtful statement will hold true. Hence, another purpose of this presentation is to develop a set of invariant equations that will have meaning both within the intrapsychic system of the patient and the social system.

The development of equations that express social and intrapsychic conditions at the same time must proceed from relatively crude formulations, in the hope that later, as science progresses, stricter statements will be possible. Hence, the present effort is presented tentatively as a work paper. The experimental psychologist and the mathematician will perhaps find my efforts naive. My interest in the equations, however, centers not so much in their value as a possible basis for quantitative statements of relations but rather as concise presentations of hypotheses that can then be explored in all their implications, both for society and for the individual.

Let us assume that in all societies there are certain types of paired socio-psychological factors that can be viewed as standing in dialectical relationship to one another. Examples of them are (1) reward and punishment; (2) activities performed under constraint and activities performed as free choice; (3) activities permitted and activities forbidden; (4) important things and unimportant things; (5) familiar situations and unfamiliar situations; (6) success and failure; and (7) painful situations and gratifying situations.

Some of these factors may be present in some societies and absent in others; but all societies can be assumed to have factors of this kind. It is not necessary to assume that all societies will have the same number of them, or that where the same factors occur they will always have exactly the same quality. Thus, although both our society and Chinese society have rewards and punishments, these are not the same in both societies. The peculiar qualities of rewards and punishments must be defined in the context of each society.

For the sake of clarity, I shall discuss one relationship in detail, and then go on to the elucidation of others.

If I assert (a) that in all societies there is reward for conformity and punishment for non-conformity, I can then say (b) that the extent to which people in a society are aware of the imminence of social punishment is a function of the relationship between the totality of rewards and punishments provided by the society.

Although such formulations are imprecise, I believe they can be used as heuristic devices for exploring various types of important relationships, and for making comparisons between societies. In the present case the formulation can be used to explore the relative ease or uneasiness with which people go about their activities in different societies. Thus, such a simple formulation can serve to compare societies. This relation can be stated symbolically:

EQUATION 1: $$AP = \frac{P}{R}$$

P stands for possibilities of social punishment, and R stands for possibilites of social reward; AP stands for "sense of social punishment."

The statement of socio-psychological relationships as tentative laws in these dialectical and symbolic ways makes possible rough quantitative estimates of socio-psychological relationships of various kinds in different societies. Societies may then be compared.

The equation states that in societies where the possibilities for social punishment for non-conformity are great and the possibilities for social reward for conformity are small, individuals in the society will tend to have a strong sense of being in imminent danger of punishment for non-conformity.

Here we must introduce an important modifying factor: a "sense of social punishment" would be a function not only of the number of the punishments prescribed for individuals who do not conform, but also of the severity and frequency of punishment. The equation states that the sense of social punishment is not alone a function of the situation with respect to punishment, but it depends also upon the situation with respect to social reward. The equation implies that in societies offering many opportunities for social reward, individuals may develop high tolerance for social punishment. It seems to me this helps us to understand some of the characteristics of totalitarian systems, where the number of punishments or the number of possibilities of punishments is increased greatly while at the same time the totalitarian government increases the number of possible rewards. I should state that I use the term "reward" here not in the sense in which the animal psychologists and the learning theory people use it, but in the sense of recognition, an added increment for something done.

PARSON: *On the social-symbolic level that is fundamentally the same. It is the social-symbolic equivalent of the gratification rewards in learning theory.*

HENRY: If you get a salary for work, that is not a reward in my sense. I mean a medal for doing your work well.

The equation $AP = \frac{P}{R}$ suggests that where the value of P is high in relation to R, individuals will try to divert themselves of AP by over-conforming and thus reducing the possibility of social punishment. Hence, any reward one receives in a society where the possibilities for social punishment are great will exert an influence on the personality which is "out of proportion" to its "real size." I put such expressions as "out of proportion" and "real size" in quotes to emphasize their impreciseness and necessary subjectivity, and because this is obviously a crude attempt at qualification.

It is common experience in our culture that little compliments and flattery go to one's head. In many people this may be attributed partly to a relatively great preponderance of P over R. One may attempt to reduce AP by striving to increase the value of R for himself. He can do this by trying hard to acquire whatever rewards the society affords. Thus, one type of person fighting for recognition is the person who is acutely conscious of imminent social punishment. Hence, we find combined in one person over-conformity and a struggle for recognition.

Reward and punishment have both social and individual reference. We can speak of *society* as *providing* rewards and punishments; and we can speak of *individuals* as experiencing these in the proportions they are administered by society. We can then attempt to predict how an individual who has experienced these socially determined proportions of reward and punishment will feel—whether he will have a strong or weak sense of social punishment. It is in this sense that the equation has both social and individual intrapsychic reference, and hence fulfills the requirements of invariance.

The next category concerns commitments and fulfillments. Every society provides statements of what one is to expect from it. One society promises the crock of gold at the end of the rainbow. We see this in LIFE magazine's success stories every week, and in the ads for perfume which promise that if you smell right people will love you. More seriously, however, our society promises we will always have a constantly rising standard of living and equality of treatment from our fellow men. The Pilagá Indians of Argentina, with whom my wife and I lived for over a year, expect that all people will share their food with them. Among the Kaingáng Indians of Brazil, with whom I lived for a year, everyone was led to expect love from everyone else. These expectations of what one has the right to receive from society I call the "commitments" of the society. Dialectically opposed to commitment, then, stand the factors of fulfillment and no power to fulfill commitment.

THOMPSON: *Would you give your definition of "powers"?*

HENRY: It entered, Thompson, into your discussion of the relationship between values and institutions. A value to all intents and purposes will not exist unless there is an institutional device through which it can be expressed. This is what I call a power. My definition is: By "powers" is meant the factors, natural resources, culture traits including technology and forms of social organization, and other things available to society for carrying out its commitments.

PARSONS: *What you stated a moment ago is what the starry-eyed liberal forgets, that just by getting assent to a value you cannot get implementation and action. It must have institutionalization, and adequate mechanism.*

RUESCH: *What about such a phenomenon as Gandhi in India?*

PARSONS: *There may be a tremendous influence from such persons; but the one thing you can predict about their influence is that there will not be a direct implementation of what they state to be desirable. I think a classic statement of that is given in system terms by Pareto.*[1] *I think he used the T for Telos, which is stated as an ideal goal, ideologically, we will say; but in the nature of the case, unless the goal is so stated as to take account specifically of system interdependence the process may not operate to achieve the goal: it may go off at a tangent.*

We have innumerable examples. One of the studies in the Harvard Center is of the wide gaps between ideological statements and the actual constitution of the system. Stalin can say, "The family is the pillar of the Soviet state," but this is not very good Marxism, in my opinion. I think he just had to say it because the family had to be consolidated.

HENRY: Now, the relationship between commitments and fulfillments may be stated symbolically as follows:

EQUATION 2: $$S = \frac{F}{C}$$

Here C stands for commitments, F for fulfillments and S for sense of satisfaction. The equation thus states that societies with few commitments and many fulfillments of them tend to produce relatively satisfied persons, while societies with many commitments but few fulfillments tend to produce relatively unsatisfied persons. It is a matter of everyday experience that our society commits itself to many things it does not fulfill. This is equally true of other societies. Among the Pilagá and the Kaingáng, individuals are led to expect things that are beyond the powers of society to give.

This brings us to another aspect of the fulfillment–no fulfillment dichotomy—the relation between the commitments of the society and its

[1] V. Pareto, *Traité de Sociologie Generale* (Paris: P. Bowen, 1917).

powers to fulfill them. This relationship may be stated symbolically as follows:

EQUATION 3: $$S = \frac{Pw}{C}$$

Here Pw stands for "powers to fulfill commitments." Societies may be committed to many grand things but lack the powers to fulfill them. Our own society is committed to the granting of equality to all men, for example, yet under the present conditions it simply does not have the powers to fulfill this ideal.

Interesting considerations emerge from a close examination of equations 2 and 3. If we assume the existence of a person X with a low value of S (sense of satisfaction), then we may suppose that he will do the following: (a) attempt to increase F—attempt to get as much out of the society as possible in terms of what its commitments are; (b) diminish C—declare to himself that he is not entitled to anything. These are two courses that the person with emotional difficulties may follow. But bear in mind that these choices are laid down for him in advance by a fundamental type of social relationship. A third course: the person with low S may attempt to increase his own powers, yet never claim what one would be supposed to achieve thereby. He thus does not attempt to garner the "fulfillments," but contents himself only with the means with which to reach them. Outstanding in this group would be those who accumulate knowledge about everything but never put it to any use.

The next pair of dialectical opposites to be considered are the permitted and the forbidden. In all society some things are forbidden and some are permitted. These may fall equally or unequally on the population. The permitted and the forbidden may have different meanings to the people in the society according to whether they give satisfaction or cause pain. Thus, it may be of little consequence to an American child to be prevented from drinking whiskey, but it may mean a great deal to him not to be able to stay up at night. It may be of little consequence to a Pilagá woman that she is not permitted to dance in a circle as the men do, but it may matter a great deal to her that she is not permitted to smoke or visit.

You can see that you have to take into consideration not simply the number of things that are permitted and forbidden, but their meanings to the people. I state this in equation 4:

EQUATION 4: $$D = \frac{Fb}{Pr}$$

Instead of talking about a sense of satisfaction, this time for the sake of variety I will state it as a sense of dissatisfaction. Fb stands for "activities not engaged in," D stands for "sense of dissatisfaction," and Pr stands for "activities engaged in."

The equation states that in any group in a society, dissatisfaction is a function in part of the relation between the number of things permitted and those not permitted. Not alone the number of things but also their quality as giving physical or symbolic pleasure is important. Enjoyment of tobacco, for example, might be considered a physical pleasure. Becoming a tribal chief might be considered a symbolic pleasure.

In rating groups in a society along a permitted-forbidden continuum, therefore, one would have first to try rating the groups in over-all terms for the number of things permitted and forbidden to them, and then try rating them for the pleasure-giving qualities of the things permitted and forbidden.

TOMAN: *Will you distinguish between "forbidden" and "punished"?*

HENRY: Being forbidden to do something under certain circumstances might be considered as a punishment. This question has arisen because I have not defined punishment. I define it as follows: By punishment is meant the administration of pain to a person by another person or group as a consequence of the performance of a given act. Such punishments may range from having people look at one or comment adversely on his behavior, to the extreme of capital punishment.

PARSONS: *That is, contingency is a crucial part of the definition. It is not just painful things that happen but they are administered as a contingent consequence.*

KLUCKHOHN: *By significant people.*

ENGEL: *It may not be actual disapproval—it may be an internalized feeling of disapproval as a response to something that has gone on in the past.*

HENRY: I do not know whether I could admit that in this system, Engel, because the conditions for the occurrence of the phantasy disapproval would have to exist in the society. This becomes internalized in the individual. Society provides the conditions for the occurrence of the phantasy.

ENGEL: *Except that that would leave out of consideration the genetic or developmental elements. In a neurotic person, disapproval which was appropriate at age three, as in the case of staying up late or drinking whiskey, may be perpetuated into adult life even though it is no longer realistic.*

HENRY: Yes, I agree. I would say, however, that the conditions of this disapproval or punishment which has meant so much in his life are provided by society. Punishments are not administered to a baby in the same ways as to an adult; the social situation provides the conditions for the development of punishments appropriate to every level of life.

ENGEL: *The people immediately in the child's environment, namely his parents, are the translators for the society and because of problems of their own, they may accentuate or alter certain aspects which are not realistic in the society as a whole. Therefore, the more personal aspects of behavior at age three may be transmitted unrealistically to adult life and projected on to society.*

HENRY: Equation 5 suggests that societies producing strongly dissatisfied persons would produce in them also the inclination to break with convention through doing the forbidden things. The extent to which such breaches are attempted, however, is related to the relationship between P and R in equation 1; for if the punishments for non-conformity are severe, the dissatisfied person may have too strong a sense of social guilt to permit himself unconventionality. In such a case breaches of convention may take place in phantasy only. This situation may be expressed in the following symbolic form:

EQUATION 5: $$W = \frac{D}{AP}$$

This equation suggests that the "willingness to break with convention," W, is partly a function of the relation between personal dissatisfaction, D, and the fear of social punishment, AP. We might suspect that where fear of social punishment is enormous, breaking with convention will not occur even in phantasy. At this point we may indicate that a D can be derived from equations 2 and 3 as well as from equation 4.

When the willingness to break with convention is examined in this way, we see that it can be referred to the total structure of relationships within a society. It can then be understood as a "normal" expectancy in societies where commitments outstrip fulfillments, where people are denied too many of the pleasurable things of life, and where the fear of social punishment is not overwhelming. We might guess that persons with a strong but unconscious desire to break with convention would protest fear of breaking even the slightest social rules and/or would proclaim com-

plete satisfaction with their lives. These would be relatively unpredictable persons who would live conventionally but indulge in sudden outbursts of non-conforming, and make bitter attacks on symbols of their dissatisfaction.

The next pair I would like to talk about is the relationship between choice and constraint. It may be stated in this symbol:

$$\text{EQUATION 6:} \qquad Cn = \frac{Ac}{Af}$$

In this equation Ac are activities performed under constraint, and Af are activities performed by choice; Cn stands for the "sensation of constraint."

The equation states that the degree to which a person in a society will feel under compulsion, tied down, unfree, is not a fixed item in the personality, but is rather the product of the balance in society between what he may choose to do and what he must do.

Where many activities are performed as choice, Cn will be small. However, this is not only a matter of quantity of things but also of quality. The size of Cn is a function of the importance of the activities that are constrained or chosen. It is likely that the matter of definition of these areas is important also. Society may define activities as freely chosen, but really constrain them. This will happen when controls are indirect and where cultural values emphasize choice as a good. The definition of constraint may be on a suprasocial level, as in India for example, where what one is constrained to do is one's *karma*.

From the equation at the individual level, the following possibilities emerge: A person having a strong sense of constraint may attempt to reduce the number of things he feels constrained to do by refusing to do prescribed things; or he may attempt to increase the number of things he can do of his own free will. It would appear, however, that the AP factor must be taken into consideration also. If a person has a strong sense of the imminence of social punishment he will not attempt to reduce Ac. Impulses in that direction will express themselves also by phantasy, in chronic irritation at the performance of all duties, or in attacks on the symbols of constraint such as persons in authority.

SPIEGEL: *You would define equations 5 and 6 as positive and negative aspects of autonomy. There is willingness to break convention, or the sense of restraint seems to refer to variations in the autonomous situation. Am I interpreting it incorrectly?*

HENRY: I hadn't thought about it. Equation 5 would be the positive aspect. As we analyze the meanings implicit in equation 6 we see that a behavior under constraint is a function of the total configuration of the choice-constraint relationships in society. A person's behavior may be the product of specific events in his life having to do with his particular experience of choice or constraint, but these are a reflection of the dialectical relationships among the totality of such possibilities in his society. What this means to me is that hunger for freedom is not something inborn in man, but its intensity and possibly even the fact that we talk about it are functions of the totality of social relationships.

The next pair I would like to consider are "gratifying" and "painful" situations. If a society creates many painful situations and few gratifying ones, the individual will tend to expect new situations to be painful. This hypothesis is stated:

EQUATION 7: $$E = \frac{Sp}{Sg}$$

Here E stands for negative expectations. By "gratifying situation" is meant one in which a need is adequately met. By "painful situation" is meant one which brings pain. "Negative expectation" means a state in which one expects new situations to be painful. To the degree that this equation approximates what actually happens, persons with high E may be supposed to do some or all of the following: Attempt to make all new situations gratifying; attempt to define all new situations as gratifying; attempt to define all new situations as at least not painful; deliberately to seek new situations known in advance to be gratifying; attempt to create new situations they hope will be gratifying; shun new situations.

I hope you understand that I do not think, for example, that seeking new situations known in advance to be gratifying can be derived only from this kind of ratio. A person who has had only pleasurable situations in life will continue to seek only pleasurable situations.

WEISS: *Can you delineate this equation as against equation 1?*

HENRY: This, of course, is one of my continuing problems. The equations, upon careful examination, appear to overlap. On the other hand, somewhat similar situations if stated in different ways can lead to somewhat different conclusions. You can state punishment, for example, as being administered by other people. Let us say you can define a painful experience as something specifically *administered* by other people—codified in the laws, perhaps. You also can state painful experience as being something that *happens* to a person in interaction with others. You will see as I go on that there are other areas about which you might raise the same question.

PARSONS: *You haven't put these together to constitute a system. You know they are interdependent, though their interdependence is not formally specified?*

SPIEGEL: *Also, these do not necessarily define any particular number of people in a situation. Can it be a two-person, three-person or a multiple-person situation?*

HENRY: What I am stating here is that society provides the conditions for the experience of pain or gratification.

SPIEGEL: *"Society" meaning extended groups?*

HENRY: Yes, and meaning, too, that the individual will experience in his psychic system the basic conditions that are provided by the society.

TOMAN: *Is this parallelism correct: In all of these terms on the left hand side you have something corresponding to tensions and on the right hand side you have activities. The equation relates an activity to its possible consequences. If I understand how you are handling this, isn't there a constant total activity and therefore an additive relationship between P and R?*

HENRY: An additive relationship? If one were to assume that all the symbols on the left hand side stand for tension, then you should be able to add up the right hand members.

TOMAN: *No, but quite aside from that, the symbols on the right hand side correspond to unit activities and the consequences of those activities. If they are units, then the favorable and unfavorable activities, or so it would seem to me, would add up to a constant sum.*

WEISS: *I don't think that is true. What you might mean to say is that instead of writing equation 1, the function of pain as* $\frac{P}{R}$, *you could* write it as a function of $\frac{K \times P}{1 - P}$.

That would be correct only if every item could be rated either P or R; but you have a lot of indifferent events which apparently are neither punishment nor award. If you put those in, then you have a different factor and P and R do not add up to 100%. I think that is essentially what you had in mind, was it not?

TOMAN: Yes.

GRINKER: *But it does coincide in general with Parson's pattern. On the left side there were all degrees of satisfaction and release of tension. On the B side they were always action systems.*

HENRY: If these suppositions are correct, then people who have had many experiences and relatively gratifying ones would be active seekers after gratifying experiences of all kinds; they would be Pollyannas; they would blind themselves to real pain and avoid anything that does not promise immediate gratification.

To this the reservation should be added that people who have had only gratifying experiences may behave in the same way. It is along such lines, so it seems to me, that we find the error in the thinking of Linton, who postulates a basic human need for "novelty of experience." [2] Actually, whatever need people have for new experience is a function of their prior experience; or more specifically a function of the ratio between pleasure and pain in the prior experience.

These suppositions raise some interesting problems with respect to social change, for when individuals have many painful experiences in society, and few gratifying ones, they seek, it seems, new gratifying experiences in a variety of ways or avoid new situations altogether for fear of pain. This may be given symbolic formulation in which the ratio $\frac{Sp}{Sg}$ is substituted for the enumerator in equation 5.

EQUATION 8: $$W = \frac{Sp}{Ap.Sg}$$

The equation here states that where the sensation of social punishment, A, is very strong, the willingness to break convention—that is, to seek a new kind of experience—will be relatively weak even in the presence of minimum gratifications. It also suggests that willingness to break convention will be strong even in the presence of great fear of social punishment when gratifying situations are zero. When Sg becomes zero, the value of W becomes infinitely great.

If what has been said in the preceding pages is true about the direction behavior and feeling will take in the presence of changes in magnitude in the factors considered, then we may have a fruitful approach to the problem of *psychogenic needs*. If a person has a strong sense of social punishment it follows, from our reasoning, that under certain conditions he will develop a "need for recognition." If he has a strong sense of constraint, he will develop a "need for freedom of choice." If one's experiences have been painful, then one may develop a "need for novelty of experience." If a child has been given a strong sense of failure by hostile parents, under certain conditions he will have a strong "need for achievement."

Since social experiences are involved in the generation of all these

[2] Ralph Linton, *The Science of Man in the World Crisis* (New York: Columbia University Press, 1945).

needs, psychogenic needs evolve out of the social field in which a person lives, they are not inborn. Thus, psychogenic needs develop out of interpersonal relations, not the other way around. Once the need is developed, of course, it then enters with its own dynamics into interpersonal relations and conditions them.

It will be seen at once that this theory of need simply applies to "normal" needs or the theory of "compensation" developed by psychiatry for the understanding of "abnormal" needs. Implicit in psychiatric theory is a mathematical model of the abnormal person: he is one who strives "too much" for recognition; who wants "too much" to be free; who hungers "too much" after novelty; and who tries "too hard" to achieve. This "too muchness" is believed, generally, to arise out of experiences of "too much" punishment, failure, and so on. If this is correct, then one must conclude that just the "right amount" of punishment, failure, and so on, must account for the "right amount" of striving, search for new experience, struggle for achievement, and hunger for freedom.

If we must take society into account when considering the generation of psychogenic needs, we certainly also must do so when analyzing their gratification. What happens to the individual with a particular need is a function of the way his social environment is prepared to respond to it.

Concerning the needs of the individual and reciprocal needs of the environment, we have the following definitions:

(a) An individual is said to have a need when he experiences malaise because he lacks something.

(b) A reciprocal need of the environment is said to exist when malaise is awakened in one person or persons (the environment) by perception of the need of another, but only when that malaise can be relieved by activity that will for the moment reduce the specific need of the other.

While a baby in a maternity ward often needs to sleep, the mother's need often is to feed it. Pilagá mothers wait for their babies to wake before they feed them; we used to wake our babies for feeding on schedule. This is an example of lack of reciprocity between individual needs and environmental need. Another example: A child cries because it is frightened and its mother slaps it for crying. The child needs tenderness, comfort, and reassurance, but its mother needs to release hostility. If, instead, she only offered him food, it still would not be reciprocal. In the first case, soothing words, explanations that no harm will come, and so on, would be an expression of the mother's need to give tenderness. In the latter case the mother's need would be reciprocal to the child's.

Let us then make the assumption that the level of tension in an individual is a function of his need, on the one hand, and the need of the environment to gratify it on the other hand. This is stated symbolically in the following equation:

$$\text{EQUATION 9:} \qquad Tn = \frac{IN}{EN}$$

Tn stands for the vague condition, "level of tension relating to need"; IN indicates the needs of the individual; and EN indicates reciprocal needs of the environment with respect to them. The equation is meant to suggest that in a culture where there is a reciprocal relationship between the needs of the individual and the needs of the environment, tension will be relatively low; but high when the needs of the environment bear no relation to those of the individual.

If we now ask, "What kind of persons are produced by societies where Tn does not equal 1?" we can obtain the answer by assuming the value of Tn to be large. Since in such societies the aim of the individual is to reduce the value of IN relative to EN, we can expect such societies to produce one or more of the following: (a) ascetics, who deny that they have any needs; (b) those who restlessly and endlessly seek some nameless gratification from environment—the insatiable and those who "don't know what they want"; (c) those who believe that others will never "do them any good" or have their interests at heart; and (d) the apathetic people, who feel there is no use trying to get anything because it will never satisfy them, anyway.

Further problems are suggested by the dichotomy: the need to satisfy self—need to satisfy others. The postulated relationship is expressed in this equation:

$$\text{EQUATION 10:} \qquad Tn_1 = \frac{IN_s}{IN_e}$$

IN_s represents the individual's need to gratify himself, IN_e the individual's need to gratify others, and Tn_1 the state of tension that depends on the ratio. The society in which social tensions are low might therefore appear to be one in which $IN_s < IN_e$. This is apparently the goal of societies like the Pilagá, where one's economic activities are devoted largely to the satisfaction of the needs of others rather than of self. In such societies, in contrast to our own, the major sanctions are organized around giving away rather than keeping. However, if there is too much emphasis on giving away, without adequate provisions of the needs of self, the individual's needs, IN, may go unsatisfied and tension may rise. This may come about when, through a defective socio-economic organization, people give away more than they receive.

Further dangers appear from consideration of:

$$\text{EQUATION 11:} \qquad Tn_2 = \frac{IN_s.P}{IN_e.R}$$

This states that where punishment attaches to satisfaction of self, tension will be high if little or no reward accrues for satisfying the needs of others. This is typical of the Pilagá: one is carefully watched lest one keep too much of the food one gets for one's self, yet praise is rarely given when one gives away what he has.

In societies where tension revolving around the need to satisfy others is high, people may devote themselves largely to attempts to escape punishment, P-O, rather than to giving to others. Generally both occur at the same time. Thus, the Pilagá, though he gives away much of his food, conceals it also or takes circuitous paths homeward when he returns to the village with food. Theoretically, the Pilagá could avoid all tension by always escaping punishment; but this is impossible for people can always find out that he has food, and there is never any real escape from sorcerers who, he believes, will kill him for withholding it.

Meanwhile, there is a limit to the extent to which one can reduce tension by looking after others, IN_e, for since one receives less than one gives away, one must hold back some of the fish one catches lest one starve. But giving away food is relatively unsatisfying, for rewards for doing so are almost nil. It is easy to see from equation 11, therefore, that tension in Pilagá society would be greatly reduced by arrangements through which people could keep what they need, without fear of sorcery, and receive praise for giving.

Culture is the summation of the integrated values in interactional systems of individuals, groups and institutions. Thus, the individual and culture are related to one another somewhat as the molecule to the total volume of the gas of which it is a part: the culture as a whole has properties that the individual, alone, lacks. The behavior of the individual cannot be understood apart from the culture of which he is part, and the culture cannot be understood without an understanding of the individuals in it.

It is by such reasoning that the way is paved for the assumption of certain generalities that hold for both culture and the individual, but in different ways. A culture may be said to administer certain rewards and punishments to individuals, but it is inaccurate to say that cultures can be "frustrated," have "feelings of inadequacy," or "over-react." Only individuals can do these things; they are processes whereby individuals adjust to culture.

But individuals adjust to certain cultural circumstances, such as punishments and rewards, opportunities for success and failure, promises made and promises fulfilled, and so on. The culture, through values and fixed systems of interaction that have become traditional, provide the basic conditions under which individuals shall experience reward and punishment, success and failure, gratification and pain, and so on.

Hence, a single system of equations can be used to describe the conditions provided by the culture and certain experiences of the individual. It has the advantage of making clear at once the relationship between culture and individual, of defining the relationship concisely, of facilitating manipulation of ideas, and finally of making a beginning at the quantitative description which is our goal.

Mathematical models of personality process are no more than a statement of the assumptions that are unexpressed in all personality theory. If we say that a mother rejects her child, we simply mean that she performs more acts of repudiation than she does of acceptance. If we say that an individual has feelings of inadequacy, we mean that he more often feels inadequate than adequate. If we say that an individual represses his feelings, we generally mean that he more often conceals than expresses or recognizes them.

Much of our thinking about personality turns upon such notions of more or less. The contribution of this paper, as I see it, is that it puts assumptions together into a single theory with the social circumstances from which personality emerges.

Editor: *Henry attempts to help dissolve the patient-society dualism by establishing invariant equations applicable to intrapsychic systems and social systems. In all societies it is assumed that paired socio-psychologic factors exist in dialectical relationship to each other. The factors are construed to be reward-punishment, constraint-free choice, permitted-forbidden, important-unimportant, familiar-unfamiliar, success-failure, pain-gratification. From these factors a number of equations were derived based on examples of conditions and responses. Henry stated that social experiences were involved in the generation of needs, in other words, psychogenic needs evolve out of the social field. The behavior of the individual is not understandable apart from the culture of which he is a part and culture cannot be understood without considering the individuals in it.*

CHAPTER NINE

GENERAL DISCUSSION TERMINATING THE FIRST CONFERENCE

ENGEL: We have moved essentially from the biological system all the way around to the cultural system. I propose now to come back to the biological again, very briefly, and mention again, without any great detail, some of the common properties that we have mentioned.

In the *first* place, if we view man in process with his environment, it is worth while to look at the common biological properties of the simplest living organisms, common to all living organisms. We would include, first, spontaneous activity which is apparent in growth, development, and various physiological processes. The limits of these activities are generically determined in many different ways, and the sources of the primary energy are internal and presumably finite, each organism having a life cycle.

Secondly, each organism has a limiting membrane; the boundary that we have mentioned in so many contexts. The intactness of this limiting membrane is essential for the integrity of the internal environment of the organism.

The *third* point is that all organisms have the capacity within limits to adapt to environmental forces and to obtain from the environment what they need for survival, growth and development. This is genetically as well as phylogenetically circumscribed and experientially modified. That is, the enzyme constitution, the physical-chemical constitution and the morphology determine as well as limit the capacity of the organism to deal with an environmental process. To paraphrase Jennings, "A cornered amoeba cannot escape by flying."[1] Some of the basic types of behavioral adjustments

[1] H. S. Jennings, "The Beginnings of Social Behavior in Unicellular Organisms," *Science*, XCII (1940), 539.

are internal metabolic rearrangements, mobility, moving toward, moving away, ingestion, digestion, excretion, spore formation, and so on.

Fourth, all living organisms have the capacity to reproduce, and thereby to continue the species. Implicit in this fact, then, is that some behavior is not self-regulatory, but species- or group-regulatory. The behavior in the service of reproduction and continuation of the species also has internal sources and external stimuli and proves to be of importance in determining relationships between one animal and another.

Energy is a concept which has come into the discussion in various connections. In dealing with the biological system we regard the energy sources as physico-chemical in nature, energy being understood in physical terms. In this area some of the problems or the dilemmas have been clarified to some extent, at least, by the introduction of the concepts of the open system applied to living organisms. Keeping clearly in mind that energy derives from physico-chemical sources, we then have to distinguish between energy and its consequences. So-called psychic energy, or social energy, is really not energy but is the consequences of this internal dynamic configuration of the organism which we recognize in different forms. Pain or pleasure may be recognized in psychological terms and social terms without being energy, *per se.*

Spiegel presented to us a scheme in which he wanted to move away from some of the hierarchical and level aspects of behavior. I would feel that there are good reasons for not doing that, that there is some valid reason for maintaining the idea of levels, at least in connection with the evolutionary aspects, that is, development in the course of biological time.

The basic biological functions that I have outlined are common to all living organisms and the energy sources are essentially the same. Evolution provides a record since the primeval state of the successful and unsuccessful efforts of development, of organismic organization to adapt to a changing cosmic environment.

PARSONS: You say that energy of the organism comes from physico-chemical sources, but mediated through the organization of the organism. In other words, what we call effort in action is not applying force in the sense of mechanics. When you try hard to solve a problem, you can't use the formulae of mechanics in order to describe what happens.

WEISS: Not as yet, but it is a good postulate that we might some day. Talk which is somewhat loose runs through the field of biology and psychology about the energy which provides the steam, disregarding the device of rails. Think of a railroad: energy can merely produce an explosion, or it can be directed into useful channels. (What we are dealing with in the organic everywhere is a limitation of the freedom of a given amount of energy to explode.) If that channel is very narrow—then it is constantly a question of will there be an explosion? However, it does not require energy to limit energy to a channel. It requires structure restraining the freedom of movements, as in the orderly movements of electrons. It is the pattern of distribution, which is not a correlate itself of energy. The ways in which a given quantum of energy can be expended are restricted. These things ought to be separated conceptually as much as possible.

ENGEL: You should not speak of "psychic energy" or "social energy." Those are the fields within which one is functioning.

PARSONS: I have no objection to what Weiss has said, except that I think my point is relevant. There is a conceptual parallelism relative to the open system idea, namely that the energy source of the organism is in the physico-chemical system which is interchanging with the environment. The energy source of action is the interchange within the organism. Between the two energies there is a direct conceptual parallelism. How that is interpreted in another set of terms is an open question.

ENGEL: I proceed from the evolutionary point of view because I think it is possible to trace, in schematic fashion at least, the steps from the biological to the psychological and the social. I shall summarize them briefly.

First of all, as already mentioned, the unicellular organism incorporates all its functions within one structural unit, and at the same time certain basic modes of behavior concerned in survival and reproduction in higher organisms have their *Anlage* in the primitive organism. However, the higher organism manifests these activities at more complex and psychological and social levels.

Secondly, the development of multi-cellular organisms requires specialization of functions and cells and organs, development of systems of internal communication and coordination, systems of external and internal perception—and here I simply remind you of Grinker's presentation of the various levels of organization within the complex multi-cellular organism.

However, it is from the developments eventually of the central nervous system with possibility of delay, development of abstract concepts, language, symbolization, and so on, that a psychic apparatus evolves, but that we must not lose sight of its primary biological origin, because certainly psychological adaptive devices stem directly from the biological *Anlage*.

Again, as Jennings pointed out, "Awareness of self and of one's behavior as an individual among individuals comes with the development of the psychic apparatus." [2] I am speaking now in the evolutionary sense, but I think this also would be appropriate in infancy. Action process comes long before such awareness in evolution. In other words, certain things are going on long before awareness of behavior by the individual takes place.

RUESCH: Does that apply to lower animals without higher psyche? They still form social organizations.

ENGEL: Somewhere along the line some self-awareness comes in. Where it comes in, I don't think anyone can say. You would say there is a difference between the amount of awareness of environment of a newborn infant as compared to a three-year-old child.

A *third* evolutionary change has to do with the continuation of the species. Here one might mention three developments:

First is the reproductive potential, as concentrated in the germ plasm, which alone retains the capacity to reproduce the whole organism.

Second, differentiation into two sexes, although originally basic bisexuality is never completely lost, increases enormously the interanimal relationships involved in continuing the species.

Thirdly, changes in the forms of reproduction and status of the young —getting up to mammals and man, one sees an ever-wider developmental span between young and adult forms, and a longer period in which the animal is taken care of, and therefore a greater possibility of experimental and environmental influence as compared to the relatively fixed, genetically determined patterns of the lower organisms. This makes another contribution, I think, to the interpersonal or interanimal and social systems in that the necessity of caring for the younger organisms develops a complex social organization whose functions include protection.

Thus, beginning with internally derived instinctual forces having to do with growth, development and survival of the individual and of the species, we can see an evolution from single-cell to multi-cell organism, with subordination of parts to the whole, and from the relatively isolated to the highly social organism, with subordination of the organism to the group; in other words, a continuity between biologic, psychologic and social evolution.

Grinker and also Shakow outlined some of the ways in which one might see the transition from the biological to the psychological. To bring it back to context, taking, for example, an imperative need like that for oxygen: The deficiency of oxygen is perceived by the organism, and a variety of internal physiological regulatory activities are initiated to compensate for the change. But, in addition, one can see behavior initiated in respect

[2] *Ibid.*

to the outer environment, such as efforts to escape, or to obtain help, or, if the deficiency is recognized, recourse to some more complicated device such as a gas mask, ventilation equipment, and so on.

In certain cultures perhaps you could say that this eventually had something to do with the discovery of oxygen, the scientific investigation of respiration, the invention of ventilation systems, and a host of complex social derivatives of the original biological need and danger. We can leave it to the anthropologists here to answer why these developments took place in one culture, and why oxygen could not have been discovered in another culture.

WEISS: In the thirty-three years or so of my scientific activity I have been exposed to the type of rationalization I have heard here, over and over again, and it is a very valid statement of research objectives but I am afraid I have not seen much implementation. Schemes and diagrams have been developed before my eyes or behind my back since Spencer, and the question is now what we have really learned. Where does it lead us? Merely a statement of the facts. Does it really lead to certain conclusions which will reduce the immense variety of our experiences to a few more common denominators and save us labor in the end? I think that is the tendency of scientific work.

We are struck with a lack of a practical, realistic, analytic approach that will go beyond the mere statement of the fact that we have hierarchical nature, that it does consist of a system of Chinese boxes one inside the other, that they are integrated, interrelated, coordinated, and all these other terms. We should go beyond these statements to an identification, if possible in quantitative terms, of just what that correlation, integration, and so on, consist of, so that we can really work with and operate with them. We aim ultimately not merely to restate the case, but to try to come to grips with it.

One of the major difficulties is that whenever we get up to something which looks organic, we introduce the word "organization." It is called "organized" or "ordered," as contrasted with the disorganized or disordered systems, without spelling out just what we mean by the term "organized." Is organization an all-or-none property, or amenable to gradations and variations? Can we arrive at any quantitative scale by which we can rate organization? Here, for instance, we have some very practical problems. We are talking about size. I think Engel said that the larger system must include the smaller one. If you proceed from the smaller to the larger one, you have to add something. That adding may be other substances, or it may be forces or relations, and so on.

That strikes right home to a basic fallacy of our scientific development, namely, we have developed as atomists, which is an historical accident. It goes back to scientific history in the Antique, Renaissance and after that, and we are still suffering from that history. What we are trying to do now, in the last twenty-five or fifty years, is to atone for our sins and repair the damage we have done by breaking up the universe into units, atoms of various degrees, and dealing with them as if they were really isolable—as if they could be picked out and dealt with in a vacuum.

In breaking down the universe into smaller systems, into the society, the group, the organism, the cells, the cellular parts, and so forth, we dissect the system; that is, we sever relations, and then we try rather awkwardly and clumsily to restore those relations systematically but frequently very inadequately. We cannot build up even the simplest protein molecule out of its units. We cannot build up a cell out of the various molecules that form it. The question is purely practical. On the other hand, we can build up a society out of individuals; so here we are up against a problem which I will now briefly indicate. I am just experimenting now to see if we can arrive at a definition of "organization." I claim, for the time being, that what we are doing is dissecting out arbitrarily a sample of space and time. We talk of the space-time concept, when we mean "space" to be that which we can cut out in three dimensions, and "time" as something that we can make stand still—a moving picture, for example.

I shall try to indicate how we arrive at the concept of organization and how we can perhaps measure the degree of organization of a system in purely operational terms. Basically we do it by comparing different samples of space or of time and establishing resemblances or dissimilarities between the samples. Let us bear in mind that each such sample consists of multiple parts of different constitutions and varying distribution. When we take such a sample, we find it crowded with phenomena of all kinds, some impressing us as having no order and others with a certain regular recurrence. For this we can test objectively.

We take samples of identical and reasonably large size, or identical duration, and compare their content. Suppose we let them contain only three types of items of interest which we could symbolize as black and red and blue points. Supposing we find these to be present in identical numbers in both samples. There are then two possibilities. We could subdivide our sample further and find that each subsample again contains black and red and blue in the same average proportions as the total sample, and that every reasonably large subsample is of that kind. In that case, we would conclude that the distribution is purely statistical, random and unorganized. The other possibility is that the sample from one part of the system will yield a prevalence of black components or perhaps be solely composed of them, while a sample of the same size in another part of the system will yield mostly red points and from still another part mostly blue points. In this case we shall ascribe to the system some degree of inner order which had led to a segregation in space of its constituent units. The rule of order may merely be that components of identical constitution segregate according to their similarities and dissimilarities. However, the over-all pattern according to which they segregate might again be unsystematic, that is, unique for the sample specimen and not recurring in exactly this form and distribution in any other specimen that we might examine. That is, another specimen at the corresponding point at which the former one yielded just black spots might yield red ones.

The next higher degree of organization is reached, however, when two systems that we compare will yield the same subitems if sampled at corresponding loci. In this case, the probability is very low that within either of the two samples a subsample from one spot will be identical to a subsample from another spot; yet the probability is very high that if samples are taken from corresponding loci of the two systems, these samples will be identical.

Cells, organs, organisms, communities are evidently instances of such organized samples following this description. You note that organization is here defined in terms of probabilities of finding resemblances, equivalences or dissimilarities between samples taken from the same system or from different systems in space. The same type of argument can, however, be applied to the time line, in which case intervals substitute for space samples, and the typical different distribution of items in space, such as black, blue and red, takes the form of typical succession of events in time.

Now systems which we have empirically identified as having some degree of inner organization of the described type have various remarkable properties which we find expressed in their behavior relative to environmental changes. The contradistinction between a system and its environment is basically again an empirical one. In cases where we have dissected our sample along what appeared to us a clear boundary line or interface, we have frequently followed a natural outline which endows the enclosed system with a certain degree of constancy, stability, durability and consistency that indicate the degree of dynamic inner cohesion often referred to under the term of individuality. Everything on the outside of that boundary line is considered environment. Now, there is an interesting dichotomy of such systems into two kinds of classes which can be distinguished behaviorally, depending on whether they tend to persist or yield to impacts from environment. In the former case we speak of elastic systems, in the latter case of plastic systems, and both types can be subsumed under the term of adaptive systems for in both cases the integrity of the system is preserved—only in the latter case in a modified form from which it will not return to the original configuration, whereas the elastic system will bounce back once the modifying influence has subsided. There are, of course, limits to elasticity as well as plasticity beyond which the system is disrupted by external force and ceases to exist; that is, it has lost its identity and individuality.

Now, if a system tends to retain its integrity, this means that enforced extrinsic changes of any of its parts are counteracted from within by countervening changes of opposite sign from the inside. This implies an interrelation between the constituent parts of an orderly nature so that the totality of action within the system will act as a conservative force. Unfortunately, there is no way of predicting *a priori* whether a given system belongs to the plastic or elastic type. I have tried to mention these approaches here merely to indicate that more precise definitions of such phenomena as organization, levels of organization, systems and system reactions are attainable. I do not imply that this brief sketch is giving an adequate description.

HENRY: What would be an example of a completely random distribution of phenomena?

WEISS: If you probe Chicago's lake water, with all the fish and other debris in it, it is random to the extent that it is the same all over the lake; and you drink the same dirt on the south side and the north side of the city. That is randomness in the sense of repetitiveness of samples. So there is no organization along that line. But if you take samples in depths in the lake, then you will find different things floating on top from those on the bottom.

That is my point; it isn't the difference merely, but the systematic recurrence of those particular differences. That is the first degree of order. But if the differences occur systematically, then of course you have another system of water, and then gradually you begin to ascribe invariance to the systematic differences and ignore the constituent part. Then you emerge with a field concept, because you ascribe to the systematic recurrence of those relations a certain stability or invariance which is greater than the flux of the component parts. Field concept emerges really out of this type of statistical consideration.

Another example: Take a cell or organism or group, in its environmental relations. To scientists it is obnoxious to hear the question frequently discussed in educational circles and other places, "How much do heredity and environment each contribute to a certain product? How much is genetic and how much is learned?" As though you could express these relations in the form of a sum of commensurable contributions. Scientifically, that amounts to the same as misinterpreting the law that the volume of a gas is proportional to temperature times pressure to mean that pressure and temperature added up to 100%, so that if one took the pressure completely out one could still have 40% of the volume left, or if one left temperature out, have 60% of the volume left.

You are always dealing with a reacting system from the very first. Isolation is artificial; the system always reacts with the surroundings, and all we can do is write a matrix of some kind where you say that a given system under such and such environmental conditions will show this or that series of changes. But you cannot consider the system and its environment as two items of a sum.

Let us now take such a system and assume that the environmental conditions—nutrition, light or whatever you want to take—are effective only along its surface. In an undivided system the whole surface is exposed. Now, you let the system grow and divide so that there will emerge two systems. Their inner partition is not exposed to the outside; so the effective fraction of total surface has been reduced. Then make it divide into four, and while more surface is created, now only half of each has access to the environment.

As we continue this quantitative reduction, then all of a sudden something very dramatic happens: An emerging condition arises which has the properties of novelty; this occurs when this system divides once more, and the new cleavage plane cuts the inner portion of the system completely from all surface contact. This condition appears not as a continuous quantitative variation of the preceding events, but as a single discontinuous step which renders some parts "inner" and some parts "outer," whatever that means; and now you can expand this and extrapolate it into all kinds of phenomena. It would be silly to speak of the property of being inner or outer as a property of the constituent units. It is obviously a property only of the collectivity or Gestalt, or whatever you call it; but it does not arise until you have a certain number of units present.

Now suppose as a result of that uniqueness, that this new core starts doing things. Then of course if the products of this inner activity, by diffusion, interact with the peripheral portion, the result of this interaction gives you a third type of product. The two systems interacting may be two persons or two groups, but they are interacting as different individuals, and no longer as equivalents. From the resulting third condition you could go on to new progressive interactions with the earlier two systematic parts, and so on in a chain of continuing complexity.

The characteristic thing is that this does not depend on the properties within the collective. In this case you have organization of a higher order emerging as a result of the processes which take place.

Here again we are merely restoring something which we ignored in the beginning. We are treating systems on the blackboard as though they were static, standing still in time. They never are. No cell, no organism, no group is ever standing still. All we are doing is artificially laying a cross-section through a time course and arresting it for expedience. Then, of course, we are surprised if this thing does not go on remaining the same as time goes on. Of course, the change is actually the primary thing. We arrest it arbitrarily. The process is the primary thing, while the static form or state is merely a cross-section through an endless chain or processes. All the problems of form versus function really resolve themselves if we take this attitude.

As I said, if we had come down from the universe gradually through the hierarchy of systems to the atoms, we would be much better off. Instead we now have to resynthesize the conceptual bonds between those parts which we have cut in the first place.

The example of the appearance of inner and outer parts is an instance of emerging organization. But there is another different type. Assume you have particles, each of which has an inherent polarity—little magnets, electric bi-pole molecules, etc., and suppose you have them swimming around in random distribution and haphazard orientation, so that again any reasonably large samples taken out will show no over-all polarity because the individual polar arrangements cancel out.

Take two samples from different places; they show no over-all polarity. Now you put a vector in from the outside, let's say a magnetic field, and what happens? All the elements will right themselves in a common order. Now take the external inducing factor away and you will note that the system suddenly has polarity, the potentiality for which it had before by virtue of its elemental properties, but which it did not have a chance to manifest till now. You have permitted the system to express something which was actually inherently present in the individual particles, but which could not be materialized. Now you have, all of a sudden, brought out an over-all property which it did not show previously.

The characteristic thing is that the frame of reference imposes a certain limitation on the degree of freedom for the distribution of energy, or if you wish, of substances or process—within the field. The distribution becomes non-random in what we will call a "typical" way; that is, in a typically recurrent way, so that it is not only non-random but it is always the same type of non-random situation.

Such considerations have led to the concept of "field" which, for better or worse, have developed in biology, and I am still not yet fully persuaded of its heuristic or pragmatic value. It is a wonderful circumlocution. I have used it extensively, but I do not know really where it will lead us. It does express a reality; it does express something which is there.

That much I wanted to say about the field patterns of inner relations. Everything else follows from here. Whenever we have such a non-random system with typical inner relations, you have either an over-all condition by which you describe the system, or you may be able to ascribe it to active interactions of individual parts. Those are two different things. I will give you an example. Some slime molds consist of separate amoebae which to all practical purposes are each a single individual moving and living as separate entities. At certain times, however, the amoebae aggregate into solid masses, uniting into a multi-cellular organism consisting of tens of thousands of such amoebae. These move now as a coherent multi-cellular organism, and soon differentiate by organized division of labor into beautiful fruiting bodies with a cellulose stalk in the center, a disc at the base and spores on top.

Here you have a real synthesis of a higher-order form from combinations of equivalent unit parts. Morphologically, this shows all the properties of an organism, an egg or any such thing, where the cells had never been completely dispersed and secondarily brought together.

As long as this is true we should not assume that there is anything more to the unity of an egg or a group of cells than there is to this reassembled body. So here we have an experimental case of dissociability and reassociability with emergent properties of collective unity, properties of organization much like those of an egg—only in an egg we cannot do it. It is not necessary to assume that the difference between the two systems is fundamental.

I am going to propose that we stick to that type of model as long as we can, for the nervous system and the psychological functions. As long as we can fall back on this type of thinking in the biological areas, we cannot deny its pertinence in the psychological sphere, pending proof to the contrary. The entity, the unity may be something else.

I can give you another sample of the same kind: A flock of starlings (starlings have recently been studied very extensively) consisting of hundreds of birds, forms a beautiful cloud. That cloud has the same morphologic properties as an organism or a slime mold. The starlings keep their distance from each other. Their mass has a completely sharp external surface or boundary line which is as sharp as the boundary of a cell. When a bird of prey gets into the starling crowd, it is surrounded by a "contractile vacuole." The bird of prey is in the center and the starlings form a perfect ring around him at a respectful distance determined by the bird of prey and the vigor of the starlings. The cloud can form wedges and assume all kinds of shapes. If they settle down on a telegraph wire they form absolutely regular spacings in the triangular form, and if a starling should sit next to another and leave a gap, then what, speaking psychologically, one might call "a tension of disequilibrium" causes unrest and the distance is corrected. If anybody can tell me whether the starling "feels" it or not, I would like to know. Anyhow, after a while the starling is going to be uncomfortable and is going to repair his positional status until he is in "equilibrium" with the rest of the system.

HENRY: I do not agree with you. You say that these are the same phenomena, that the cohesion of the amoebae and the cohesion of the starlings, their reaction when they are threatened, constitute the same phenomena, but they are not analogous.

WEISS: I said "until proof to the contrary" is furnished. I do not know. I have never been a slime mold and I have never been a starling so I do not know whether they are homologous or analogous. In the first place, the form of the slime mold is not to be explained by cohesion. The cells in the center form a stalk of cellulose, and the cells that get to the top become spores. Each amoeba therefore receives its assignment within the framework of the social organization of this whole, as you would call it. If you divide such a body in two, then there will appear two fruiting bodies. That is why I brought you the other picture first, where "inner" and "outer" were determined by their position within the whole. This happens here, too, on a much more complex scale.

We have phenomena of the same kind in what can experimentally be shown to be an arbitrarily composed group. The starlings may react the same way; although their reception for distance and their executive apparatus of shifting along the telegraph wire are different from the receptive and executive apparatus of the slime mold, the formal pattern of behavior is the same.

My point is that we are able to bring many of these things into certain formal conceptual schemes that work, without having to worry about the reducibility of these things to phenomena on the next lower levels of organization. This is essentially what I was driving at. For the time being we have to do both—conceptualize as well as analyze. We have to describe phenomena on each level, but much more concisely and precisely than we do now. We have to say what we mean by organization, by integration, by coordination, and then try to work on each level in its own right. That is the scientific birthright of the psychologist, the anthropologist, the cell physiologist, and all others. At the same time we cannot help but be struck by the correspondence of the rules that we find emerging between various levels. Whether that correspondence is based on reducibility—whether the higher level behaves as it does because it is made up of units of the lower order which follow certain regularities—is something we have to keep in mind because of scientific economy. Whether it will turn out that way is something for the future to tell.

I think we should approach the task with an unbiased mind. There is too much religious warfare these days, and people want to have things their way. In science there ought to be no injunctions. We should not be doctrinaire and hold that because behavior on one of the higher levels of organization does not yield to reduction, to regularities of a more elemental order, a treatment of the higher order in its own right is unsound. I think this would be a wholly illegitimate and shortsighted proposition. We should have an amicable brotherhood in these different lines of approach, and nobody should encroach on the other fellow's rights or step on the other fellow's toes.

PARSONS: I agree with what Henry was saying a while ago. If I could only substitute social systems for culture in what you said in your concluding statement—you said society's social systems do not project, displace, repress. Those are mechanisms of personalities as systems; there is a fundamental analogy between personalities as systems and social systems, but the mechanisms are not the same. That has been a source of primary difficulty between sociologists and psychologists. They have assumed that the mechanisms must be the same.

WEISS: That is not true, even in physics. The laws of wave mechanics are valid for an acoustic wave, an electric wave or a light wave in the same way. The formal relation of reflection, diffraction, extinction, and so on, applies to any type of wave.

Purely as a statement of fact, animal society and personal society are said to be integrated. What do we mean by that? We mean the individuals are not random parts of a larger sample, but they are somehow connected with the sample as a whole. In circumscribing the sample we proceed empirically, and we state in one case that the unit is the species and in another case it is the family and in the third it is the individual, and so forth.

I think the discrepancy between the social and the psychological interpretaters is due to the arbitrary definition of the boundary line of the system they are interested in, whether it be the individual or the group.

In the ant colony, irrespective of the total number of individuals, the proportion of different castes is more constant than the sum or size of the colony, just as in the slime mold and the starling, and so on. Therefore, there is an invariance to that relation, let us say, of queens to workers, to soldiers, and so on.

Secondly, that relation is not by pre-established harmony, but by actual interaction, so that when you reduce one component, the others will reduce themselves proportionately. Again, keep in mind that this need not be so. There is another system wherein the reduction of one part of the system will immediately accrue to the advantage of the others, and then the system will change greatly.

If you reduce one caste in an ant colony, the others will substitute for that group; altruistically, if you wish. We can play around with the term of "altruism." I am convinced the ant does not know this, and so I see no value in carrying this beyond the mere statement of fact. If the analogy is carried to the point where you say man *ought* to behave, *ought* to cooperate, *ought* to pay attention to the super-individual needs of the community because the ant does it, then I say we are out on a dangerous limb. If some biologists should point out that some other animals are less socially conscious of who may eat each other when they get anywhere within reach, and furthermore that they are very solitary animals and have remained so during a long evolutionary history, then where will we be? If man ought to take his cues for his social behavior just by looking at the ant, then he had better give up. I think he should have the courage to develop his own social norms according to his own conscience, irrespective of how the animals behave.

We can point to any number of animal groups which do not cooperate. Just picking ones that have societies and saying we ought to follow their example is fallacious. After all, in an ant society each man is put in his place, which is exactly what the Russians and Germans have done. It is really dangerous, in my personal opinion.

One more thing: It is an arbitrary matter how we circumscribe the system we are considering. It is an arbitrary definition. That is where most of our problems of the day arise. A species has circumscribed what is the self-maintaining, self-perpetuating, conservative unit. By inter-breeding and by the evolutionary processes, that group has become stabilized. Whenever two species get into contact, then something happens. Either one or the other is not quite adjusted to the new conditions, and they are going to compete for a new equilibrium.

As long as they are in isolation, they are stable. One is as good as another. It is no good saying that an amoeba is any worse than a bird. They are wonderfully adapted as long as they stay within the environment to which they are adapted. What has happened in human society and human culture, and my anthropological friends may correct me if I am wrong, is that our cultures have developed in a certain degree of physiologic isolation in certain environments of relative insulation. They have adapted to those conditions, and one is as good as any other. You are either adapted or not adapted. If you are not adapted, you will be eliminated in due course of time.

Then what happens? Modern man has brought these diverse cultures in confluence, and when groups of different potential and different development all of a sudden have an impact upon each other, the trouble arises.

I see no end to this process until we have redefined the new group within which stability, equilibrium can be attained, and I can see no intermediate stations on the road to an integrated entity except mankind as a whole. The groups have been relatively stable and sound and healthy as long as they were independent. Now that they have become confluent, either physically or through means of communication, I think the process cannot end until a new circumscription of a self-perpetuating and self-continuing unit has been found. Again this is an arbitrary circumscription for a particular purpose, only in this case the purpose has been validated by survival, not simply by our academic purposes.

Frank: The question of time has been emphasized by Weiss and may justify further discussion if we are to discuss various systems. When we start with an organism in a biological environmental system, we may observe that organism moving through time, entering into a variety of close interpersonal relations, then in the cultural system, then in the social system, where it develops new properties out of its original organic endowment, or it may be said to transform its organic functions into these new patterns. Here we see how the child emerges as a personality as he learns the various patterns and relations required by these different systems, assumes a variety of roles through which as an adult he participates in these systems.

This looks like a self-perpetuating process in the sense that human organisms as adults not only reproduce through child bearing, but also rear their children to live in these several systems so that in turn these children will become adults capable of full participation like their parents. Here is where we may ask how those who are studying the formal properties of these systems can contribute to the development of a unified theory of human behavior by showing how this self-perpetuating process operates. This means, as I see it, explicitly recognizing that each of these systems exists and continues only insofar as individuals are indoctrinated patterns, and brought into the reciprocal relationships with all other individuals in and through the operations of these systems. It also implies that however we may describe the formal properties or patterns of these systems, they will appear in the activities of each constituent person operating in those systems with greater or less deviations and distortions, as indicated earlier.

Here our own personal ways of thinking and organizing experience may make considerable difference in how we may approach this situation. Some of us may find it more congenial to approach a unified theory by emphasizing the distinctive properties and separate operations of these different systems. Others, including myself, may be more inclined to seek a unified theory of human behavior by focusing primarily upon the individual human organism-personality and observing how he, in the very course of his life career, becomes a participating member of his group as he learns to use the patterns for action and for relating himself which are provided by more experienced persons who induct him into our symbolic culture and our social order wherein he lives as an idiosyncratic personality. In this way we may look upon weapons and tools, language and other forms of symbolic expression and communication, institutions, and all the other innumeratable dimensions of group living as being utilized by human beings and giving rise to these different systems or organizations with their various properties.

WEISS: It does. As a matter of fact, you might keep in mind one more very marked evolutionary step which comes into the cultural and symbolic level. Originally we had to rely on genetics in order to improve the viability of a species. That was a slow process. Now we do not have to breed generations to pass on an improvement; we do it by communication. The time unit of trial used to be a generation. Now we can try out things infinitely faster and keep them on record, and thus there is an entirely new time scale of development.

FRANK: Today we may say that we are beginning to assay these several systems as well as the ecos or biological surround in terms of what they do to and for the human personality. We are finding that many of our traditions and our historically developed patterns and institutions are no longer desirable or tolerable, but are producing deviations and distortions of various kinds which may be lethal or at best destructive of social order and profoundly disturbing to individual personalities.

SPIEGEL: It seems to me we came together because we all felt in some way that problems considered in different disciplines are related to each other, and that we would all do better work if we could find how they are related; or, to put it another way, if we could in some way bring different insights into the same data into one frame of reference.

In pursuing this goal we approached it in three different ways. One has been to attempt to identify the main elements in any particular discipline or field. Another has been to attempt to construct some sort of model in which these main elements can be related to each other. Those two things, as I said before, probably go on simultaneously, if they go on at all, so that each one of us has had some notion of the identifiable systems and some notion of the way they could be related to each other in a conceptual model. Thirdly, I think we have all seen the need to grapple with the problem of how interactions between particular foci or particular disciplines can take place; that is, how to build a bridge or dig a ditch to get from one level to another level. Those seem to me to be separable as problems.

Since we are dealing with the same data fundamentally (and this is a point that Ruesch has made repeatedly), the thing that separates us or makes us different has been the way we have assembled our data, or codified them, or made observations upon them. If so, then as a group we can try to see the similarities in the way we have all approached it, and the divergencies.

THOMPSON: Also, we differ on the units that we consider significant for research.

SPIEGEL: I do not know whether we can separate the units we consider significant for research from the problem of what we consider identifiable anyway, as units of observation. Perhaps you can make a differentiation. I wonder if it would not be a matter of grouping different research units in larger areas of observational units.

I would like to specify what I think accounts for some of our differences. There have been but minor differences, really, in how we identify the observational units. It seems to me that when the anthropologists have talked about "culture" we have not seen any real difference of opinion as to how they identify their material. We have not differed over what goes on at a psychological level or a biological level. Maybe they have existed and we have repressed them; but at least they have not emerged.

PARSONS: That is a very important observation. A generation ago any such meeting as this would have broken up over such thoughts.

THOMPSON: We would not have considered that such discussions were relevant to our own specialty.

SPIEGEL: The main misunderstanding or difficulty in understanding each other comes at the point of producing a conceptual model. We have had some competition as to who drew the prettiest pictures. Speaking for myself, I have had some difficulty in knowing exactly what frame of reference to use in understanding someone else's model. In certain presentations, such as Parsons' presentation and Henry's presentation, we have had that difficulty. This again may be a matter of insufficient information.

RUESCH: You mentioned three factors. I think there is a fourth one. Not only elements, models and transformation hypotheses or bridges, but the location of the human observer takes its place in the model.

SPIEGEL: That is important, and I should have included it. The identification of the position of the observer with reference to what he is observing was implicit in what I said about the ways we go about taking our observations, but it is sufficiently important to warrant its being isolated.

Maybe it is easier to start with the model problem. The models have had a great deal in common, and perhaps they are more similar than they are different. For instance, if one takes the difference between the model I was using and the models Henry drew,[3] I do not think the differences are so large, although he brings out levels and I brought out foci in interaction with each other.

Perhaps what makes the difference is again a matter of how the observation is made, because his particular model is an observation made primarily from the point of view of time—that is, the big axis is the evolutionary axis in time. If you look at the evolutionary axis, then, to use an expression, you start with the biological.

One arranges larger and larger organizational units; that is quite true. One arranges them on a time scale to show they happen to become larger and larger organizational units. It is in that sense that the problem of reduction-progression comes in. What then ordinarily happens is that you have to ask yourself how it all originally started. From what original properties in the cell was this or that derived?

If you do not set it up that way, but if you set it up on a present-time level, and ask the question, "How do they all interact with each other?" then you simply focus on a different property, one which seems to me to be implicit anyway if looked at in a space-time sense in all the interrelations.

The models have much in common, and probably their differences do not emerge from the kind of problem which Weiss was just bringing to our attention, that is, of ascribing an unreal existence or ascribing ex-

[3] See Chapter Eight.

istence as an entity to something that is only part of a pattern phenomenon. I do not know whether that is true or not.

Our problem is: How does the somatic process, the psychological process, the role behavior in small groups, the role behavior in extended groups, the manifestations of a particular culture—how do those all impinge on each other at the moment when you are making the observation? How do those all affect each other? I think the difficulty is not a real one. It depends upon what the focus is at the present time or over larger time segments.

There is one other aspect that I do not think is a real problem of the model, namely, that some of these models do start out with the human individual and then put him in the middle of a field which radiates out from him—as in Frank's model, and others. Still other models try to put the human being in the total field without specifying him so much as an entity.

With respect to the problem of the interconnections between the foci or between the levels, the main source of my difficulty has been that the bridges which have been constructed in front of our eyes, so to speak, have not all been bridging the same thing. For instance, Henry's presentation seemed to me to be a way of bringing what is going on inside the individual—his feelings of autonomy, of constraint, and so on—right into the middle of a larger unit, and I do not know what that larger unit is. I do not know whether it is a small group, whether it is an extended group, or whether it is the culture. It does not fit into any conceptual scheme that I, at least, have developed on other grounds.

If the bridge-building had been such that these equations which have to do with anticipation of punishment, or anticipation of satisfaction, and so on, have been constructed into or related to a person's particular role so that I could conceive of him as thinking, "If I play this role I will get more satisfaction or less satisfaction, whereas if I play another role I won't"; or "There are no roles I can play that will lead to satisfaction," then I would see how to use the bridge as an actual bridge in the larger conceptual scheme.

PARSONS: But the roles are also an organized system, with limited possibilities.

SPIEGEL: Yes. By means of the role system, then, energy is channelized or restricted, varying from society to society and culture to culture. As a matter of fact, throughout all this discussion I have missed any concrete description of roles, yet it seems to me to be necessary as constitutive of a bridge between two other levels. Kluckhohn's schema of the core value system, too, must require a bridge to the role structure, which is the limiting and constraining factor in any social system. In Parsons' presentation I felt I was also seeing a bridge being built or a channel being dug between the motives of the individual and the way roles are structured in social systems; but what I missed there was the point where you get off the bridge. No roles emerged concretely in my mind which would represent the pattern variables. Again, it may be only a matter of time before we solve it.

GRINKER: I have felt the lack of a fundamental description of the changing form of energy, from its physical-chemical level into forms which in every presentation have been related to some kind of purpose. Weiss used the word "adaptation," which he defines as an end result. He says that a system is successful if it adapts; its presence is an indication that it has adapted. But that is a circular process of reasoning. Yet, in every other presentation we have heard, in some way or other, the idea of need, and the location of the need and gratification, have been introduced. The reverse, too, has been used—the lowering of tension, all of which implies a process of reduction of need-tension.

We have gone to the extreme when Henry said that society furnishes the psychogenic needs of the individual, which I would not agree with at all. Society furnishes the form in which the need is expressed; but the need itself arises with the organism. And at this point I would like to ask Weiss whether the need is not the fundamental biochemical physical-chemical process extending itself in various forms. The organism needs to form relationships, to form systems. It needs a kind of organization which becomes greater, wider, larger in time, or whatever quantitative measurement you wish.

WEISS: I question this because I think the term "need" is only a convenience—an atavistic, historic and traditional circumlocution for some state of deficiency in the system. It is an actual state of the system, like a potential. The question is: Do you believe that need is physically expressed at the time it exists in a deficient state of the system—which, if so, is something that could be described even though we cannot describe it at present? Or do you conceive of need as something which pulls from the future, so to speak?

ENGEL: Originally the need is an expression of a disturbance in some physical system within the organism.

FRANK: Much of our current thinking tends to reductionism. Because all organisms not only start with the need for food and elimination and must continue to eat and eliminate, we may try to reduce all human activity to the expression of those needs or to some basic instincts. It seems clear, however, that as the organism grows and develops and learns to live in our cultural and social world, the coercion of internal biological needs seems to diminish. Increasingly the child and the youth may be freed from the coercion of their own organic processes as they become more and more responsive to culturally and socially defined events and situations. For example, the child's eating is governed by the meal patterns of his family rather than by primitive hunger; indeed, we may say that he "gets hungry" when mealtimes come, just as he learns to eliminate at specified times and places in response to the appropriate vessel. By emphasizing the way the growing child learns to relate himself to the public world, we may escape from the concept of primitive needs and biological motivations which apparently are observable in much of our animal experimentation from which we have extrapolated to human behavior.

GRINKER: Then I would like to find out what is psychological and what is biological. Parsons talked about reduction in tension, increase in satisfaction, and so on. We must find something that expresses a process, which has nothing to do with its form but has a basis in the biological organism.

PARSONS: I would agree with Weiss, with one qualification: In science as activity, as distinguished from science as a system of propositions, there has to be continuity. Looking back from the point of view of a nature scientist, you can see that these terms have had connotations which clearly had to be dropped. To operate with violent neologisms actually impedes scientific work. I have deliberately used traditional terminology, but have tried to look at it in the context of system states as much as possible. The difficulties with those terms have arisen from necessity of describing the phenomenon but in the absence of a generalized formulation of the system in which it belonged.

TOMAN: At the level of human behavior "need" means something to us; but "need" does not mean anything at the chemical level, or in a homeostatic system in the cell. We need not postulate "need" just because we see motion.

WEISS: The word "need" is a perfectly good word. As soon as everybody realizes it has no connotation as a future goal, there is no danger in using it.

RUESCH: As long as we deal with non-identified human observers, and with non-identified particles, you are safe in using the word "need."

But as soon as you deal with an identified human observer and identified objects, you may run into difficulties. The characteristic system deals with an identified human observer and identified human particles.

EDITOR: *The last session of the first conference was not introduced by a presentation but plunged into a general discussion. Engel recapitulated general biological properties found in all living organisms from which behavior extends and evolves. Our whole conceptual processes and methods were subjected to vigorous scrutiny by Weiss, whose remarks need to be read carefully. Spiegel then attempted to analyze the approaches used by various members of the conference in attempting to achieve a confluence of insights.*

In general it can be stated that an immense amount of information concerning the concepts and operations of various disciplines was imparted in a brief time during the first conference. Crucial problems common to all systems under scrutiny were posed and discussed, and considerable agreement was reached. We came to know much more about other fields of investigation, and were ready to begin comparisons with a view to establishing similarities and differences, upon which to build alternative theories.

SECOND CONFERENCE

Comparisons Between Systems of Organization

Multiple Origins of the Uniqueness of Human Society

Homeostasis and Comparison of Systems

Comparison of Psychological and Group Foci

Comparison of Psychological and Group Foci—(Continued)

The Relation Between the Small Group and the Larger Social System

Social Systems and Culture

CHAPTER TEN

COMPARISONS BETWEEN SYSTEMS OF ORGANIZATION

Presentation by Roy R. Grinker

I THINK perhaps it might be wise to begin this second conference[1] with a statement of impressions about the first conference. In looking for the essence of what each individual said, we noticed that the variance between the points of view was not random, but fell into four groups, with considerable overlapping between the groups and among the individuals.

Group I we called the *Observer Emphasis*. Here the accent was on a specific analysis of the methods of observation and research, in order to arrive at the precise location of the identified human observer; and of the effect of observational methods on research, on the conclusions reached and on the conceptions and assumptions employed in the process.

Group II we called the *System Emphasis*. The attention was on a precise definition and description of the various organized systems or levels necessary to the study of human behavior.

Group III we called the *Conceptual Model Emphasis*. Here the aim was to elicit the assumptions behind any particular description of human behavior through the construction of a visual model of the assumed relationship, no matter how crude. It was obvious that this point of departure is intimately related to the *Observer Emphasis* but the accenting is different.

In Group IV the interest was in formulating hypotheses which can

[1] April, 1953.

account for the transitions from one system to another and also for the transactions taking place between the systems. We therefore called it the *Transformation Emphasis.*

These four points of view signalize the road to our ultimate objectives. What is now required is a more orderly and systematic attack on these areas. With this in mind we proposed the following program: to attempt to define the systems we are using for the description of human behavior. The definitions should be formulated from the point of view of an identified human observer whose position with respect to an assumed system is known, and whose methods of making observations can be specified concurrently with the isolation of the circumscribed system. The major fault, as I see it, of the last meeting was the presentation of conclusions from particular fields without revealing the mental steps and the operational procedures used in their development. As a result we busied ourselves at attempting to close the gaps.

Now how should we go about creating the bridges or transitions between systems of organization and conceptual communications? There are at least four possible procedures. Each one can be identified by the observer's frames of observation utilized during the processes of analysis. Observations should not be made from a single frame of reference but from several, either simultaneously or in succession. I shall exemplify the difficulties involved in considering similarities and perhaps differences between somatic and psychological systems.

But first, those categories of function which we may conceptualize in whatever way and on whatever level must be capable of being derived from the structural and functional properties of the living organism. Furthermore, foci, using Spiegel's word, which we identify within a living field through structure, function and transactions with other foci, and to which we attribute characteristics of a system, should be considered as derived through a process of stages of evolution, differentiation and development from earlier and perhaps simpler forms and functions. This, contrary to Spiegel's, would be my basic assumption.

The first method of comparison would be to take similarities and differences between *structures* or *system determinants.* By structures I do not mean static morphological structures, as you can well realize, but patterns. Here the observer is within the system. This method of comparison predicates similarities in intrinsic cause and effect relationships based on genetic derivation. For this reason I am glad that Emerson is here because he can discuss in greater detail the methods of comparison. According to his scheme, this method would be that of homologizing. Organization is characterized by boundaries—that is almost redundant—which are semi-permeable, surrounding open living systems. Boundaries permit exchange of energy in many directions, that is between the parts, the parts and the whole, and between the whole and its environment. The organization is capable of differentiation, specialization or development of gradients of activity. There is a capacity to transmit or conduct forces capable of maintaining and changing part to part and part to whole relationships. Relationships such as reciprocal relationships and phasic relationships may all be included in such an organization. Structurally, both somatic and psychological systems constitute an apparatus for transformations of energy. They both constitute an organization with semi-permeable boundaries; they have the capacity for specialization and gradients, and they have apparatuses or patterns for communication. The determinants of these systems may be represented in the somatic field by the hereditary constitution of the organization and in the psychological field by the psychological "id."

The second method is the comparison of similarities and differences in *functions*. Here the observer is outside the system or its boundaries. The mental process is that of dealing with analogies—the favored method of psychological interpretation. Interpretations given to subjects under therapy are usually in terms of "it is as if." According to Emerson, this means that the functional resemblances are due primarily to the action of environmental forces on genetically dissimilar structures. The best example he gives is in the analogy between genes in the somatic field and symbols in the psychological field. Both have a capacity for repetition, duplication and change. I speak of function as integrative, or in other words, opposed to disintegration—it is the capacity to maintain or defend itself against randomness. If we can use the term for an open system, it would be negative entropy.

In the somatic system the primary functional process subsumed under the term of a *living organization* is characterized by needs and need satisfactions for maintenance of somatic homeostasis. I touch on that word a little gingerly because, during our last meeting when we began to deal with similarities between somatic, psychological, and social systems there was a great deal of argument about this term. On the psychological side, such needs and need satisfactions can be compared with what has been termed pleasure and unpleasure or what the psychoanalytic school calls the pleasure-pain principle. From these needs, need satisfactions and frustrations can be derived a number of functions.

In discussing the question of derivation of systems and the analogue of satisfying particular needs, I would like to introduce another comparison: irritability and motility on the somatic side; tension and consciousness on the psychological side.

Somatic learning in the sense that bodily surface contacts result in self-discrimination enables one to differentiate self from not self and create an image of self and its boundaries. However, much of significant somatic learning is inside the organism and has to do with conditioning of the vegetative nervous network. On the psychological side, the counterpart is the function of reality testing.

On the somatic side we have the process of growth; psychologically, learning.

On the somatic side we have propagation; on the psychological side, memory and recall.

The common ground or genetic derivations for these functions has been implied in the concept of instincts representing the transition between somatic and psychological functions. In other words it is a borderline concept between the physical and the mental.

The third method is an analysis of *functions of systems* and *transactions with other systems*. Here the observer uses three or four systems simultaneously. This is admittedly a very difficult thing for one observer to do, especially in transactions of larger foci. It can be approached by multi-disciplinary operations or, theoretically, by establishing a focus on one system and looking at two other adjacent systems as if with a divergent squint.

I want to refer to a letter written by Thompson, the essence of which is significant to this kind of comparison. She states that multiple observers are required for transactional analysis; many points of view are gathered simultaneously rather than from the single fixed position of one observer. It is a little difficult for anyone to visualize the term simultaneity as applied to the larger systems: for example, the ecological, which she considers as extremely important. She even makes the statement that the problem of man in nature is more basic than the transactions of man with man.

The problem of multiple observers dealing with such large systems simultaneously is one that I think should be discussed later. Thompson likens the issue of the individual and the multiple points of view to the contrast between classical and modern physics, and between Modern Art and Renaissance Art. Her second point is that circumscribed significant units are thus revealed to be merely parts of larger units which a scientist must study. Her third point is the difficulty in science of relinquishing the idea of circumscribed systems. She says that we must give up two-dimensional analysis; that is, the analysis of two-dimensional interactional cause and effect relations. She says that we must have at least three dimensions of behavior and her favorite dimensions are the psychological, the social-cultural and the ecological.

One night Toman and I performed a little experiment, naively, based on the possibility of comparing the somatic and psychological systems. We attempted to find out if we could make these comparisons by dealing with the somatic limiting functions and the interpersonal functions of man in social groups, identifying psychology as the link or bridge between the two, and not by its internal structure-function. The result was that we were in complete agreement about what we saw as the basic principles of somatic functioning; at the very least, we were in agreement about what is known. Whenever we came to the rather naive experiment of talking to each other about the relationship between the psychological and the somatic, we seemed always to go directly to the social: to man's relationship to man. This highlights the fact that while we were dealing with the transactional functions of the psychological, we were talking either of the somatic processes, or of the relational processes of man to men, losing the psychological focus.

As a matter of fact in our research in this Institute with multi-disciplinary techniques we are either actually observing and measuring somatic correlates, or interactional correlates of man and some participant-observer. We deal with the psychological only as a self-reporting system in which the person himself states how he feels in relation to what is going on inside him and in relation to other individuals. Furthermore, we cannot deal with the psychological system as a focus except when a developed self-differentiation enables the organism to perceive itself to be in transaction with a not-self and can experience its inner feelings as an observer.

That brings up the problem: When is such a psychological system derived? Can we speak of the psychology of the infant in its first days or first weeks of life? Or are we dealing then with a somatic focus which has not yet differentiated itself in or out, self or not-self? At that period the stimulus and response to a need seems to be a part of the child himself; the needs and satisfaction or frustration are still inside and self.

The basic similarities and differences between systems can only be approached through understanding the processes of communication. Ruesch has certainly done a service in pointing that out. We must study the communication of parts to the whole, and the whole to other wholes, foci or systems. Such communications are essential for understanding the determinants of relations between systems.

In the somatic organization we can generalize and state that communication occurs by means of signs—be they electrical or chemical. In a system of social interaction in which the individual is already differentiated, communication is through symbols. I would like here to attempt a definition and say that the essential characteristic of the psychological system, in this frame of observation, is that it constitutes the area of transaction between somatic signs and interpersonal symbols. Through such transaction the psychological system differentiates, grows, proliferates and maintains its defense against disintegration. It is associated with varying degrees of awareness or consciousness based on the capacities made possible by the structural configurations of the species and the individual.

PARSONS: *You are saying essentially that somatic phenomena are psychologically significant so far as they constitute signs which enter into this psychological permeation process.*

GRINKER: Yes. Also, the neurophysiological processes may be described as functions of parts of the organization within or at its boundaries. But when we are talking about the relationships between the psychological system and its adjacent foci, we are dealing then in terms of the whole organism's activity in motility, perception and symbolic relationships to others. In other words, a projection of all internal surfaces upon the outer boundary.

Another and more abstract kind of comparison concerns the relationship among the parts to the whole of any system or organization. Then it is noticed that the over-all system maintains a fairly stable self-perpetuating equilibrium. But there is a contradictory tendency: the component systems become involved in the changes associated with growth, specialization, division of labor and loss of individual autonomy. As expansion and more complex organization develops, the integrative processes become looser and more susceptible to disintegration. Whether such expansion constitutes a function of living organisms essentially different from the need function is a moot question. At any rate there are problems concerned with the balancing between the need processes and the expanding processes in all systems or organizations: the part in conflict with the whole, the individual with the group, selfishness versus altruism, etc. It is the need of the part or the need of the whole versus the trend toward expansion and the forming of more and more complex organization.

One of the tasks that we had assigned to each other was to discuss similarities and differences. But it is very difficult to perceive differences; we usually make comparisons based on similarities and then say, "yes, but." Some physicists, like Schroedinger, attempt to show that continuity of observation and causality are impossible.[2] Yet the fact that we constantly see similarities and derivations between one system and another makes it clear that the human mind needs to maintain continuity, to close gaps

[2] Erwin Schroedinger, *Science and Humanism* (London: Cambridge University Press, 1945).

and finish circles. Clearly our stressing of similarities must be related to the basic need for continuity.

Derived systems characterized by expanding organization and varying degrees of integration may develop differences, but in a certain way. For one thing, their own special functions contribute differences of quantities or of types of organization, of kinds of communication and of degrees of integration. Secondly, similar functions expressed through different forms of communication give rise to dissimilar effects. They may all be subsumed under the most general abstractions, yet their appearance at different levels of transactions is different.

CHAPTER ELEVEN

MULTIPLE ORIGINS OF THE UNIQUENESS OF HUMAN SOCIETY

Presentation by James E. P. Toman

I SHALL restrict my presentation to some simple questions which I believe we will have to deal with in formulating a unified theory of human behavior. Let us recognize the smallness of the mass of human protoplasm. If we were to call the entire human race into this conference, according to a rough estimate it could easily be seated in a lecture hall thirty miles long by thirty miles wide. We could see all mankind from the speaker's stand.

First, let us observe that somatically these people are not remarkably different today from what they must have been thousands of years ago, aside from small matters of dress, hair styles, and so on. Yet if they brought to our lecture hall today all of their belongings, everything which has been made by mankind, a tremendous mountain of materials would be checked at the door, in contrast to the small heap which would have been brought by our cave-dwelling ancestors. Certainly we would be struck by the enormous expansion of tools, of instruments for observation and machinery for carrying out production of other materials, of vehicles, and so on, in the very recent historical period. If we could also see, just outside our great lecture hall, the buildings, roads, subways, dams, and all of the physical material that man has attached to himself, in the way that a hermit crab attaches mollusc shells to himself, we would be struck by the size of the shell in comparison with the man inside.

We have accreted, built or modified for our own use a tremendous volume of materials, which is constantly growing and to which may be added all of those things which are contemplated for eventual usage, things which man hopes someday to turn to his own advantage. The stack of belongings to be checked at the door in the future is almost impossible to conceive.

It is not the mere fact of operation upon physical things which is characteristic of man. It is more important to note that he differs remarkably from most other species in the time scale with which he can make alterations in his physical environment, or utilize new forms of energy for the performance of work. Although in each instance we can find primitive examples of these processes in other animal groups, none of them is much more than an alteration which can be carried out by the following generation of the same species without reference to that which has gone before.

Although it may very well be that an element of what we might call the passage of a culture is already present in certain insect societies, we usually tend to think of hive-building and other characteristics of insect societies as built into the central nervous system and relatively incapable of change, except in an evolutionary sense.

What is unique in the origin of human culture? I doubt whether any single factor will give us an adequate explanation. Man's brain is not qualitatively different as far as we know from that of other mammals, and certainly the difference in complexity between it and the brain of a chimpanzee is not as great as the difference between that of the chimpanzee and the rat. Nor can the difference be simply the question of physical complexity of communicative systems. Intricate systems of communication exist between members of certain insect societies, at least, and even among fairly simple mammalian groups. Furthermore, even the element of education of the young has its beginnings in species lower than man. Here I am thinking of the reported ability of adult cats, for example, to develop mouse and rat killing in the young kitten. There seem also to be examples of educational practice among certain of the primate groups.

Whether we look at the anatomical and functional differences in brain, or whether we look at the problem of communication between members of a species, we see at first only apparently quantitative differences. We see in simple species the beginnings of the complex layers and fissures of the brain. I know of no function that can be examined in the human brain with any of the present neurophysiological methods that cannot also be examined in the brain of a laboratory species.

HENRY: *I wonder whether what Toman has been saying is related to Grinker's point that differences in functions appear as a result of large apparent discontinuities arising from a large number of small differences.*

TOMAN: Yes. I was thinking of accumulation of small differences not only in a particular category, but as the product of the various differences seen quantitatively between man and certain other species. I pose the thesis that none of these categories is really qualitatively different to begin with, insofar as ability or quality of behavior is concerned, and yet, when taken together, they lead to a human society which differs certainly in a most remarkable way from the other animal societies known to us.

Human society is an expansive and changing thing which, unlike most animal societies, no longer appears to have strong internal regulation and stability from one generation to another. The time-scale of evolution has been contracted enormously and what the end of this expansive process may be, we cannot readily foresee.

Certainly one property that distinguishes this society from that of other animals is the extent to which almost all transactions are between people rather than between the individual and some aspect of nature at first hand. This is a progressive trend changing rapidly even within our own generation.

Another important difference is in energy utilization. Even in the most complicated insect societies, the animal's own muscle power is used in the construction of dwelling places, for example, and the energy is derived from chemical transformations that go on within the animal. In contrast, our human society has learned many round-about ways of utilizing energy for the performance of work; we do not have to eat atoms in order to produce atomic energy.

RAPAPORT: *Analogously, before the concept of energy was well known, there was another concept—namely that of force—and the organism was seen as simply transforming one kind of force into another. Levers, muscles, etc., can be seen as purely mechanical devices without any transformation of energy being considered, which is a purely anatomical view. Then the classical physiologists of the nineteenth century interpreted the organism as an engine for the transformation of energy much as the technological counterpart of that time, the heat engine, which transformed energy from one form into another. Now a new concept is arising, namely that of information, which has very little to do with energy. It can be roughly defined as a degree of organization. The energy transformation in the intellectual process may be minute, but the transformation of information that accompanies it may be vast, just as, for example, the mechanical energy used in firing a gun is trivial but the energy released as a result is tremendous. The mechanical part of this is only incidental; it is just the pulling of the trigger. So, analogously, we may perhaps think the actual energy transformation in intellectual process may be entirely trivial but the thing that emerges is the amount of organization. Now mathematical theories are developing to account for and to measure it, and to relate one part to another and to see how it transforms.*

Laws are now being developed in relation to the entropy concept, whereas previously we were preoccupied with the conservation of energy; the law that energy can never be increased in a closed system but only dissipated and decreased through friction and other losses was somehow integrated into the law of conservation of energy where the losses were accounted for. So now we have an analogous law in entropy: that the amount of entropy will always increase, the amount of information will always decrease in a closed system. Perhaps some day we will be able to formulate the law of conservation of information which is analogous to the law of conservation of energy—if we can find ways in which information is transformed.

There is an interesting parallel between the way people think about technology and the way they think about biological problems. When there was anatomy, there was only mechanistic technology of levers, pullies, etc. When there was physiology, there was biology of energy transformation. Now, when technology has advanced to a state where not the energy transformation but information transformation is the most important, biology keeps pace, or at least is trying to do so.

TOMAN: A striking general trend which seems to distinguish human society from other animal societies is that its great over-lay of culture is most unstable. Those beginnings of social interrelations, communications, energy utilizations that we see in animal societies, presumably can be begun anew or found again within a few generations of a particular species if all of the cultural over-lay in even the most advanced species were removed. This certainly does not seem to be true of human society, where an absolute requirement for expansion is the complete interpersonal continuity of communications. The continuity of the educational process makes for the continuous ability of human beings to relate their own experience to others and to add successively from one generation to another. In this the human society is very vulnerable to disruption.

Let me emphasize that it is not the human brain as such which is the source of this disruptability, for the same rules of instability hold for all mammals at all levels of neurophysiology. Experimental animals may be made epileptic, neurotic or psychotic. The peculiar instabilities which we recognize in human psychopathology may reflect more the peculiarities of our society than of our individual brains.

Because of the basic vulnerability of human society we must be preoccupied with two different levels of potential disruptions. First of all, there is the level of disruption in the individual, which we can call psychopathology. Since in such a coordinated unit as human society the bizarre behavior or inability to function in a useful way of even a few individuals can potentially have cataclysmic consequences for the many, psychopathology becomes socially important. But at a higher level we must deal with the question of societal psychopathology, if we can call it that, in relation to the laws governing conflicts between large groups within human society as a whole. That is something about which I can certainly say nothing authoritative, as a neurophysiologist, but I think it poses a major problem for our attempt to arrive at a unified theory of human behavior. Hurricanes, earthquakes, or the accidental approach of large astral bodies are not likely to disrupt our society badly in the near future, but rather many of the unsolved conflicts within the human race itself. I would like to conclude with a question: To what extent can we speak at the present time of any generally accepted laws of human behavior that are useful in an interpretation of the internal conflicts within human society?

EDITOR: *Toman gave a twist to the method of comparisons among systems, using the susceptibility to disintegration rather than structure or function. He emphasized that man's soma and brain show few qualitative changes from other mammals, but multiple small differences have resulted in huge social and cultural instabilities and vulnerability to disruption into personal and societal psychopathology.*

CHAPTER TWELVE

HOMEOSTASIS AND COMPARISON OF SYSTEMS

Presentation by Alfred E. Emerson

HUMAN society is undergoing an evolutionary process and this is related in terms of broad causations to the evolutionary process in the organic world. In order to draw the conclusion of similarity in process, one has to draw certain analogies. Grinker mentioned the fact that I analogize the gene in the genctic system with the symbol in the human societal system. If it is valid to draw such an analogy, then one can describe evolution in a symbolic system that partially parallels evolution in an organic system, and add the important and absolutely necessary time dimensions to the social system.

One can relate different levels of organization and integration in time. Some of the primary units of biology are levels of integration. For example, the cell came first, the multicellular organism was created out of cells, the segmented organism was created out of multicellular organisms.

Other levels of integration involve group relationships and this fact seems to me fundamental for the concept of behavior in relation to integration. If the protoplasms are either continuous as they often are within the cell, or contiguous as they often are between cells, the integrating mechanisms are biochemical or biophysical in nature, for example, the nerve impulse. If the system has separated so that there is no protoplasmic interconnection, one may still find some passage of chemically integrative substances between individuals through a mutual licking or odor, but one also finds an augmentation of what I would call the sensory reception and response systems which integrate the group. In such instances, while there is a reduction there is not an exclusion of the biochemical mechanisms. So the individual organismic system relies in large measure upon biochemical and biophysical factors of which the nervous system, the hormones, the gradient mechanisms, the enzymes, the genes are examples.

Groups exhibit an augmentation of behavior and also a sequence in time. Sexual integration between individuals occurred before family integration which brings together the young and parents. The family integration preceded the development of the strictly societal integrations which incorporate interactions between adult individuals, based on a division of labor. All of these systems show division of labor between the parts and an integration of the parts, linking them into a whole. It is not always generally recognized that integration and division of labor are not ends in themselves but serve a function and that function is the controlled regulation of the necessities of life and the relative optimal conditions of existence. There is evolution in time leading toward increased homeostatic control. As the cell evolves, homeostasis increases. The multicellular organism shows an increase in homeostasis of the whole system of cells, although homeostasis within a cell may be greater than between cells.

Some biologists have been loath to recognize the group as a system. We have many erroneous concepts of group behavior based upon inability to conceive of the group as an entity or as more than a statistical summation of individuals. Fundamental groups, for instance the sex pair, are units. Darwinian individual sexual selection is an example of an erroneous conclusion from the treatment of the individual as the most inclusive entity. The difficulties of individual sexual selection are immediately resolved if the sex pair is seen as a single unit. The problems of mutual adjustment between the sexes becomes a problem in the development of sexual homeostasis and the selective unit is the integrated sex pair, not just one sex individually choosing the other.

Take sexual coloration, which was one of the major problems in the discussions of sexual selection in the late nineteenth century! Darwin attempted to explain this by showing that the female would select the male coloration on the basis of stimulation, or aesthetic qualities, or what not, and that that was the reason the males evolved sexual coloration. This problem is resolved to a marked extent in modern times by the concept that any mechanism that integrates the sexual pair is selected if it leads toward a greater degree of group homeostasis. It is not a matter of the individual as the ultimate choosing organism but a natural selection of the unit, which is in this case a group unit.

The question of what constitutes homeostasis is also answered in recent times by biologists. It poses a very interesting and profound problem. The function of sex in biology is without any question not efficiency of reproduction. The asexual methods of reproduction are superior as reproductive mechanisms to the sexual devices. Sex is not an increase of reproductive efficiency but an increase in controlled variability which is necessary if natural selection is to operate in an evolutionary process. Sex, then, becomes the homeostasis of variability. This proposition seems anomalous: Homeostasis means self-regulation or self-stability and yet one of the stable products of self-regulation is variability itself.

We may now pass on to the evolution of the family system and you may notice that behavior as an integrative system becomes more obvious. The stability of the family lies unquestionably in the degree that controlled conditions for existence for the group system is attained. The adaptation of the mother to the young and the adaptation of the young to the mother increase the chances of survival of the group, and the group is the unit. You could not possibly claim, for instance, that the mammary glands together with their hormonal basis for growth and their potential capacity for growth are functional only for the individual organism. In other words, there is no survival value for the mother, the unit organism, in the possession of mammary glands. She may even have suffered hazard as an individual in the development of both her sex and family functions. The uterus as well as the mammary glands have survival value in terms of *group* function. Features may evolve that are harmful to the *individual* as the survival unit, as long as they are beneficial to the *group* as the survival unit. The part identified as the individual organism has to be integrated with the whole group unit.

Society moves in a similar direction. As a specialist in social insects I find that time sequences in the evolution of societal systems involve an increase in organization, an increase in integration, and above all in the functional interrelationship of these two in terms of increased social homeostasis. The social system regulates the optimum conditions of existence, just as beavers by building dams regulate the optimal conditions of their existence and maintain group homeostasis.

Part of the increase in homeostatic control involves numerous periodicities, so that if a system starts to move beyond optimal conditions there are regulating devices for bringing it back. If it goes below, there are regulating devices for bringing it up. So it fluctuates periodically along a general level. Many periodicities are examples of homeostatic control. Again it sounds a little anomalous, but not so if it is considered as a dynamic self-regulation involving periodicity. Consider the matter of optima for instance. The optimum conditions for a certain activity may be present at a certain temperature and not at another. So there are mechanisms for responding to the seasonal variations to bring the physiological and behavioristic aspects into functional relationship. These involve time sequences, and you may have time sequences in innumerable biological processes. Again the emphasis is on the fact that behavior is to be looked upon in the same way as physiological regulative devices; namely, as a system of a division of labor between individuals, of integration between individuals, all of them leading toward an increase in homeostatic control at whichever group level it be—sex, family or society. Again, it is necessary to emphasize the fact that these constitute an evolutionary order, that one transcends the other so that the levels of integration follow by integrating units at a lower level into a higher level system. At the same time it is quite possible for an included unit such as a cell within a larger system to undergo evolutionary change in partial independence or partial dependence with the more inclusive system.

Transitions of mechanism from one system to another almost invariably involve analogous rather than homologous mechanisms. Behavior, surely, in its integrative functions is analogous to hormones. Analogical comparisons are unavoidable and, as a matter of fact, most science deals with them. Here in this group we certainly have to consider analogies if we are going to integrate various sciences because we have to deal with different mechanisms of organization in the systems with which we are concerned.

This brings behavior into a certain perspective—that of an increase in homeostatic control of the group system—in this particular instance, society. I would state that human society is moving on a behavioral basis toward an increase in social homeostasis without having left out of consideration individual homeostasis. Individual homeostasis is still primary, but it is now gradually becoming incorporated into a higher level. I would also add that we can transcend the species and bring other species into still more inclusive organizations. In ecology we refer to these as ecological community systems. They incorporate the external environment within the system and become what we call an ecosystem. Such a system results from the species reactions to the external environment and also regulates the external environment in terms of internal functions of each species. The inorganic environment becomes regulated in a homeostatic direction within the ecosystem as a whole. The latter may include other species than our own, for instance, the human relationship to domestic animals, to domestic plants, as well as interdependent adjustments to the wildlife of the planet. These all are indications of the evolution of ecosystems. Our focus here, however, is on the societal and intraspecies system so far as humans are concerned.

Bringing behavior as a whole into perspective, now, we have to consider another aspect—the innate versus the learned. In insect societies nearly all behavior is innate and not learned. Experience does not vary the social behavior to any marked degree. Behavior integrates insect society, and leads toward homeostasis, but the integration is automatic and inherited. You do not have to reason and learn how to digest your food. Digestion goes on automatically, and automaticity may occur in the behavior system also as is characteristic to a very marked extent of the insect social systems. This does not mean that insects cannot learn. I refer you to the very remarkable modern experiments by the German, Karl von Frisch, on bee societies which indicate the interplay of learning with innate behavior. Bees can and do learn and utilize their learning to a certain degree. But still a very high percentage of the societal behavior is innate. I think a large percentage of human behavior is not innate but is conditioned and learned. In the vertebrates, starting with the fish and moving up, there is a marked increase in the capacity of the nervous system to become conditioned. This has survival value because of the versatility of response that is attainable in contrast to the limited responses possible in innate behavior. This difference reaches a level that almost looks qualitative, as has been pointed out.

The higher mammals can learn a remarkably wide variety of things. I knew a dog that would respond to over one hundred words and phrases purely by sound. Higher mammals certainly can do a lot of learning. What they do not do is to symbolize their signals in such a fashion as to pass learning on to the next generation or to another individual directly. In other words, what they pass on is through the germ plasm rather than through symbolization. This gives rise to the marked difference between animals and humans in cultural evolution—the evolution of accumulated symbolic systems and communication systems. Perhaps a few examples of cultural evolution may have occurred in animals, but they are so weak as to raise a question of whether they have occurred at all. Animals do learn signs, they learn communication, they have learned behavior, but they have not reached a threshold where they can pass this on by communicable symbols to the next generation. Each dog practically has to learn its own system of response and this dies with the dog. Very little of what is passed on from one generation to another was originally a conditioned response. Symbolic communication produces almost a qualitative difference from animals. I am sure that it was quantitative as it developed in time; as it is now manifested, it is practically qualitative.

Humans reach the point where instead of depending upon germinal evolution of the genes they can symbolize a meaning or a concept and pass that on directly. They invented language and that was a tremendous change in threshold of response. It reminds me of the statement about information and the tremendous change that could follow a certain trigger effect. Symbolization is a sort of evolutionary trigger that profoundly differentiated humans and which lead to an integration in time with all the other humans. We are integrated in time with the cultural system. Now this integration in time also includes the organic, the physiological and the individual systems. Remember that the genes and the gene patterns in any organism, plant or animal, are a product of a long process of selective adjustment through millions of years. Any given individual organism at the moment is a product of its past. It is what it is because of past events that affected its ancestors and selected its ancestors and gave direction to the process of evolution. All living organisms are decidedly integrated with past evolutionary sequences. We are partly what we are because we had fish ancestors adjusted to a marine environment. But the mechanism of integration in time becomes vastly different with the advent of the symbolic systems in cultural evolution.

My other point is that in spite of the change in the mechanisms of integration between an organism and a group, in spite of the changes that involve innate behavior contrasted to learned behavior, in spite of the changes involved in individual learning as contrasted to symbolic learning which integrates us with a society to which we belong, in spite of all these actual differences, the direction still has similarity. Every one of these systems is moving toward a higher degree of division of labor between parts of a whole; every one of them is evolving a greater system of integration of parts; every one of them is moving toward an increase in homeostasis.

This homeostatic adjustment is never perfect. It can never be expected to be perfect. Everyone knows that if even a simple machine is to do one thing well, that in itself presents limitations upon its doing another thing well. Under a certain optimal temperature, for instance, some physiological activities will be better than others. This is evident in the evolution of certain organs which were originally internal but functioned better at cooler temperatures and therefore moved later to the outside of the body. An optimal temperature is never optimal for *all* the processes going on inside the body. Compromise is an absolute essential. There are conflicts, competitions and incompatibilities that have to be resolved in an evolutionary process through compromise, and this means that there can never be perfection. Perfection of adaptation either at a behavioral level or at a physiological level is an illusion of idealistic philosophers and not a reality at all.

Now this gives us some understanding of the background of the tremendous problem of the relationship between cooperation and competition. Conflicts exist both within the individual and between the individual and his society. Conflicts also exist between certain groups within the society and among societies. Competition itself may be interpreted at times as a mechanism for the development of increased cooperation. These are not opposites in biological systems. Evolution always leads toward greater homeostatic control, and in this process competition may be utilized as the mechanism for developing a greater degree of division of labor. The latter is the basis for a higher degree of integration and homeostasis leading ultimately to greater cooperation so that it is a fallacy to treat competition and cooperation as opposites; they may in large measure have similar functions and similar attributes, and no sharp line separates them.

For instance, the social hierarchy of chickens involves individual combat to establish status in the flock organization. Once this status is acquired and is learned and is known, then the chickens function better as a flock than they do before that status is acquired, and the status is the result of competitive interactions. I would suggest—and this is only a suggestion —that in part homeostasis can be interpreted as controlling optimal competition. In other words competitive systems themselves are regulated in the direction of more optimal conditions of competition, because if competition is too weak, homeostasis, and therefore survival, is threatened. If competition is too strong, certain destructive events also happen. Consequently, competition is *not necessarily* bad, nor is it *necessarily* all good; there is an optimal level of competition that has survival value.

Now one final point: Toman mentioned the fact that with increase in social integration, division of labor and organization, there is a trend at the societal level in the direction of catastrophic instability. I would say that there are many fluctuations within the system, but that the system is consistently moving toward greater homeostasis which is a greater regulation of the conditions of existence, even with these potential catastrophies.

I maintain that human society is moving definitely toward increased homeostasis and I equate increased homeostasis with progress. I emphatically state that all these systems are moving progressively and by that I mean toward better and better homeostatic control regardless of whether it is the group or the individual, regardless of whether it is physiological or behavioristic, regardless of whether it is innate behavior or learned behavior.

I do not think organization is the only trend. Some people have stated that the evolutionary process produces a greater degree of complexity. Usually systems do become more and more complex, but I do not think that is the end. An increased homeostasis demands an increase in efficiency of specialization. If things are specialized, they have to be integrated, or else the specialization has no function. So there is an increase in complexity, and in organization. Why? Because there is a natural selection toward an increase in homeostasis. That is the fundamental function. Survival involves an increase in homeostasis.

RAPOPORT: *Perhaps there is an interesting analogy between, on the one hand, the biological invention of sex which telescopes the time scale of the evolutionary process by increasing the variability of potentialities, and on the other hand the biological invention of uncommitted portions of the nervous system which makes it possible to learn new behavior patterns which can be selected. On the one hand, the invention of sex made possible very much more rapid evolution than hitherto because it made possible genetic variation—all the possible combinations of genes which were not possible when biological variation had to depend on mutations alone. Analogously, there is the portion of the nervous system which is uncommitted, so to say, the random portions which await experience in order to guide behavior, instead of practically all the nervous system being committed, as perhaps in the case of social insects, to predetermined patterns of behavior.*

PARSONS: *I was very much struck by what you said about the control functions of sex relative to variation. The human use of sex is in part to aid in the establishment of a fundamental control mechanism of behavior. I think this could be regarded as a reinterpretation of Freud's great discovery of the fundamental importance of infantile sexuality. Infantile sexuality, I believe, is one of the major components in the process which makes internalization of value patterns possible in highly generalized terms. In this way, the control of the symbolization process is the basis of the homeostatic control of the civilization process. This is linked with the generalization of certain factors of the sexual components of the mother-child relationship.*

EMERSON: My restatement here is obviously and necessarily an over-simplification. We all have to over-simplify in this discussion, but it is a danger that should be recognized. As to sex, I agree with you, and I would say that in many instances a system that first functions in one direction may take on other functions in sequence or contemporaneously.

One gene, for instance, has numerous functions. One developmental process may have many functions. A clear-cut and easily understood example may be seen in the gill bars which were originally a part of the breathing mechanism of the fish and which evolved into a jaw. They changed their function from breathing to eating. Then that jaw became partially incorporated into the middle ear of the land vertebrates. So it changed its function from eating to hearing. Similarly, I would not state by any means that the sole function of sex in all aspects of sexuality throughout the animal and plant kingdoms was the control of genetic variability. In other words, sex may take on many functions, for example group integration of human society. Human sexuality has many other functions than the original or prime function of sex in the biological system.

One other point: The concept of homeostasis is complex. The physiological homeostasis within the body may apply to temperature; it may apply to sodium ions; it may apply to calcium ions; it may be applied to glycogen in the nerve; it may apply to sugar in the blood; it may be involved in neurophysiological mechanisms or biochemical mechanisms. It may include a hormone; it may incorporate gene systems; it may control nerve impulses. So it is a very complex concept to subsume under the one notion of self-regulation. Many different things are being regulated, not a few simple things. Some of these we know about physiologically, but, unquestionably, innumerable aspects of physiological homeostasis are unknown still. One might almost say that it is such a big generalization that it does not have direct utility as a concept. But I think quite the opposite. It is a remarkable concept in that you can objectively measure it and compare it.

For example, I have equated it with progress—human and otherwise. Some persons will challenge me and say, "What do you mean by progress? What right have you to assume that human progress has occurred from the days of the cave man to the present?" When I say, "What do you mean?" they answer, "Well, can you prove that we are any happier than the cave man?" The pursuit of happiness is put forth as if it were the prime concept. Happiness has some value as a scientific concept; probably the pleasure-pain principle that is basic to certain psychological theory is tied with happiness to a certain extent. But I claim on the whole that happiness cannot be adequately described or defined. You cannot adequately measure it and you cannot compare one organism with another adequately in terms of happiness. Whether happiness is involved in evolution or not is an unscientific question. I do not know how to tell whether the cave man was happy or not. I do not know for sure if I can always tell whether I am happy or not, and I know very well that it is sometimes difficult for me to tell whether my colleague or whether my child is happy or not.

On the other hand, not only can I tell whether a cave man had homeostatic control over his environment by the use of fire, and whether we have a better homeostatic control over our environment by the use of our modern heating system, but I can tell whether a cave man had a homeostatic control over his diet as contrasted with modern man. Not only can I look at the anthropological and archeological indications of his degree of homeostatic control, but I can move, as I did a few years ago more or less by accident, to a Pigmy village in the Congo and look at the Pigmies in relationship to modern civilization in terms of their homeostasis. I can compare the Pigmies to the animals they are living among and hunting. I can compare termites in terms of homeostasis to humans, and I can compare termite societies in terms of homeostasis to the individual organism. It is a remarkably useful concept because it allows us to measure objectively and compare what it has heretofore been almost impossible to compare scientifically.

KLUCKHOHN: *It seems to me that what you are emphasizing is, as Parsons said a moment ago, increased range of control, all the way up from fire to atom bombs. Would it be possible to take this term progress, about which I think we can raise some question, turn it the other way and say that maybe you can go out and measure the increase in individual breakdown, the increase in conflicts within a society or between societies? Perhaps this increase in control is not necessarily for the benefit of individuals!*

EMERSON: That is a good question, but we now have a tool that we can use. We can compare objective observations in a manner that, I think, was formerly extremely difficult on philosophical and scientific grounds. Just imagine now being able to compare the invention of the atom bomb with architecture, human architecture with the architecture of ants or bees, groups with individuals, levels of groups with levels of individuals! You see what a tremendous tool it is for comparative study on objective scientific grounds.

KLUCKHOHN: *Yes. The only question is the possible element of value judgment in that word "progress." It is not necessarily progress.*

EMERSON: Now remember this is a complex thing and homeostasis demands compromise. Psychiatry is not my field, but I would argue that the person in a psychotic condition may be attempting to feel his way toward integration, rather than showing only the effects of a disruption of it. In other words, the individual may be holding on to himself by attempting homeostatic control of certain things within himself. He may be acquiring a certain balance that has been out of kilter. What is good in one connection may be harmful in another, and this shift in emphasis is part and parcel of adjustment within the organism and between groups all through the animal and plant kingdom. This is simply a manifestation of the complexities of interaction on biochemical grounds, or in any other aspect of the organism. Most of you would agree that therapy re-establishes an individual in a homeostatic social system.

RUESCH: *We must distinguish two things here. We have talked about communication, growth, control, organization and integration. We have entirely different orders of abstraction when talking about the physiological, the psychological or the zoological universe. The theory of theories is a higher derivative function and the others are lower derivative functions. Grinker pointed out that he could translate physiological into psychological—psychological into physiological—by means of analogies. Theories of theories do not rely any more on analogies, but they take the data of a lower order and derive functions of a higher order. In other words, the theories of theories are not content-bound. But the theories themselves are always content-bound. For example, growth theory, homeostasis and information theory are theories of theories which are not content-bound; they are closer to what we might call mathematical functions. But as soon as we talk about the ego, or as soon as we talk about the hermit crab getting something, we deal with content-bound specificities.*

Now, on the lower level, namely, the psychological-social level, one can compare by means of analogies. In the psychological universe, for example, there is something analogous to the social functions. But as soon as we relate social systems to the evolution of man we deal with an entirely different order of abstraction in which we actually relate derivative functions and not raw data.

EMERSON: I admit that there are different dimensions in the system but they are not totally unrelated one to the other. In other words, they are not entirely distinct; they have a relative distinction.

RUESCH: *Well, in that sense quite relative. In other words, when we are talking about functions of functions we have to use different rules and different symbols, and different operations from those used when we talk about functions directly.*

EMERSON: I would hope that my discussion would take into account the basic assumptions of the scientific method which I recognize has its philosophical implications. The philosopher can to a certain extent criticize the assumptions and the philosophy of the scientific method. I still admit the legitimacy of somebody questioning the scientific method. But I wish to be consistent with what I would call scientific method which, I take it, is the system for acquiring knowledge, for studying relationships and for making comparisons. I think it is relative rather than absolute, and mostly objective rather than subjective. I am not disregarding the possibility of making the subjective objective and studying it scientifically, as the psychologist would; nevertheless, I think it would be on the whole an objective study of sense perceptions, their relationships, their cause and effect sequences and their interpretations, and I would want to stay consistent in that.

GRINKER: *You are looking at the increasing difference in integration as a process related to homeostasis which has value meaning. We could just as well take another value. For example, we could assume in place of an increasing tendency to control the environment that there is an implicit trend toward higher, more complicated organization in the life process, without imposing a system of values on it.*

EMERSON: That is true. I would argue against the possibility that something innate is driving organisms toward greater complexity, or greater this, that or the other thing, that is unassociated with survival value in terms of homeostasis. This, by the way, links up with the process of the evolution of adjustments. It is another way of stating what has survival value in Darwinian terms.

I wish someone would clarify the term value. Some people say science stops where value starts. I speak of survival value, but possibly I am using the term differently. As I use it I do not think there cannot be a science of values; there can be, but it may entail a semantic difficulty. In any case, somebody spoke as if this might be internal, and we are finding the relationship because of our particular set. You might accuse the scientist, for instance, of having a certain set philosophy in that he discovers relationships that are associated with that particular viewpoint, as if that viewpoint were within himself as contrasted to the external world. Now this is a great philosophical problem. Because of our sensory experience we discover order, but we do not insert that order; the order is there and was there before the human mind ever came into existence. I think that we are in the process of discovering order, or finding its dimensions, and relating one system of order to another. That is external in the phenomenal world rather than an innate attitude on the part of the human.

FRANK: *One point may be significant in this topic: The growth and development in an organism apparently requires a certain amount of instability so that the newborn infant may fluctuate physiologically quite widely. Likewise, the adolescent goes through a period of physiological instability while he is growing rapidly. Thus whenever a process is starting, or an organism or organization is undergoing any considerable alteration, especially an irreversible change, there may be at least a transient period of greater instability which seems to be essential if these alterations are to take place.*

EMERSON: Multiple systems and multiple compromises are involved both in time and contemporaneously and between levels. For instance, the infant in certain respects has less homeostasis as an organism than the adult. But he has a family to take care of him. As the family increased its homeostatic control, it could take over the homeostasis for the infant. You might say that an infant human has less homeostasis, let us say, than a horse, which I understand can get up and run at a fair pace across the meadow within a few hours of its birth. To that extent it has more homeostatic control than the human infant. Why can the human infant survive with less homeostatic control? Because it is incorporated into another system which takes over that function for it, namely, the human family and society.

DEUTSCH: *At this time I would like to say that I find two things very relevant. One is the statement made by Emerson about infant homeostasis; and the second, which seems at first glance contradictory, Toman's statement that the most important thing about human society is its changing and expanding character. The concept of homeostasis is a concept extracted from one relatively simple set of processes and perhaps we should try to avoid the premature closure of our theoretical system. I wonder whether the concept of homeostasis was used to describe two sharply different things: (1) goal-seeking feedback, and (2) goal-changing feedback. In homeostasis, so far as I understand the term, the emphasis is on stability, and the word stability has occurred as often in Emerson's discourse as the word homeostasis. You have a system which keeps something, that stays what it is or becomes more so.*

EMERSON: The "stasis" part means relative stability.

DEUTSCH: *Yes, I mean it is an Aristotelean concept. The very striking thing in certain types of feedbacks is that they do not remain unchanged. Learning means that even the center of the system may become different from what it was before. The philosophers will argue about this at length, but in modern technology they may find devices such as a land mine on which you can sit six times but which explodes on the seventh time. Such a land mine is not homeostatic; it is an extremely crude learn-*

ing device. A major difference between a society and an organism is that a society can relocate a vast amount of its members; while an organism even if it has a generalized set of cells in the brain—an internuncial pool, let us say—can at best only relocate a very small fraction of its resources. Human society within a hundred years has shifted something like 75% of the American population from agriculture into urban and non-agricultural occupations. To the best of my knowledge there is no organism in the world of any complexity which can do a thing like that. You have a little bit of dedifferentiated embryonal tissue, but a society is characterized more by goal-changing feedback than by goal-seeking feedback.

We could use growth—I am still thinking about our search for a "theory of theories"—rather than homeostasis as criteria. We could even begin to measure growth, and that is undertaking a comparison. We can compare growth in terms of increasing openness. Growth may be defined as the range of intake of information from nature available to a particular society—for example, the range of memories that are stored and can be scanned for data or orders for behavior. From this approach, one can estimate to some extent the range of unpredictability of future behavior. As an indication of growth, or the range of recombination, I would say that the usefulness of the concept of homeostasis is slight. It excludes, for one thing, a consideration of the combinatorial aspects, both in the thinking of the individual and in learning in society. It excludes, therefore, a consideration of independence of the system from environment; but such a consideration would be needed if we are to form a theory of the range of possible future outputs of a system vis-a-vis the range of possible future goals that may be chosen by it. However, all of these changes include homeostatic processes as special cases, together with the value concept and the culture concept.

EMERSON: These questions are very profound ones and worth considering carefully. I am not positive that you are not correct, but I would take a somewhat different viewpoint. In my discussion of the function of sex, I showed that the greater degree of variability was itself controlled at an optimum and became homeostatic. There is one point that I did not raise in the question of evolution, but which you raise: that is what I call circular causation, and you call the feedback system. I think we can demonstrate that the order of cause and effect is not always linear but may often be circular, given a time dimension in which the system is observed. For instance, in evolution it is quite common for us to group the factors which are causing evolution: (1) variability; (2) consolidation of pattern through isolation; (3) guidance through selection. The mechanism of variability itself has been guided through selection. So instead of this being a linear arrangement of factors in the cause and effect sequences, selection is operating upon the initial set of factors with which we started and is guiding the variability. It is also guiding the isolation and the isolation is in turn consolidating the genetic factors in the unit systems responsible for variability. The feedback or circular causation system is inherent in the evolutionary process, it seems to me, and leads toward homeostasis or the optimal control of the degree of variability and freedom (and the degree particularly of versatility) involved in human evolution.

DEUTSCH: *Let me make just one point here. The concepts of optimum and versatility are inherent in what I say. By optimum adjustment you mean adjustment to a set of conditions which, it seems to me, are invariant for the period of observation. But where there is limited universal change, the problem of preserving or enhancing adjustability, versatility or learning capacity involves already a considerable problem of adapting over a range of conditions taken to be considerably larger. Ideally, in the extreme or limiting case, learning capacity would have to be an infinite quantity— "life everlasting" in a world of unending change. The concept of "optimum" means, it seems to me, that for all the implications of the invariant situation, you know what are the conditions, the species and the individuals to be coped with. It seems to imply a limited range. Learning capacity, by contrast, implies a very large range, and possibly one not yet delimited.*

There is a second consideration. Given a certain set of conditions, there is probably more than one set of possible adaptations. Small step adaptations are likely to follow the line of high probability. In other words, supposing that two or three solutions are possible, which is the "best"? The most probable one is likely to be found soonest. But according to actual events in nature, it is often the improbable solution which, when found later, may prove most successful. To some extent a combinatorial system is apt to produce what we might call "great" solutions, such as the elegance of a mathematical proof. There are three dimensions in evaluating any such solution: the improbability of the solution, the organizing power or relevance or adequacy of the solution, and the economy of means with which this organizing power is achieved. This again involves internal combinatorial resources.

All I suggest is that homeostasis is part of this learning process. But homeostasis is not a broad enough concept to describe either the internal restructuring of learning systems or the combinatorial finding of the solu-

tions. It is too narrow a concept because it is change rather than stability which we must account for. A theologian describes even damnation in the extreme case as exactly the state where the mind of the sinner is completely closed. He has achieved perfect though uncomfortable stability in hell.

EMERSON: Homeostasis and goal-seeking are the same thing from my viewpoint—with the complexities and compromises associated with them. We must, however, take account of the semantic problems. The human mind conceives a concept and then limits it by definition. A good way to define a term is to make something that is opposite. Thus we are constantly building opposites and limiting concepts to define borders of meaning, to bring them into relief, so that we can look at them.

But sometimes that relief is spurious, based merely on semantic considerations. For example, Deutsch said versatility and homeostasis to his mind were not compatible or were opposites, or inconsistent. To me they are not inconsistent at all. Versatility of adjustment is one of the most remarkable types of adaptive evolution that I know of, not incompatible with the idea of homeostasis. I certainly would not treat stability in homeostasis as an absolute stability, but as dynamic and relative. The concept does not mean absolute stability, but includes these periodicities, fluctuations and versatile responses associated particularly with the human level.

We must also pay attention to our methods of observation. We look at the individual one moment and measure him alone as if he were a closed system but we know all along that he is not closed; he exists in relationship to outside systems. If you bring those other systems into consideration as really related to the individual, many of these problems resolve themselves.

EDITOR: *Although* homeostasis *had been mentioned before in several previous contexts, Emerson discussed this theory in some detail with reference to its applicability to all forms of organization. For this group, homeostasis became an attractive unifying principle, and it is alluded to often in future discussions. Homeostasis is used, not only as a narrow concept alluding to stability of the internal milieu of the living organism but as a principle encompassing growth, evolution, social organization, increasing complexity of organization, increased range of control, etc. Some conference members wondered at the all-encompassing expansion by Emerson of the homeostatic concept, the value judgments attached to it, and the possible*

conflict between stability and expansion. However, Emerson included growth, change and optimum variability as homeostatic, but in so doing he involved the sacrifice of some contributing systems, organizations, individuals or units. Thus, in its larger scope homeostatic processes have survival value if one applies it to "multiple systems and multiple compromises, both in time and contemporaneously, and between levels."

CHAPTER THIRTEEN

COMPARISON OF PSYCHOLOGICAL AND GROUP FOCI

Presentation by John P. Spiegel

I HAVE been interested in the criteria for the identification of the systems, or organizations that we use in our descriptions of human behavior. The question I ask is how can we separate and identify the various systems or levels of abstraction which are obviously in transaction with each other in any situation of human behavior. Let us assume that behavior occurs in a field of such transacting systems. What are the properties of the field and what are the characteristics of the transacting systems?

Looked at in this way it would seem that any system in the field can be characterized by three different sets of properties: its constitutional determinants, its integrative determinants and its system or field determinants. In the first set, one is speaking about the kinds of processes which go to make up the fundamental "stuff" of the organization or system; in the second, one is concerned with processes which integrate the system itself or maintain it as a bounded organization; and in the third, one deals with processes which take place precisely because the system in question is a component of a larger group of systems, all of which are in transaction within the field.

To describe transactions between the systems from this point of view avoids the polarity between structure and function to some extent. Structure and function are presumably different aspects of the same process. If one is examining the process at a brief moment or time, then little change is observed. This static effect we call a structure. If we study a process over a longer period of time where we can notice the changes, then we call the process a function. Even so, we are essentially describing different aspects of the same process.

The systems that can be tentatively isolated as transacting within the whole field are the Universe; Somatic system; Psychological system; Group, meaning the small primary group; Social system, defining society as a system of extended small primary groups; and Culture system, identifying culture somewhat as Emerson did, as the behavior of the society in terms of shared symbols and meanings. I will not take up time with any extended discussion of all the foci of organization, or systems, but will only attempt to compare the *Psychological* and the *Group* foci.[1]

PARSONS: *All of the empirical phenomena that you are describing for at least four out of the six systems consist primarily of symbolic behavior so that it cannot be a differentiating criterion. Psychological system is a behavioral system, and it is certainly infused with symbolism and certainly group and society are too.*

HENRY: *What is the Universe, in your model?*

SPIEGEL: The Universe as a focus describes all the transactions taking place between individuals of any particular species, and the physicochemical aspects of the surrounding environment. In other words, it describes the ecological transaction in the larger sense. If one examines any specific focus of organization, one has to assume that it is functioning in an ecological system. Biochemical processes of the Somatic focus have to be isolated from and are transacting with larger chemical processes which occur in the focus of organization which I call the Universe. A specific, small primary group exists in a geographical place and is in some sense in transaction with that place. If one examines a culture simply from the point of view of its symbolic properties for the behavior of the larger social system, then one notices that the symbolic properties of that particular function were developed in a particular geographical context—an ecological context—through a long history of interplay between that social system and the kind of physicochemical world in which it has existed. So that one has to include the Universe in any description of behavior.

There is a step-by-step progression in organization from smaller units to larger units, but that is not the point. At any moment or time in which one examines human behavior, all the evolutionary steps are transacting simultaneously and none can be ignored.

[1] Cf. Figure 1.

RUESCH: *What do you mean by Culture?*

SPIEGEL: It is the symbolic behavior, the system of meanings and values, through which a society understands itself and the world in which it exists.

RUESCH: *But this is an abstraction. Does something like Culture really exist in nature?*

SPIEGEL: It is an abstraction, yes. I think that all of these foci are abstractions. They are ways of organizing the raw data of experience from which we make abstractions. An individual is an abstraction from the group.

RUESCH: *But when you are dead that is not an abstraction! Do I understand you correctly that the order of the abstraction that you use for Culture is different from the order of abstraction for the individual?*

SPIEGEL: It has to do with the step-by-step progression in time, in history, and so on, but I am not here concerned with a hierarchy of abstractions. I am interested rather in a conceptual model which may help to order and show the interrelations of the observations we make about human behavior. I have no specified individual in this scheme. The individual can be in any place and can be looked at from any of these foci. But with respect to Ruesch's question about death, I would certainly define death as a concept abstracted from the totality of human experience. What any one person says about death depends in part on his unique experience and in part on what the culture in which he lives has to say about it. In one culture if he is dead he ceases to exist. In another, he still has a role in afterlife in some other part of the Universe—for example, Heaven or Hell. In a third, he is a migratory spirit returning to earth repeatedly in various forms and thus has to die over and over again. In western scientific culture he may not even die all in one piece! His cornea may live on as a window in someone else's eye.

Now I want to compare the psychological focus with the primary group. For this purpose we will match their constitutional, integrative and system determinants. This may have the advantage of permitting us to be fairly concrete about types of distinction without having to refer them to one unifying, all-embracing concept such as homeostasis (Table 3).

Let us start with the constitutional determinant. We can describe the *constitutional determinants* of the psychological focus as being composed of *zonal* patterns of transactions, of *modal* patterns of transactions and of *generalized* patterns of transactions. Now by pattern of transaction I mean a process that already takes place between the individual and the environment. It is a bridging concept.

Zonal patterns of transaction would include such processes in the individual as the oral, visual, tactile, kinaesthetic, anal, genital transactions, etc., between the developing child and the environment. In other words, the child relates himself to his environment primarily through patterns of

TABLE 3

COMPARISON OF PSYCHE WITH GROUP FOCI

PSYCHE	*GROUP*
Constitutional Determinants	
1. Zonal Patterns of Transaction	1. Number of Group Members
2. Modal Patterns of Transaction	2. Somatic Characteristic of Group Members
3. General Patterns of Transaction	3. Psychological Configuration of Group Members
	4. Status-role Configurations in the Group
Integrative Determinants	
1. Cognitive Integrations	1. Recruitment
2. Communication	2. Communication System
3. Valuation	3. Allocation of Members to Roles
4. Learning	4. Motivation of Members for Roles
5. Scheduling	5. Defensive Integrations
6. Defensive Integrations	
System Determinants	
1. Social Roles	1. Status and Functions of Group with Reference to Extended Social System
2. Identity, i.e. Historical Configuration of Role as Stored Memories	2. Position of Group with Reference to Communication System in Extended Social System
	3. History of Group, i.e. Stored Memories of Group

transactions that are initiated through body zones. When a child is first born, his main but not exclusive contact with or transaction with the environment is through the mouth.

Actually I borrowed these concepts from Erik Erikson.[2] By *modal* patterns of transaction I mean a more generalized pattern of interaction, one which was initially zonal like an oral pattern, but which now includes

[2] *Childhood and Society* (New York: W. W. Norton, 1950).

all incorporative transactions with the environment, becoming generalized in behavior so that one can refer to that pattern all behavioral transactions between the individual and the environment having to do with intake, or with receiving. One can make finer distinctions such as the distinction between receiving and retaining, referring these back to the zonal situation of interaction, such as sucking and biting. Sucking is purely an intake process; biting more a hanging on or a retaining process.

RUESCH: *That distinction may become untenable. Modal is coexistent with zonal from the very first moment on. The child does not consist only of the mouth when it is born. Some might say that breathing is dominant because otherwise the child could not exist.*

PARSONS: *The major problem there is whether there is need for selective allocation. Breathing can proceed while all other somatic functions go on. If you are walking down the street or riding around, or talking, breathing is coordinated with it. But there are other activities which exclude alternative usage of the body. I think that is a very important consideration. If you are doing one thing you cannot do another at the same time.*

SPIEGEL: Turning to the third of the constitutional determinants: by *generalized* patterns I mean those transactions of the individual with the environment which facilitate zonal and modal patterns that result in pleasure—love satisfaction. By generalized, I mean it includes the organism as a whole. Those which block zonal and modal patterns result in aggressive, hostile transactional patterns. Those which disrupt zonal and modal patterns lead to pain—anxiety patterns.

Under the patterns general to the individual as a whole I have included three different types: pleasure-pain type; aggressive-hostile type; and pain-fear, or anxiety type. These patterns of transactions are related to goals. Disruption, for example, is an interference of such a degree that the eventual attainment of the goal becomes impossible. If a child has a need which has to be satisfied in transaction with the mother, and if the possibilities of fulfilling this need are seriously threatened, for example, through separation from the mother, this transactional pattern simply ceases; the pattern becomes disrupted, leading to anxiety.

The list of integrative determinants that I am giving is not a complete catalog. I am more concerned here with the method than with the particulars.

1. *Cognitive integrations* have to do with the formation of symbols. Perhaps it would be best to describe them as the Gestalten of the patterns of interaction between the individual and environment. It seems to me that

the actual notion of Gestalt includes the substrata from which we get both signs and symbols.

2. *Communication* can be described as a sharing of the Gestalten of the signs and symbols which refer to these interactional patterns.

3. *Evaluation* includes discrimination at the level of the symbol formation with reference to various interaction patterns. Evaluation also includes judgment; and includes preference or choice of one pattern of interaction over another.

4. *Learning* can be described as self-corrective, regulative behavior in which the patterns of transaction and the symbols that refer to them are restructured and changed as, for instance, when the child finds that intaking patterns of transactions can be generalized from the mouth to more elaborate varieties of transaction with the family.

5. *Scheduling* includes all planning, sequential structuring of patterns of transactions as means and ends.

Then lastly there are the *defensive* functions. I am not sure that is a good word, but I use it to refer to all the integrative functions that have to do with the settling of conflict and incompatibility. The model for this actually is repression or separation. That is, when two patterns of transaction are incompatible with each other, the defensive process separates them and attempts to immobilize one of them by repression, projection, and so on.

Now, let us look at the *system determinants*. The system determinants at the level of psychological focus have to do with *role behavior*. The patterns of transaction which are at first so zonally and somatically oriented in structure have to be built up into various forms of role behavior. A child has to learn what it is to be a child, to behave like a child in its various roles toward sisters, brothers, mother, father, first in the environment of the family. Then it must learn the elaboration of roles in the group and in larger and larger groups, by assembling these patterns of transaction in various configurations. This is what we call role behavior. It represents the entry into the psychological focus of the group and society focus. That is why it is called the system determinant. It comes in because the role behavior is the social behavior of the human being.

EMERSON: *Could you equate role behavior with* ego *or* superego?

SPIEGEL: I tried in the past to equate the constitutional determinants with the id, the integrative determinants with the ego, and the system determinants with the superego. It can be done, but it is forced.

I have classified social roles within the system determinants because that is the way external factors enter into this particular focus of organization. Now, perhaps, whether or not these things are consistent will come out better when compared with the group focus.

Under *constitutional determinants for the primary group* I put: (1) number of group members; (2) somatic configuration of group members—that is, the age, sex, somatic characteristics of the actual members of the group; (3) psychological configuration of group members; (4) the status-role configuration within the group—that is, the group as more than simply a collection of people of various ages, societies, etc., but as a collection of status-roles.

The *integrative determinants* of the group are: (1) *Recruitment*—there is loss and there has to be replacement. (2) *Communication system* within the group refers to such things as how orders are given and how orders are received, who speaks to whom and so forth. (3) *Assignment* or *allocation of role:* Who among various individuals in the group is functioning in what role? This again is an aspect of leadership functions in the group which, integratively speaking, can be reached through different mechanisms; either by a leader appointing it or by a group voting on it, or in some other way, role must be allocated. (4) *The relation of motivation to the assigned roles:* Motivation in the individual is what I mean. Conceivably if somebody is functioning in a role for which he has feeble motivation, or no motivation, this will interfere with the integrative processes in the group. So integrative processes all would have to take into account disparities between motivation for role behavior and the assigned role.

SHAKOW: *Doesn't that appear as part of your role structure in human behavior?*

SPIEGEL: Yes, at the level of the *individual*, but now we are looking at it from the point of view of the integrative processes within the group. One difficulty one always will have in differentiating these foci is to decide where to assign or allocate the process. Is it going on in the group or is it going on in the individual?

PARSONS: *It is going on in both. Do not ask yourself where it is located, but what is its system of reference. You will analyze it differently, according to which is the relevant system of reference.*

SPIEGEL: To continue, I have lastly (5) *defensive* processes within the group. What happens when conflicts or incompatibilities occur within the group? How are they handled—by splitting up the group into two groups, by the isolation or expulsion of one individual or two individuals from the group, or by some other mechanism for settling and handling strains and incompatibilities within the group?

System determinants for the group again mean the entry of the external wider social system into the group focus. The categories are: (1) *The status and function of the group* with reference to the social system. By this I mean its status in the division of labor within the social system. In this way a group becomes characterized as a family group, or an occupational group, etc. It becomes identified as one among the variety of groups in the wider social system. Then there is (2) *the location of the group* with respect to communication processes in the social system. At what point in the on-going distribution of information and communication in the wider social system is this group located? Is it, for instance, in a hierarchy in which one group gives orders to another group which passes them on down to the particular group that we have under observation?

I have had some difficulty characterizing the time scale of these different foci. But one of the things that characterizes any group, or characterizes any individual, is its *history*. Although it is difficult to describe, it belongs among the system determinants of the psychological focus. The psyche has a history and its history is one of its determinants. The same is true of the group. The group is not only what it is constitutionally, integratively and in relation to other groups, but what it was; it is shaped by its history and traditions.

DEUTSCH: *It could be described as stored memory. An essential part of the group is its stored memories.*

RUESCH: *But history is nothing but the accumulated traces of past experiences available as of now. The position of your observer is different in your constitutional, integrative and system determinants. In the first two, he is an internal observer; in system determinants, he is an outside observer. When you look at a social system or at a group from the outside, you do not care essentially for their detailed structure. That is something which you care for only when you are a member and inside of that group.*

KLUCKHOHN: *How do you characterize an interviewer?*

RUESCH: *An interviewer is always operating at an interpersonal level; he conducts interpersonal interviews and then deducts certain things about the group, but he does not look at the group as such; he looks at it as a collection of individuals. You cannot interview a group; you only interview an individual. You can observe a group but you cannot interview it.*

KLUCKHOHN: *If the interview is always interpersonal, which naturally it is, where is the interviewer, in the group or out of it?*

RUESCH: *It depends entirely on his function in the group. He may be a stranger in the group, admitted as if he were in the group but still with the status of stranger; or he may remain relatively outside like a war correspondent. He even may observe what is going on in the group without the others knowing that he is there. But as soon as he is identified, he is assigned a different status.*

PARSONS: *If he is a member of the group, it is participant observation. If he is not, it is non-participant.*

RUESCH: *They are really not opposites; they are nothing else but successive positions assumed by an observer because of the limitations of his communication apparatus, especially his perceptive organs. We can observe now here, and then there, and then we put it together.*

SPIEGEL: I have really almost finished describing my model. I was interested in the categories in order to see whether or not one can rely on them to isolate or describe the foci, because one often loses a particular focus. If on the one hand you look at somatic processes and on the other hand you observe the group, the psychological processes of the individual, as Grinker stated, seem to get lost in some sort of squeeze play. I call this phenomenon "system fading." I am trying to be specific about what happens to the apparently lost elements. I think the same thing will happen with other foci; for instance, as between the psychological focus and culture, the social system will tend to drop out. So I was interested in trying to be as specific as possible about what one includes and what one leaves out.

PARSONS: *I think there is one thing you have not considered that I would emphasize very strongly: That is, however we finally conceive of human behavior (I think it is in a very fluid state just now), some kind of energy concept is involved in motivation, defining motivation as that which gets action done. I think we currently are making the transition from force to energy because we use ideas of energy transformation. Now, the critical point is that the energy source is in the organism and in the personality as a system. A psychological system has one single energy source; the group has a plurality of such energy sources. I think of the group as a plurality of members between which direct transfer of energy is not really possible. That introduces some complicated questions!*

SPIEGEL: Nevertheless, I am trying to get away from describing energy transformation. I am not at all sure that energy concepts are appropriate to an analysis of human behavior.

PARSONS: *I am thinking of the point that Emerson made: Where you have continuous or contiguous tissues, then biochemical interchange* is possible and seems to predominate. With the breaking of spatial continuity, the interchange has to involve communication, and the behavior becomes extremely important. I think there is an analogous difference as between the component parts of the individual personality system. A gap arises when energy passes from personality to personality and a new order of mechanism has to be involved in transaction.

EMERSON: I find Spiegel's analysis holds pretty well when I translate his terms into what you might call group versus individual biology. Nearly everything he says fits. I would emphasize, however, that you must not treat any of these categories too rigidly. They do diffuse and overlap and they do fit the same point. You have to think of them both dynamically in terms of time and also complexly in terms of the function of each unit as it spreads throughout the system. Any attempt to define rigidly each one of these in one system of relationships, I think, would be a gross oversimplification. If you frankly accept the fact that such definitions must be only definitions of relative influences, then it will be the beginning of an analysis that is fairly adequate.

RUESCH: Parsons, are you looking for quantum mechanics of social forces when you raise the question of energy?

PARSONS: In trying to state the problem of the behavior side, I have found the idea of inertia extremely interesting. Instead of assuming that the combustion of the gas must make an automobile go, you take the logical equivalent of the assumption of mechanics; namely, that a process such as motion will continue unless interfered with by counteracting forces. That works, I think, very well in the theory of social interaction in analyzing the two fundamental types of non-continuing processes. These two are learning, i.e., the socialization processes which are a change in the patterning of the system itself; and the processes of deviance (as contrasted with social control, to use sociological terminology) which are the processes of continuing adjustment through the interplay of the different parts of the system.

Now, let me add one other consideration relative to learning and socialization. Whatever the case may be as to plurality of constitutional components in a motivational system, there is always a fundamentally important learned component in the actual structure of the goal system itself. Generally speaking, our goals are acquired tastes. In the biological sense there is no constitutionally-given success drive.

The question is essentially that of analyzing the process of energy flow and transformation. Becoming attached to learned goals involves the processes of liberation and inhibition of energy so that there is an orderly sequence of different kinds of activity which all fits into a system. In other words, this is a dynamic aspect of homeostatic or equilibrating processes, involving several different units, but units which develop by differentiation and growth in the history of the system itself.

RAPOPORT: I think I understand what you are trying to say, at least in part. I am certainly in favor of trying to find concepts in the social sciences analogous to those in the physical sciences. One can then fit data into the concepts, operate with them, make deductive statements in terms of them, and so on.

In physics the important concepts are quantitative invariances. The important thing about the energy or the momentum of a system is that it is being conserved. If a quantity is not being conserved, then we seek some sort of quantitative law to tell something about its time course.

In our work in mathematical biology and sociology we try to find concepts in the social sciences to use in the same way that the physicist uses his concepts. However, I do not see what purpose is served in trying too rigidly to find analogies for concepts. They may or they may not be there. About forty years ago there was an attempt to develop a social mechanics in terms of an inverse square law of action at a distance—a direct borrowing from physics. It was assumed that some sort of social mechanism operates exactly the same way as gravitation operates in physics. An attempt was made to build up an entire theoretical system on the basis of that analogy. It would be nice if such things were found, but one should not be disappointed if they are not. In fact, other things may be found in a theory of social sciences which have no counterpart in the physical sciences. Even in physics itself, the concepts of thermodynamics, for instance, are not all analogous to the concepts of mechanics. Some are and some are not. Thermodynamics deals with such things as mass and inertia, but it deals also with temperature and entropy which have no counterpart in mechanics. So one should expect to find concepts outside of physics which are new but which nonetheless are mathematically expressible, and are somehow connected with observable, measurable referents.

PARSONS: Essentially we are searching for a fundamental invariant factor, invariant in time and fundamental to the theoretical interpretation of the stabilization or homeostasis of the system. Or a factor which, if it varies, can be used to account for changes in the state of the system.

RAPOPORT: At the risk of sounding trivial, I can point to a very obvious invariant: the number of us in this room. Now, that of course is a trivial notion. Nevertheless, beginning with some such simple concept in the study of social groups, one might proceed, step-wise, to more and more complicated analyses.

Bavelas has made interesting studies on the structure of the group, meaning by structure a rigid establishment of communication channels.[3] Now having established such a structure in a group, he examines the learning curve of that group with respect to a particular problem, such as discovering which color is common to several groups of five marbles, for example. If people can talk to each other only along these channels, the group will exhibit a learning curve which is analogous to the individual's learning curve, except that it will be a function of the structure of a group and to only a small extent a function of individual characteristics of the participants. In other words, the particular variable, the structure of the group, happens to be more important in this case than the constitutional variables of the members of the group. Here is valid example of a variable which can be used to explain an aspect of group behavior.

PARSONS: To continue with the case of numbers, my colleague, Freed Bales, has made studies of the distribution of participation as a function of the numbers in the group. The proportion of participation given by the top man—that is, the one who participates the most—increases steadily as the size of the group increases. This cannot be explained by supposing that by chance you just happen to get more dominant personalities in the larger groups than in the smaller groups.

FRANK: Spiegel has raised the question of how we can reconcile apparently two divergent views so that we can deal with the individual as an individual either somatically or psychologically, and we can also deal with the individual as a member of a group. Some of our difficulties and confusions here seem to arise from resort to two sometimes divergent, if not irreconcilable, conceptions of the individual personality. When we deal with the individual organism as a member of a class or group, we seem to have little difficulty in retaining a unified conception of the organism viewed individually or in a crowd. But when we discuss the individual as a personality and deal with him psychologically, we tend to rely on one set of assumptions in the clinic and then employ another set of assumptions when we observe him acting in a group. As suggested earlier, a somewhat similar dichotomy has been encountered in physics and it may be necessary for students of human behavior explicitly to adopt the doctrine of complementarity. One promising clue to a resolution of this difficulty lies

[3] A. Bavelas, "A Mathematical Model for Group Structures," Applied Anthropology, VII (1948), 16.

in recognizing that the same individual personality may exhibit different and seemingly contradictory behavior according to the fields in which he finds himself which he may perceive differently, interpret in different ways and find occasions or provocations for dissimilar patterns of behavior.

GRINKER: *I would like to bring up a question that cannot be disposed of simply by stating that the individual is a myth (as we would agree) and that we cannot find characteristics that set apart a single individual from his participation in the group. I would like to go back to what I said about how difficult it is to pick out the determinants of a psychological system—which Spiegel has brought out clearly in his attempt to define the psychological system and to compare it with the group system. His definition has a particular bias in that he is going to use it for comparison. At the same time in his constitutional determinants, he is dealing with somatic function. They are derived from somatic function, zonal, modal and all the general determinants.*

PARSONS: *But they do not function somatically.*

GRINKER: *That is what I want to bring out. They do function somatically up to a point. He has concepts which can be immediately derived from somatic processes—as a matter of fact, it is a question whether any of these so-called general constitutional determinants in the psychological focus are not largely somatic. They have a certain element of the psychological insofar as the individual can report them to us. But when it comes to the integrative functions we find that they are all group-derived. They are derived from interaction during the course of time. Of course, they depend a great deal on the spontaneous unfolding of maturity which enables the individual to learn. But his learning is in relation to other individuals and cannot be isolated from it.*

SPIEGEL: I have not separated the individual at any point, even in the constitutional determinant.

GRINKER: *But you have separated these foci in some sort of logical consistency and attempted to define them in accordance with various criteria: constitutional determinants, integrative, etc. You are talking about an integration which is not of the system itself. It is in the system only in relation to some other level or setting, but it is not a function of the internal organization. What I am trying to do is to find out where we stand with the psychological system. If we derive it from the somatic system, we lose it when we integrate it with the group because there we* find that the specific characteristics of the integrative determinants of the psychological system are group-derived.

PARSONS: The system is the system of interaction between organisms and an environment or situation. The system is not the organism. Certain components of that system's content come from the organism—the zonal pattern, for example. Other components come from the situation of which the social-cultural situation is the key part. But the fact that the integrative part has cultural content simply reflects the fundamental point that Emerson made—that this is passed on through symbolic process, not through the genes. The personality is a system; it has not evaporated as a system. It seems to me that suggesting that it has evaporated is equivalent to suggesting that since everything that composes the organism biochemically came from the environment through food intake, etc., there really is not any organism at all.

DEUTSCH: The suggestion that personality "is" a combination of soma and environment recalls a stock argument in philosphy to the effect that a thing is "implied" in its antecedent conditions; thus, in the parts of the thing there already is the whole. This argument almost necessarily assumes that the number of possible combinations of such parts is very small, and that the probability therefore of getting from them just this combination is very high. But if you take all the many ingredients of an organism together, the most improbable combination of all is that of the organism. Similarly, the works of Shakespeare are not simply "implied" in the production of a million monkeys writing on a million typewriters for all eternity. It would take almost eternity for them to be produced in this way, and almost another eternity for them to be found and selected from all the other combinations of letters produced by the same process. By contrast, the organization principle consists in making the improbable happen now. Thus, integration can be defined as all those processes which specifically change the combinatorial probabilities implicit in the unassembled backgrounds of the system.

EMERSON: If you take recognized levels of integration as having differences and at the same time relationships and therefore certain similarities, and if the psychological system is not defined in such a way that you create a dualism, these matters would be resolved fairly well. The psychological would be an analogous system at a behavioral level to the physiological systems at a somatic level, which means both serving a function, like integration, and integration that results in homeostasis.

PARSONS: *Behavior enormously extends the range of possible homeostatic integration. Symbolic behavior extends the range beyond non-symbolic behavior tremendously. That is where culture comes in. The fact is that the material of culture cannot come spontaneously from the interaction of organism and environment; it would take a million years for a child to learn by his own invention what he can learn by socialization in a few months.*

EMERSON: *This brings us to the fundamental question of what guides these evolutionary processes, cultural or otherwise. Biologically, the guiding principles is natural selection. It distinguishes possibilities and performs a choice. Incidentally, this is also evident on the psychological side. Now, if the intelligent mind with its learning process discovers principles of action, such principles provide guidance in choices. But the guidance itself is the effect of the process of evolution and was done under the conditions of natural selection. In this way you can bring these two fields into relationship and also admit the possibility of the effect being a cause of the cause. A circular causation system is set up which brings these things into consistent harmony. To my mind, it is the guiding force of natural selection that explains the fact that the so-called improbable becomes probable. The existence of this guiding force has been experimentally demonstrated without much doubt so far as the genetic system is concerned and I think that a sociologist can experimentally demonstrate it so far as social evolution is concerned.*

PARSONS: *Such a selective process, at least in certain sociological circles, is called orientation. We talk in our field about exactly the same thing you talk about in yours—under a different term.*

RUESCH: *Returning to the question Grinker discussed a moment ago, of what happens to the psychological focus, let us start out with one observer—the psychiatrist—looking at a patient. The observer has a psyche and the patient has a pysche. The observer has a limited capacity for observation and he now decided to devote his entire capacity to the observation of psychological phenomena; he is not interested in genetics or other somatic phenomena. Subsequently, he decided to add "x" numbers of other individuals for observation who also have a psyche. His capacity to observe and evaluate is still the same; he has not changed. What happens now is that the phenomena observed appear to him in a lesser magnification, as it were. Since the number of neurons he can devote to all these observations is the same, he must use concepts which are more global. Now, let us assume that our observer finishes by studying 100,000 people.*

He cannot enlarge his perceptual or conceptual capacity, but he can use global terms which denote derivative functions of other abstract functions about what he observes. Under those circumstances, the people he studies gradually lose what we call psyche because by definition psyche refers to detailed information about an individual's psychological structure.

GRINKER: Yes, that is clear, but that is just because of the difference in closeness of the object.

EDITOR: Corresponding to his model of system functions presented at the first conference,[4] Spiegel compared psychological and group foci in regard to constitutional, integrative and system determinants. This brought into consideration the differences between the individual as an individual and as a member of a group. Spiegel emphasized the development of role behavior of the personality within the group as contrasted with his individually developed somatopsychological structure-function. The conference wondered about the energy sources, flow or transformations involved by the personality or personalities within the group. Are there analogies between the social and physical sciences?

In further comparing the psychological and group systems, Shakow used a different method. He first raised the question as to the realities of similarities and their theoretical productivity. Are we over-simplifying in seeing analogies or over-complicating our assumptions? Sometimes our terms are too diffuse and are parts of systems without empirical references. Often we confuse homology with analogy.[5] To what extent is it justifiable to separate artificially the individual and the group? Finally, is homeostasis a scientific truth or a literary notion?

One method of comparison is to ascertain parallel concepts appropriate for two systems. What in the group are parallel to cognitive, conative and effective aspects of the psyche or parallel to the id, ego and superego in personality, or to conscious, pre-conscious and unconscious, or to original, maturational and learned? Another method is to seek supra-ordinate concepts common to both systems under comparison such as integration, communication, in-ness and out-ness, self and not-self. But in comparing psyche and the primary group there is always the problem of interaction which complicates comparisons.

[4] Cf. Chapter Two.
[5] Cf. Chapter Thirteen.

It is much easier to compare soma and psyche, for between them there are many parallels[6] *and they can be kept separate. Such parallelism does not exist between the individual and the primary group and their interactional relationships are extremely complex.*

[6] Cf. Chapters One and Eleven.

CHAPTER FOURTEEN

COMPARISON OF PSYCHOLOGICAL AND GROUP FOCI—(*Continued*)

Presentation by David Shakow

SOME basic principles and essential areas have to be dealt with in the comparison of these two system: The psyche develops only through group interaction. Dewey said a long time ago that all psychology is social psychology. The question is: Can we separate the individual and the group? It seems possible that we can deal with different kinds of behavior. Some behavior is in unpeopled fields, some may be in people-imaged fields and some in peopled fields. The question is whether there are not degrees of involvement, even though on the whole the psyche has developed through group interaction.

The statement is also made that behavior takes place only through an individual and this behavior is in the end individually motivated. I shall give as an example the statement of Paul Lazarsfeld who says that he can predict learning behavior adequately by using three sociological, non-psychological variables: the economic status, religion and size of the place in which the person lives.[1] He implies he does not need to know anything at all about the psyche. It is true that you do not have to know about the individuals in order to make that particular prediction; but that this is not psychological is quite a different matter. He uses these three indexes which really stand for a background of psychological vari-

[1] *Mathematical Thinking in the Social Sciences* (Glencoe: Free Press, 1954).

ables which are really quite important. For, of course, in the end it is the individual who learns; the group does not learn.

Now, the functions of the two systems have to be taken into account when we attempt to develop central schemes which cross each other. A principal function of the psyche of the individual is the gratification of its needs to the fullest. On the other hand, the family as a primary group has several functions. It has the function of providing facilities for the gratification of its members' needs under optimal conditions appropriate both to their role and status within the family and outside; certain kinds of gratifications for adults, others for the child. It also provides, largely for the child, training in the delay of gratification and the acceptance of substitute gratifications under optimal conditions.

There are, moreover, two different kinds of functions which are subserved by these two different systems and they work into each other. This is what I meant in speaking of the importance of the interactional relationship. In the psyche, we observe both the intra-individual activity—that is, the internal communications and other activities that go on within the individual—and also the interactional activities with others. In the primary group, we observe the interrelationship between the spouses, the parents, between the parents and the off-spring, and between the off-spring.

Spiegel's model could not deal with the time relationship because he did not have the permanent persistent structure which is the continuation of the separate individual actions. A complete conceptual system would deal with the structures of both the primary group and the individual, structure being used in the permanent-persistent sense. I define function somewhat differently for there is a distinction between structure and function. The structure consists of the memories and background basis for the previous single functional acts. I think in structure one deals with the units of the system.

I shall make a comparison with Parsons' system and then see where the difference arises. As far as the functions are concerned, one would want to know where the act takes place; that is, the setting of the act—in Parsons' language, the situation. The actor is taken care of in this system by the structure. The execution of the act, that is, what the organism does, I described in my presentation when I developed a psychological need-gratification system.[2] We will not go into it again here.

I will, however, bring out briefly some of the points that I made, to compare them with the presentation of Parsons and his group at Harvard. My scheme, of course, is very simple and cannot be compared with their highly developed system. Nevertheless, it covers some areas missing in theirs.

[2] Chapter Three.

TABLE 4

COMPARISON OF PSYCHOLOGICAL AND PRIMARY GROUP SYSTEMS

	SHAKOW			PARSONS		
	Aspects	Psychology	Primary Group	Aspects	Psychology	Primary Group
STRUCTURE (PERSISTENT)	(a) Units	Cognitive/conative/affective combinations	Individual Members		Below?	Below?
	(b) Organization	Personality	Family		4-variable need-gratification system *	Roles
FUNCTION (ACTS)	(c) See (b) above			Actor	Ego Alter	Social System (Family)
	(d) Setting	Internal/external Environment	Group Internal/external Environment	Situation	Social Non-social	Social Non-social
	(e) Execution	Need-gratification Sequence	Group Need-gratification Sequence	Orientation	(1) Motivational (2) Value	(1) Motivational (2) Value

* 1. Need system
2. Allocative processes
3. Defense and adjustment mechanisms
4. Need-disposition structures

I am going to divide my system into structures which I define as memories and previous experiences, and into function—meaning function in the sense of acts. The former is the persistent relatively permanent system. The aspects of structures to be accounted for are the units and the organization of these units. The units of the psychological system are conative, cognitive and affective combinations, and the organization is personality. In the family group, the units are its individual members.

The functional aspects of the acts in personality are composed of the setting or situation corresponding to the internal-external psychological environment, and the execution indicates the particular need-gratification that is activated. As I understand Parsons, he is less interested in structure than in function or action of an actor with a particular orientation in a particular situation. In Parsons' scheme he makes a differentiation between motivations and values, but I have not broken my aspects into detailed parts. His orientations I call executions.

PARSONS: *You may treat the actor either as point of reference or as system. For the analysis of function, of the act, you treat him as point of reference. His orientations are the consequences of what you call structure. But you do not analyze it unless, having described his act in that term, you can ask why he did act this way, and proceed to an analysis of the structure.*

First, we make that distinction between the actor as point of reference and as system. Secondly, we wish to derive the categories of the structure from a frame of reference that we can use in describing function. We did not get far into the matter of personality but we made a beginning. The idea would be to link the two, but to use them differently. One is the analysis of the function in this sense; the other is the analysis of the structure of the system which functions, which seems to be a separable problem.

Under structure, I define member in role terms, because the same person is also a member of other groups. If you take this concept of need-disposition (which is an attempt to reconcile two emphases, the need aspect and the disposition to act outward), if you take that concept, then a role expectation pattern is one kind of need-disposition used in a personality. It is an organized subsystem of the personality structure.

RUESCH: *I think that you are talking about concepts which are complementary to each other. If you talk about roles, you might just as well talk about the rules that govern role behavior. If you are talking about structure, then you are talking about function. If you are talking about internal functions, you imply the existence of external functions. These functions are always complementary to each other, indicating that at any moment you can only have one but not the other; the next time you can have the other but not the former. Therefore, you can only get fuller information by studying the system over time. At one time you can get information about the situation, at another time you can get information about the actor. The distinction is, in other words, an observer-determined or an observer-linked property of the system rather than a nature-linked property of the system.*

Shakow: To continue with the discussion of the functional aspects of the group: the group's internal and external environment and the group's need-gratification sequence would be the same thing. I am still sticking to the relationship between the psyche as it is seen in the individual and the primary group. This corresponds in Spiegel's presentation to the relationship to other groups and to a wider sequence.

Parsons: *Instead of saying group need-gratification, you could talk about individual roles as contributing to group function. In that way you would have something analogous to a group need-gratification.*

Shakow: I do not mean now that this is a group, but in the end I think that the individuals in the group have several kinds of needs which grow out of their relationship to other individuals in the group and that is what I am talking about, not group in the sense of a unit.

Parsons: *Then, for a group function, the analogy is essentially with group system-maintenance.*

Deutsch: *Suppose, for example, a group is confronted with slums. The disturbance for most members of the city is quite marginal. The only people who really suffer from it are the few people living in the slums and according to Marx only the ones who really suffer should really be concerned about it. Actually, it is quite possible that a different group of persons will take the lead and go into action there; in most of them there is no personal need, but in some sense a group need.*

Parsons: *There has to be a personal need if they try to do anything. It is not the same need.*

Shakow: In your analysis, you try to do a lot more than I do. Here I limit myself to parallels between the family and the individual, focusing only on their relationships to each other, not with the family as a group in interrelationships with other groups. I am not dealing with the primary group in all of its different functions.

SPIEGEL: *There are two different ways of proceeding. One is by assuming that there must be common properties like needs and looking for them in both the psychological focus and the group focus. The other way is to try to be specific and concrete in making definitions and then look for the analogy or homology. I was entranced with the possibility that if you took the second way you might not get into so much danger as if you used the first method and said there must be needs and then identify the parallel issues on the basis of assuming that they already exist—a procedure that is often misleading.*

RUESCH: *There is a third possibility. The need of the individual is reenforced by the presence or actions of others. Therefore, when you talk about the individual you talk about an individual whose feedback system is within himself. When you talk about a group, you talk about mutual individuals whose feedback system includes other people and that, I think, is the essential difference. Let us not forget that any motivation, though attributed to the individual, is reenforced by others: The assumption of the individual as a separate and isolated entity has only limited value.*

PARSONS: *As a way of amplifying the parallelism under function, I might ask what do we mean by gratification in the system? Essentially I would interpret it as continuing to meet certain conditions of stable system function. Gratification is a term indicating that a certain part of the system, a certain unit of the system, is not the disturbing facet. It is a stage in a phase process. The group is also a system and it has conditions of stable functions. The parallel of need-gratification in the personality is needing certain of those conditions for certain parts of the system at certain phases of their function.*

SHAKOW: In a complete description of the primary group, everything is interdependent. But if you are limiting yourself now to its relationship to particular individuals within it, you can describe it without relationship to other groups.

SPIEGEL: *The trouble with the need concept is that it is always a two-system reference. If you speak about need, you are always implying satisfaction of the need outside of the system, so that some other system is brought in.*

PARSONS: *I would put it the other way. I would say that it is the organism-environment interaction as system. That is the system, the organism is not a system and the environment is not a system. It is the interaction of the two that constitute a system.*

SHAKOW: I did not mean to give the impression that I thought of them as separate and apart. It is a matter of the observer; at one time I want to observe one and I emphasize its aspects, and at another time I want to observe the other. When we talk psychologically, we speak "as if" this were an independent system. When we talk from the point of the sociologist we talk "as if" it were an independent system. Now we are trying to tie the two together! They are not separate units.

In these problems interaction is most important, whereas the psyche-soma system can be thought of independently. You could develop a system in regard to the psyche or with regard to the soma quite independently of knowledge about one or the other. You cannot deal with a psyche and a family group independently.

PARSONS: *You do it really by giving different names to the same thing. You exclude one component from your system because you have other names for the things that do not interest you. You have a complete phenomenological system with no somatic references in it and many of your terms are ways of covering the impingement of the soma.*

RUESCH: *All our discussion today has been turning around two sets of things. One set was related to properties of systems, such as death. Now death is something distinctly observable and occurs with and without observers. Somebody may die whether you observe him dying or not. We all agree to that.*

The other set of things that we have been talking about are the properties of the observer. His capacities are obviously limited. We cannot make simultaneous observations. We are bound to the language. We have to report things that occur all at once in successive statements. One of the foremost observer-bound qualities is the distortion of temporal and spatial aspects of events. Thus we encounter a dilemma: we are talking about variables determined by the events in nature; and at the same time we talk about events that are determined by the characteristics of the human observer—I do not mean the individuality of the observer but the human machinery of observation.

It seems very fruitful if one can distinguish those functions which are relatively independent of the human observer and get agreement on them; and then separate from those the functions which depend on the process of observation. For example, I pick out something that is on the blackboard—such a term as situation. Now situation is existent in some way but is largely dependent upon where the observer sits. For example, if the observer sits in this room, he makes one sort of observation. If he has wired the whole house with microphones and sits in another room and listens to what goes on in the rooms, he gets a different sort of picture.

PARSONS: *But the situation of this conceptual scheme would be from the point of view of the system being observed, of analyzing it. From the point of view of the actor, the observer may or may not be part of the situation.*

RUESCH: *I mean that the very concept of situation is determined essentially by the observer. The observers, such as we are here today, reported words and sentences that sometimes referred apparently to the thing "out there." Sometimes they referred to the relational process of what they saw, when they saw it and how they could express what they saw, not referring to that thing "out there." When we listen to these reports we always have to figure out whether this man, scientist or observer is referring to the thing "out there" or to the process of observation and himself.*

PARSONS: *The thing "out there" depends on symbolization. I think we should probably infer that on pre-symbolic levels, objects simply do not exist as entities independent of the relation of observations. It is only through special symbolic elaboration that this "out there" can exist at all, apart from an observer.*

RUESCH: *Right. But our whole process of observation and symbolization is more adequate for certain functions than for others. When we deal with an area where the symbolization and observation process is adequate, we can forget about the technicalities of communication. But when we come then to the kinds of things for which they are less adequate, then we have to concern ourselves with the processes of observation and symbolization. In this latter case we are not really saying something about a thing "out there."*

SPIEGEL: *Can you say which is which in our discussion?*

RUESCH: *You can do it in any psychiatric interview and probably here. When you deal with denotative words, the observation and symbolization is more efficient than when you deal with connotative statements. As soon as people start to make connotative statements it usually means that their denotative system is inadequate for what is going on and then discussion and disagreements arise because the observation and symbolization system is inadequate.*

RAPOPORT: *Sometimes it may merely mean that that person has been so trained. He may simply not have acquired the habit or ability of making denotative statements.*

RUESCH: *But sometimes it is due to the fact that all contemporaries in that generation do not possess denotative concepts for certain processes. For example, there are certain fast moving processes which neither sense organ nor machine can register. They are therefore globally connotated because we have no way of specifically symbolizing these processes. In our language all processes that more or less conform to our time scales are very adequately presented. When we deal with functions that are much slower than our own time scale, or much faster, we begin to fail. The same applies to space scales, to growth scales, and so on. But in our system construction we do not take cognizance of that fact.*

PARSONS: *That is a major function of psychotherapy to train the patient to symbolize more nearly denotatively.*

RUESCH: *In psychotherapy the psychotherapist who is not present in the original situation divides the words of the patient very carefully between what he thinks are the more denotative statements and the ones that he thinks are more connotative. He takes the denotative statements and assumes that they have reality value, and then he takes the connotative statements as if they were deductions and sees how they fit to the denotative statements. That is not only done in therapy; it is done in this room also, and therefore we should be aware of it. As soon as we deal with something denotative, we take it as if it were the thing itself. When we feel that statements are becoming connotative, the referential property of the statement points to what is in the head of the observer who is, presumably, making an assumption.*

EDITOR: *In another comparison of psychological and group systems preliminary questions were raised regarding the possible methods and their complications. Shakow attempted to compare the two systems according to his considerations of the psychological system presented in Chapter Three. He then put his comparison alongside that of Parsons to determine agreement and disagreement. To say the least, the discussion became a little sticky as the multiple terminologies referring to the same things (or not) were the subject of controversy, sometimes with definitions hanging in the air. Ruesch rescued us by making some definite statements concerning the problems of communication that were involved.*

CHAPTER FIFTEEN

THE RELATION BETWEEN THE SMALL GROUP AND THE LARGER SOCIAL SYSTEM

Presentation by Talcott Parsons

FIRST I would like to say the contrast between the small scale partial social system and the large social system is not of the same order as the shift from personality or psychological to social system or from organism to the psychological. The phenomenon of social interaction is such a critical focus point that wherever two or more interacting organisms or personalities [1] constitute a system, it becomes a special kind of system distinctly different from other types of interaction. There are continuities all the way from the two-person interaction to the United States of America as a social system.

In the context of the microscopic-macroscopic range of the group, I want to make two main points. One is, I think, of such importance as to be scarcely capable of exaggeration: namely, that with all the variation from version to version, case to case, with reflecting historical differences in development of foci, etc., all the way from the study of cellular behavior, there should be some qualification for pre-symbolic behavior. Two, that in the large-scale analysis of social system and cultures we are dealing with a common conceptual scheme. Its fundamental logic is similar to that of physics.

[1] Particularly on a symbolic level.

For example, in classical mechanics the concept, particle, is not a class of empirical entity, but it is a concept which can be applied to a very wide range of kinds of empirical entities. In treating a celestial body as a particle there is obviously no suggestion that it is a simple entity, internally undifferentiable. Every astronomer knows that the sun is an extremely complex system, but for purposes of celestial mechanics it is treated as a single body. By the same token, while the sun may be a particle, so may a molecule of gas be a particle. Again, we know that the molecule is a very complex system on another level, but there is no reason whatever to think that the particles now dealt with in atomic physics are ultimate entities which can never be subdivided.

It is harder to apply that sort of logic in our field. To say that a complex system should for certain purposes be treated as a single unit which is a part of a larger system and in this respect internally undifferentiable, is not to assert it is undifferentiated; it means we ignore the differentiation for this particular purpose. Our analyses always involve the articulation of two microscopic-macroscopic levels: the unit level and the system level.

To turn aside for a moment: A system is made up of units or parts and we deal with them as entities. Then we deal with the system which they compose as entities, which brings us up to a next higher level. But then that system may be treated as a unit in a still larger system and so on in principle indefinitely in both directions. Now, when you shift from a system of a plurality of actor units in interaction to units which are no longer actors but are subunits of their personality, that, to my mind, is the shift from the social to the psychological. In observing social interaction, what emerges is contrary to the thinking of a generation or so ago when society was set over and against the individual. Now, society is seen to consist of an immensely ramified network of social subsystems and ramified not only in the sense of an immensely differentiated variety, but of wheels within wheels within wheels on many, many levels.

The unit of such an interactive social system at the psychological range (that is, at that threshold) is never the total personality but is always one part of that total personality because of the crucial factor of multiple participation in different subsystems. Perhaps this multiple participation has the same order of significance that Emerson spoke of sex as having in a biological sense. It is a complex way of interweaving personality with the social system. It could very well have something to do with the stabilization of variability, as in cultural change, because personalities are the guardians, as it were, of the cultural accumulation of a society and a whole system of checks and balances for handling it develops, for not all the interacting eggs are in one basket. They participate with many others in many different social groups and not just with a few others in one. (This idea of a check on social change sheds light on such phenomena as the incest taboo which prevents this closest of all human groupings from becoming a self-perpetuating entity, by forcing its members to ally with people from outside their own family.)

There are many of these subsystems. They are differentiated from each other in all sorts of different ways and size is one. I will however suggest three significant characteristics that differentiate the face-to-face group from others.

In pointing out these three, I do not say that primary groups are all alike in other respects—in fact, they cover an enormous range. Look at the difference between a family as one extreme type where there is a tremendously heavy emotional investment and the ad-hoc committee of five or six persons called together to do an hour's job. They are both primary groups, but they are not identical groups.

The first characteristic is that on the role-level primary groups cannot be very highly differentiated. The more elaborate role differentiations must cut across primary groups. In the face-to-face group of ten or twelve, only that many different roles can be allocated to the members, but there are far more than 500 different kinds of roles in American society. This is a simple function of size.

SPIEGEL: *Does this differentiate a primary group from a larger social system?*

PARSONS: It does; and it can help account for certain common features of such groups. For example, some functions have important places in other parts of the social system but have no place at all in the primary group just because of its small size. On the other hand, the primary group provides for some functional needs that are common to all human groups of whatever size. To mention only two: first, the integration of the group so that the members cooperate. Beyond two in numbers there will be some differentiation into leaders and followers in the group. A limiting case would be that of five people, all of whom took exactly equal responsibility in performing a group task of any complexity. The second functional need common to all groups which the primary group always provides for is what I would call expressive leadership. By this I mean being in the position of focusing the positive emotional attitude of the members and facilitating their emotional adjustment to each other. Recent work of R. F. Bales seems to show that even in four-man groups these roles tend to develop. These two aspects of leadership are not always combined in one leader and this partly accounts for the strain of the interactive process and leads to displacement of aggression. The displacement seems to be divided between the instrumental leader and the person considered least competent.

SHAKOW: *The face-to-face situation makes possible certain modes of communication which are not possible otherwise—by written word or by mechanical transmission. Ruesch's work is a most dramatic demonstration of the importance of visual cues, tone of voice and things of that sort. We all know the difference between trying to settle a matter by correspondence and sitting down to talk it over.*

DEUTSCH: *There is one very big difference; when there are permanent channels between two or more persons, messages get stored in them. If you imagine that the channels are long and the messages are slow, you begin to get equivalents of memory. Certain primary groups have common memory. Probably the family has more stored memory per person than any other group in this society. The ad-hoc committee has no common memory.*

PARSONS: That brings me to the second characteristic of the primary group: the difference in the communication system. Eight men sitting around a table for several hours to make an appointment are totally different from the same eight men giving written recommendations and corresponding with each other.

RUESCH: *One can analyze that in the following way. First, let us take the number of roles that one person can assume with relation to one other person. Then let us consider the number of changes that one person can undertake with the other person, within many or within a few roles. A person may have a stationary role or may switch forth and back between two roles. In the face-to-face group, one observes many switches. In the long distance group, by correspondence, you cannot observe such changes. It is most difficult to detect the change of attitude of the friend whom you have not seen in ten years.*

DEUTSCH: *The difference between face-to-face groups in memory is very important in all the problems of national assimilation. The members of a minority or ethnic or regional group are in situations where they have very limited numbers of face-to-face contacts with the out-group. So long as there is a minimum of face-to-face contacts with a few of the in-group, and a lot of memories with a large number of the in-group even though they have not seen them for ten or fifty or 100 years, there will be group identification. Actually, the face-to-face contact is important because it provides an opportunity for checking and correcting memories.*

PARSONS: My third point is very simple. The scope of general participation in group-decision varies inversely with the size of the group. The bigger the group, the harder it is for any given individual member to have an important voice in it. It should be clear that it is participation in group *decision* not in group *function*. Members of the University faculty participate in group *function*, for we each do our teaching and research. But one member of the faculty of arts and sciences with 350 members does not have the voice in faculty decisions in general that he has in a department—a committee with ten members.

KLUCKHOHN: *But the cultural patterns make a big difference in the way large or small groups handle decisions. This is true of Navaho Indians, for instance, who do not want to act without unanimity. No matter whether they have ten people, or 200, they will patiently strive for unanimity. Differences in group decision came up last summer in our study of the Texans, Navahos and Mexicans. In the old Mexican culture, it would not have made any difference whether there were ten people or 200 people, the patron in the village always made the decision.*

PARSONS: I believe that is true, but it is not relevant. Some cultures will place greater emphasis on wide participation than others. Nonetheless, other things being equal, it is more difficult to implement the wide participation of 200 people than it is of five. I am only trying to pick out factors which, other things being equal, would operate to differentiate small group phenomena from large group phenomena.

I wanted to say just a few words about a theoretical development. In the last few years Bales worked out an analysis of the process of interaction, including a set of twelve categories, six positive and six negative, for the classification of acts. He explicitly treated the small group as a social system. But we later found we could integrate these small group categories directly with the scheme of analysis which I had derived mainly from the analysis of large social systems. I think we can translate back and forth between large scale social systems and small groups as a result of having brought these two sets of categories together.

I thought finally I would mention a study in which Clyde Kluckhohn, Sam Stouffer and I have been engaged for some time. Our problem is to analyze the processes which Spiegel mentioned concerning the allocation of roles, with special reference as to why different kinds of people take the place they do in the occupational system. We tried to study the boy at the high school level. From what you can learn about the high school boy, how can you predict where he will end up in the occupational system? We know there are two massive sets of facts: One factor is *I.Q.*, or better, what is represented by I.Q. which is the only measure of ability we have besides actual school performance. Stouffer has worked out what he calls an aspiration index on which is based the predictions of probable occupational level. Regardless of anything else, those with high I.Q.s come high on that index. The other factor is *family status.* Indexes are worked out from father's occupation, both parents' education and community of residence. These two factors are correlated but clearly independent. What is proved by these statistics on 4,000 cases is that there is a very substantial residual variance which is not accounted for by either family status or I.Q. There are considerable numbers of boys with high I.Q. and low status, and those are the ones we are most interested in. Some are living up to the promise of their I.Q. and some are not. We are interested in some of the factors that make the difference.

A group of graduate students working with me has been engaged in working data into three main theoretical sets, all of which have to be correlated and integrated with each other. I cite this because it illustrates an approach to tying these two system levels together: the psychological and the group.

First we have been working on a very careful analysis of the occupational system in structural terms. The occupational system is studied as a reference system. We tried to develop a qualitative classification of occupational role and to integrate that with a hierarchical classification. We have simply taken the stated occupation of the father of a sample of our boys and classified it by our scheme. The important thing is that the classification is built on general theoretical categories; it is not an ad-hoc classification.

The *second* phase is to identify and formulate the analogous components in the role structure of the groups in which the boy participates, where his own orientations are either formed or at least are identifiably manifested as socialization process. Then you can predict where he will probably go later on in the occupational system.

In practically all sociological and anthropological thinking the job world and families are treated just as different kinds of social structures and attention has been focused on the difference. But then we cannot explain why boys who are brought up in certain families land where they do, in another role in the occupational world. They are being socialized for the occupational role, not only for familial roles. The thing is to put your finger on those features of the family role-system that are relevant to future occupation.

HENRY: *You find a boy occupying a certain job position; you analyze his family structure; and then you say he occupies his particular job because he occupied a corresponding position in his family. This is essentially an untestable system of influences.*

PARSON: Of course, the ideal thing to do, if we could, would be to make these predictions and test them out by follow-ups. Once we have a body of data on role behavior with reference to our prediction of occupational future, we will then have the complete role in the family, role in the peer group and role in the student group. Eventually we will have all four roles. If they form a coherent picture, I think that is something, although not a final pinning down. We are working to get a mass instrument whereby we can get data on matters which can be handled statistically.

HENRY: *As you know, I have done some analyses of family interaction. The kind of data you have in mind is very intricate. To match it against identical data on the boy's job situation seems to make the design very complex. I imagine one could get a good account of family interaction over a period of years from a social worker. But will you ever be able to say with assurance that the role he plays on the job is related to his family role?*

PARSONS: Well, essentially I think it centers on a four-fold classification. The first would be technical and instrumental performance; the second would be collective responsibility; the third would be expressive orientation; and the fourth, cultural responsibility. By that I mean orientation neither to a pragmatic goal nor to a collective goal but to the maintenance of certain standards, as you would find in the person concerned with science.

The first thing we did was simply to classify occupations in these terms. We had to carry it out to a thirty-two-cell table. It turns out that the overwhelming majority of occupations fall into five cells. There is a scattering with some empty cells, but considerable minor scattering in several others. Now we are just getting ready for a pilot interviewing program. We are going to take sixteen boys. We have eight people to do it, and they will have two apiece, conducting three hours of interviewing with each boy. We are working out an interview guide focused around these role components. Then we are going to take the interviews and analyze them very carefully with a view to refining indices of what we want in our variables. We may have to go through this stage two or three times before we feel we have sufficiently clear-cut indices to entrust it to a condensed questionnaire.

SHAKOW: *In the family you have actual data regarding the boys' roles?*

PARSONS: Yes, but the only basis on which we have used that technically is to help Stouffer to build up this occupational aspiration index. We put in the boy's own declared aspiration. There was a screening question which said, "If you could do just what you like, what would you most want to be?", and then, "What do you really think you will be?". That, of course, was the one that was treated much more seriously. Then Stouffer built this into an index with the boy's response when he was asked whether or not he expected to go to college, and then correlated this with whether or not he was in the college preparatory course, then his declared aspiration fitted into a Guttman scale.

We are thinking of the family particularly as the socializing agency. The third part of our conceptual scheme is going to be the theory of the socialization process itself. The first step toward that has to be to identify in the personality of the boy the analogous components. This should facilitate a double prediction. We are trying to predict from certain characteristics of the family system as a small social system what kind of a personality it will produce in the boy. Then we are going to try to predict from that personality what occupational role he will eventually fill. This means we have to bring personality theory into it in a way as to fit with this technical role analysis. We have to build our own theory.

RUESCH: *In my own experience, it has been extremely difficult to predict specific features. The things that are not specific, frequency of change, for example, are more likely to yield results. You do not need to specify whether it is to this role or that role, or whether it is effective or not effective. Formal qualities are much easier to predict than these specific content-bound factors.*

HENRY: *Into what part of your general theoretical system did you fit this research?*

PARSONS: It has served to focus a great many highly generalized theoretical problems. One reason progress has been so slow is simply that whenever we began to investigate specifically, we raised problems that we had to follow on to the most general theoretical level. Only when it was straightened out theoretically could we go back to the original specific problem. This has been going on for two years.

GRINKER: *You ended your theoretical discussion by saying that you had twelve categories—six positive and six negative—which related to all groups. This meant that the size of the group had something to do with three criteria: the degree of specialization, communication and the participation in group decision. Then you jumped to this particular experi-*

ment. Then you said that the derivation of an individual from a small primary group would determine in large extent his participation in a large group. In other words, you compare a small group for a role in a large group, which would correspond to your idea then that a small and a large group can be described by the same categories. Is this an experiment, or a part of this basic thesis?

PARSONS: Yes. I brought it in as a case where with reference to a common theoretical problem we have to analyze both small groups and large social systems and relate them to each other.

SPIEGEL: *This means there is a relationship rather than a high degree of similarity.*

PARSONS: I mean there is such a high order of continuity of theoretical problems that the same fundamental theoretical scheme is equally applicable. This is different from empirical similarities.

SPIEGEL: *It seems to me just like our experience this afternoon when we all felt we were losing the psychological focus. By stretching the similarities, especially at the theoretical level, you lose the primary group. I predicted at that time that the psychological focus was not the only one in danger of being lost.*

PARSONS: If you mean by that this should be a focus of the same order of generality as the others, I would think it was in danger of being lost.

RUESCH: *Should we say that loss is one of the characteristic functions of such a comparison? We should not deplore it, but expect it.*

PARSONS: In terms of the empirical in division of labor research, I do not think it is lost at all. It is perfectly clear that there are certain observational methods you cannot use with large scale systems, but you can with small. There are two great advantages of the primary group for research purposes. One is the possibility of microscopic observation in full detail. The other is the possibility of fuller control of variables. That is why I emphasize the theoretical continuity, for the primary group offers powerful research tools. If this theoretical continuity is genuine, then you can generalize from levels where things are demonstrated most freely, to other levels.

GRINKER: *It seems to me that when we are studying the transactional process in which three systems are involved, we stand closest to one of them as an observer. That one becomes lost as we view its transaction with the other two. Here we see, as I pointed out this morning, that as we look at the transactions between psychological and the somatic on one side and psychological and the social on the other, we lose the psychological. When we are talking about the transactional relationship among individuals, small groups and larger groups, we are closest to the family or the primary group. The only way to bring out each one of these groups is to place it in a different position in our scheme.*

A second point is related to Parsons' procedure. You use the family values as the criterion of the contents of your prediction—family values as evidenced in the boy's aspiration. I cannot exaggerate the number of variables that you ignore and yet you stake a great deal on the one variable which you have chosen. Suppose you have the family constellation understood, the values known, and yet you are dealing with the family today of the boy who is reaching out for occupational status as shown by his aspirations. Still the developmental family of the past is not understood. There are "x" number of people who have been involved in this primary group who are not represented at the time you asked about the boy's aspirations.

PARSONS: Part of the risk you speak of is reduced by the fact that this research is not all one indivisible package; it need not *all* fail, or *all* succeed. Parts of it might be successful in varying degrees. The mere fact of having established certain of these analogies (in the strict biological sense we were talking about this afternoon) between roles in different kinds of social systems, is in itself a considerable contribution—to say nothing of the advantage of showing empirical consistency as between the roles played in the different systems. Then pinning that down to an analysis of certain components of contemporary personality would be another contribution. Showing that it was possible to categorize personality orientation and role orientation analogously would be a contribution. Then the most ambitious research of all is that which would involve the socialization process itself; I think it is the most difficult and the most likely to fail.

Of course, these data might not be suitable data. This thing is ramified in innumerable directions. There is a good deal of research going on now about the analogy between the socialization of the child in a family and the process of adjustment to other new group settings in later life, for example, adjustment to military life, is being analyzed by essentially the same conceptual scheme as ours.

◇◇◇

EDITOR: *This discussion really only stated a problem with suggestions for solution. In what way is the individual's adjustment in large groups of diverse kinds affected by various types of socialization in the family setting? This question is an attempt to answer scientifically what the psychiatrist does every day. He uses anecdotes from the early family life of a subject in attempting to predict his behavior in larger social groups which will be structured by the subject to fit his past. Or putting it in reverse, we attempt to explain a patient's current social difficulties on predicted or sought for patterns established in the small family group during childhood.*

CHAPTER SIXTEEN

SOCIAL SYSTEMS AND CULTURE

Presentation by Lawrence K. Frank

FOR a unified theory of human behavior, we need a conceptual framework which will enable us to recognize the many dimensions of human behavior as observed in the *cultural-social* environment in addition to the geographic environment. This calls for a concept of the organism-personality whose varied behavior we are seeking to understand.

One promising approach to a unified theory is to follow the growth, development and maturation of the human child as an organism-personality from conception on. In this way we may observe how a young mammalian organism, with all the wisdom of the body, undergoes successive alterations and passes through sequences of transformations whereby he learns to live in a cultural-social field which is being maintained by the transactional processes of many human beings. Such a field need not be regarded as a separate independent organization, a more or less superhuman system or mechanism, as our classical social theory has long conceived it, seeing the individual primarily in terms of how he adjusts to that system or mechanism. Rather, this field may be viewed as we are learning to conceive of other fields, as arising from the patterned transactional relations of *all* members of the cultural-social field, each of which carries on continual intercourse with other members of the group. Viewing his conduct and feelings as circular, reciprocal, transactional, occurring between and among persons, all the varied patterns, rituals, institutional practices and symbols of group life appear as so many different modes of communication in and through which each person can approach, negotiate and seek consummation. In this way we may view the economic, political, legal and social patterns and transactions as defined and prescribed modes of human behavior which each member of the group must utilize if he is to communicate with others. Likewise, we may see that other persons in turn must utilize these same modes of communication so that all members of the group conform with greater or less fidelity to these sanctioned patterns.

It is to be noted that this approach differs from that long accepted in our social sciences. We have regarded the individual participant primarily in terms of his adherence to or deviation from these modal patterns and the prescribed use of these group-sanctioned symbols. This, it will be recalled, was the model of classic physics, and has been immensely productive. But this social model, like the physical model, either ignored the individual actor or reduced him to a more or less automaton who was assumed to act always in accordance with the accepted beliefs about individual behavior. Those who deviated too far from these assumed norms were regarded as criminal or insane.

Today as we strive to develop a unified theory, we find it difficult, or at least awkward, to think in terms of transactional processes through which the individual person relates himself to his environment (geographical, cultural, social and private) and through which the environment is related to him. This conception implies not a series of different environments, but rather the idea of an organism in a geographic environment who is enculturized, and socialized, and through those processes learns to establish and maintain a number of different modes of relations and communications with different *dimensions* or patternings of the organism-environment field.

This point is fairly crucial since it is just here that we are most likely to create a variety of constructs which we then reify and begin to treat as if they were actual properties of the geographic environment and operate more or less independently, above and beyond human participation or intervention.

By conceiving these varied transactional processes as occurring in a field which arises from them and in which human behavior is carried on, we may be able to develop a conceptual model more nearly adequate to the problem we face and providing a nearer approach to a unified theory of human behavior.

It should be emphasized that this approach enables us to derive from observation of organism-personalities the recurrent regularities and the systematic relationships which are observable in all human conduct. Viewed as products of transactional processes, individual members of the group must conduct all their life activities by evoking similarly patterned relations from others. It is also to be noted that through this approach we need not reify the various data on social life, such as prices, wages, votes, marriages, divorces, crimes, etc. In classical social theory, we have treated these as entities and invoked various superhuman "forces" to account for both their short term and long term alterations. If we view these data as so many categories of human behavior channelled into different modes of social, economic, political and legal communication, we no longer need to conceive of superhuman systems or mechanisms (the economic system, the political system, the social system) which have been guiding or coercing the individual to "adjust." We may regard the persistence and stability of the institutional practices in a group as derived from the goal-seeking and purposive striving of the many individual human actors in the group who utilize group-sanctioned symbols and practices in order to relate themselves, to carry on their varied transactions with others. In the same way we can see cultural-social change taking place as individuals with increasing frequency deviate or depart from accepted patterns and begin increasingly to explore for and to utilize new patterns which supersede the older as rapidly as they are accepted by increasingly large numbers in that group.

It may be useful to recall how the individual member of a group is subject to a similar coercion by his cultural-social life when he communicates through language with others. He cannot communicate with others nor can they communicate with him unless he utilizes the group-accepted consensual patterns which are recognized, accepted and responded to in verbal and written communications, however idiomatically he speaks. In much the same way we may view the coerciveness of economic, political, legal and social patterns as arising from a similar dependence upon common patterns of communication. Thus, repeated emphasis upon the need for a more adequate conception of the place and function of the individual in the group and of the cultural-social life as arising from the patterned behavior of the many individuals composing the group seems justified as a crucial point in the development of a unified theory. Insofar as we attempt to formulate a field concept, we must at one and the same time recognize and fully account for the more or less coercive group patterns and practices in and through which each individual person relates himself to others, participates in the public world, and thereby meets its many requirements and utilizes its privileges and opportunities in his life career. Equally we must recognize the idiosyncratic organism-personality as the source or agent of all the activities observable in group life who, while participating in the consensual public world, always does so in his idiomatic, individualized manner of living as if in a private world of his own.

As pointed out earlier, we may trace the successive steps whereby the young mammalian organism is successfully inducted into the cultural environment and the social environment, transforming his basic organic needs physiological capacities into the patterns of functioning and of activities that are becoming progressively goal-seeking, purposive striving. We can also trace his increasing orientation to the symbols and rituals through which he learns to establish his ever-widening range of transactional relations with the surround, especially with other persons. As suggested previously, we may see the personality emerging as the child learns to participate in his cultural-social world, to relate himself through all the prescribed patterns and practices, especially through language. He becomes increasingly capable of communicating with others in and through economic, political, legal and social patterns essential to interpersonal and group relations. But insofar as each individual child is a unique organism, developing his idiosyncratic feelings, we may regard the personality as the individualized way in which each child learns to participate with others.

It seems necessary to emphasize and re-emphasize that this personality process is not a passive adjustment to or acceptance of the consensual world with its demands, restrictions and privileges. Rather, it appears to be a very active transactional process wherein the individual imposes, imputes or invests emotional or affective significance into each situation, person and event. This means that the human personality is engaged in a continuous process of patterning his perception of whatever he selectively observes according to his cultural-social models, but always modified, often warped and distorted, by his own idiosyncratic perceptions and feelings. While we may on the one hand emphasize regularities and group-sanctioned patterns in an individual's behavior, we must, for an adequate conception of the individual personality, give equal recognition to the idiosyncratic, the idiomatic, in all the individualized ways in which the individual both conforms to and deviates from what is accepted and required by his group.

Here we should acknowledge explicitly how these deviations from modal patterns may seriously threaten the group life and at the same time lead often to tragic self-defeat. In view of the undeniable dependence of the individual upon others from the moment of birth onward, and the clearly exhibited eagerness of the child and the youth to live in the public consensual world of the adult, we may find it increasingly necessary to look more carefully at our various theories of how stunting and distortion of individual personality takes place. It may be appropriate to suggest that the denial or failure to recognize the idiosyncratic organism, and the attempt to block or to coerce that organism into conformity to patterns that are either uncongenial or incompatible with his idiosyncratic needs, capacities and rate and mode of development, may be one large source of the tragic wastage of human personality.

We are not dealing with passive individuals awaiting a stimulus in order to respond, but rather we are observing goal-seeking, purposive striving. In this striving, we observe individuals scanning the world and either attempting or failing to evoke the kinds of situations and relations in and through which they can pursue their goals and attain their deferred or symbolic consummations. It should be noted that this conception of communication goes beyond the bare idea of sending messages. The individual member of a group which relies upon socially sanctioned modes of communication of necessity must code or translate his message in such a fashion that it will be recognized, accepted and responded to by the individual or group to whom it is addressed. This means that in all human communications the individual person is concerned not only with the selection of the appropriate mode of communication, but what he says or transmits is governed as much by the recipient as by his own intentions or purposes. This means that human communications are likely to be attempts primarily to evoke responses instead of just transmitting information or sending messages.

It is also of equal significance that all human communication is essentially a circular, reciprocal and transactional relationship. Moreover, each individual is continually exposed to a large number and a considerable variety of different kinds of communications to which he may exhibit a selective reception. He may decode or translate what he does receive largely according to the meanings and the feelings which he has imposed upon the sender of such communications.

This highly complicated situation in which all human communications take place, where two or more individual personalities are involved, each with his or her own highly individualized concerns, has given rise to continual efforts to establish and maintain patterns of communication having the minimum of ambiguity. As the development of the law, especially civil law, shows, it has been a constant struggle, with never a clear outcome, to establish certain practices and modes of communication regarding such important transactions as involve land, property and sexual relationships. The immense load of civil litigation is eloquent testimony to the great frequency of failure in communications which involve what the lawyers call rights, titles, interests and obligations as declared by common law and by statute.

The patterns of communication utilized in economic transactions have had a similar history of repeated efforts to establish and maintain unequivocal modes of communication. With equal emphasis we might similarly describe the patterns and practices of political transactions in terms of how each group has established certain modes and patterns for individuals to relate themselves to each other and to various groups through what we call electioneering, voting, legislation and public administration.

Since so much of our individual and group living takes place apart from legal, economic and political practice, although always subject to their limitations, we should recognize the immense variety and diversity of modes of communication that are carried on with limited interpersonal relations, in the family and in many small group activities, and in and through the many so-called informal relations that make up the texture of human living.

As we observe these different categories of communication, we have moved from the more rigidly prescribed modes and patterns to those where the individualized or idiosyncratic aspect of human relations is not only tolerated but may be especially prized and sought, as in friendship, in marriage and in more intimate groups of individuals. All of group-sanctioned practice and rituals and use of symbols may be considered as modes of communication which each individual utilizes in his own way, but with a sufficient degree of conformity to function as a valid communication to and from others. In all such communications, the role of language is central since these transactional relations almost always involve some form of verbal or written communication.

The adequacy and the effectiveness of modes of communication are governed not only by words but by the use of those more or less standardized ceremonies and rituals which have been established for the different transactional processes and by the complex of patterns which we call roles. It may be useful at this point to consider roles as group codified patterns for communication since each role serves to focus and to guide the activities of individuals in such a way as to facilitate their recognition by others, and to evoke from others a readiness to receive and to respond. Taking a role or, more precisely, patterning one's activities, verbal and otherwise, according to the prescriptions or requirements for a given kind of communications, serves not only to reduce the inescapable individuality and ambiguity of most human communications, but also serves to channel human activities into the recurrent patterns and regularities through which the social order is maintained.

Needless to say, any individual may attempt to communicate in language and to exhibit the patterns of a role which may or may not be relevant or appropriate to what he is attempting to communicate. Indeed, it seems clear that just as in the use of language each person will speak and will act in ways that may appear to him appropriate and desirable but which may be meaningless or completely misleading to whom he addresses himself. Moreover, individuals may, with little or no outward indications, seek certain goals or fulfillments which are considered appropriate for one mode of communication but which they may seek through another. Thus we find individuals turn alternately to economic transactions or political transactions for attaining much the same goals. Likewise, we may observe individuals relying upon all manner of verbal persuasion and seduction to obtain responses from others with little or no adequate compensation, using deceit, fraud and whatever means will enable them to exploit another individual. It cannot be denied, however, that many individuals are, so to speak, actively seeking to be thus deceived and exploited.

The foregoing may become more immediately contributory to a unified theory of human behavior if we will see each individual member of the group as existing as an organism in the geographical environment of nature, exposed to all the impacts to which organisms are subject, but living in this multi-dimensional cultural-social field where he is also exposed to all the approaches from other individuals in his group. Here we should see each individual as having developed an extensive repertory of modes of communication both for approaches to other individuals and eliciting their responses, and for responding to their approaches. This means that he is expected to receive an almost bewildering array of messages, to be able to decode or interpret them, and to reply or respond in terms of what will be meaningful to others.

To formulate this multi-dimensional situation in terms of a conceptual model that will enable us adequately to discuss these multiple channels and modes of communication, we may have recourse to a variety of analogies which may offer some illumination and at the same time may involve some unnecessary and misleading features. Thus, we may think of the individual as both a sender and receiver of messages, being tuned to a variety of wave lengths through which he both sends and receives the various kinds of communications. We may also conceive of the individual as operating much like a radar set insofar as he is continually sending out impulses which then come back to illuminate and define the cultural-social world for him, subject to the continual corrections to which he must submit in the course of his varied transactional relations with other persons.

Another analogy would be that of an individual growing, developing, being enculturized and socialized, and in that process becoming increasingly engaged in various fields which operate like an electromagnetic continuum. This implies that there is one such continuum in which he is immersed and which he helps to sustain by all of his activities. Through that electromagnetic continuum, the cultural-social field, he both sends and receives diverse communications which may be regarded as so many different kinds of perturbations or waves which the cultural-social field is capable of transmitting, always with more or less noise or distortion.

Returning to the child, we see how the child is inducted into a human way of living and during the first five or six years of life is expected to master extraordinarily subtle and complicated patterns of behavior and the beginnings of different modes of communications. We may say that each generation of children must learn these patterns, undergo various transformations, take on various roles assigned as masculine and feminine in all their variations, striving to master what the human race has been struggling with from the beginning of human living. All this learning takes place in the context of interpersonal relationships, through processes of communication as the organism is transformed into a personality capable of entering into and actively participating in the maintenance of the cultural-social field. This does not mean that the child recapitulates the history of culture, but rather that in each generation we see how a child is expected to learn to live in a cultural-social field at that time, always as mediated and translated by parents, teachers, and other experienced adults. Thus we can focus on the recurrent patterns and regularities of the cultural-social field, or focus upon the idiomatic personality, invoking the principle of complementarity for the assertion that both statements are valid, depending upon which point of observation we may select.

For a unified theory, it seems necessary to reconcile these seemingly diverse approaches, just as physical theory has had to reconcile particle physics and quantum physics, and to accept seemingly contradictory observations. In this connection it may be appropriate to recall that earlier in the nineteenth century scientists had made many observations and some careful measurements on heat, light, electricity, magnetism, sound, mass and gravitation. Each of these different kinds of data were then reified: heat was considered a substance, electricity a fluid, and so on. Physical theory made a great advance and began to develop a more unified theory when these different data were recognized as different ways in which fundamental energy transformations were propagated and recorded so that each one could be regarded as a manifestation of the same basic event according to the kind of instrument, measurements and recordings that were employed.

It may also be pointed out that much of our thinking has been governed by the statement of problems in which we were concerned primarily with position, velocity and the impacts of seemingly inert particles. For such problems it was both necessary and desirable to develop a technique of ever more refined measurements. The basic problem, as Schroedinger has pointed out, was to find some order in the disorder of events, such as is shown by gas laws where a large number of convergent events average out into certain recurrent relationships for which the concept of cause and effect has been both useful and appropriate. More recently, as Irving Langmuir has indicated, we are recognizing the problem of divergent events and we are also becoming aware of the problem of organized complexity as exhibited by those persistent configurations which are found in atoms, crystals, plant and animal organisms, ecological complexes and cultural and social organizations and the human personality. These organized complexities call for conceptual formulations and for methods of study which recognize their multi-dimensionality and attempt to reveal the dynamic processes operating in fields to produce often different products, as contrasted with the problem of the relation of two variables to be studied in an anonymous data.

PARSONS: *Frank's presentation raises a big underlying problem. In biology, ontogeny is said to repeat phylogeny. Analogously, the human embryo has certain features of the fish at certain points of its development. To what extent does the child's development recapitulate cultural history? Of course, the sociologist would object that the child's development is within an already established culture and so it does not tell much about how the culture itself developed. The problem is one of linking these two things and the way biologists have linked them would not necessarily work for the child and the social group.*

EMERSON: *There is a tendency to recapitulate the evolutionary sequence in the individual's life cycle. However, there is another significant factor. At any given stage the organism has to meet its immediate environment by adaptive adjustment. If the environment of the embryo or of the young developing organism is different from the environment of its ancestry, then there occurs what is called caenogenetic development which literally means new development, something recent. That will tend either to cover up or obliterate the recapitulative tendencies. The latter is called palingenesis or old development as contrasted to caenogenesis.*

Quite often these may occur simultaneously in the same organism. An example is found in the uterus when the embryo is recapitulating the gill bars of its fish ancestry, yet at the same moment it has placental membranes never possessed by any fish ancestor, to adjust itself to the uterus. Those membranes are homologous with the breathing membranes of the reptilian egg. The human embryo has a yolk sack that it does not use which is associated with this reptilian ancestry. At the same time those membranes are caenogenetic as contrasted to recapitulation back before the reptile. Obviously there is a peculiar mixture of tendencies each of which can be partially analyzed and which are integrated into a given new system. Now, I would say that the same thing was possible in the development of a child. However, with culture and learning coming into the picture, the patterns of the developing child's personality are not wholly generically determined in the sense of biological genetics. I would therefore question the complete analogy with recapitulative influences dependent upon biological heredity.

PARSONS: *But, cannot the idea of recapitulation be applied, with many qualifications, to the relation between the development of socio-cultural systems historically, the origins of which are entirely obscure, and the development of the individual within such a system? Is not cultural evolution a chapter in biological evolution?*

EMERSON: *We cannot predict from one level to the other, but since the biological and the socio-cultural levels show other parallels, they might well show these parallels also.*

PARSONS: *This parallelism was assumed in a very schematic and naive way a generation or two ago. Then the evolutionary approach was discredited, but now I think we can approach the problem in a much more sophisticated way.*

FRANK: I agree. During the first five or six years of life a child is expected to learn what it took the human race many thousands of years to learn. Now, I would ask another question. Are we seeing in the clinical picture of the individuals who have psychological difficulty, parallels to what have been the major difficulties of the human race in building up society and culture?

GRINKER: *I doubt the analogy because the child does not go through the stages of development that took society so many millions of years to accomplish. What he learns is the existent status of development at the time. That existing state has some relationship to the historical cultural evolution, but now the child is the focus; he does not recapitulate the whole business.*

EMERSON: *He is interacting with the parents and their present existence, and this is in part explainable on the basis of historical development. Some lines of order ought to relate the two.*

RAPOPORT: *It is possible to relate the use of word magic in some of the primitive societies to the use of word magic by the child. Both use words and thereby expect to get what they want.*

HENRY: *Frank's parallel between social and personal evolution is relevant when we consider psychogenically determined gastro-intestinal disturbance. We may assume that man has had to adjust more and more to emotional and symbolic problems in his environment. The resulting stress on the organism's gastro-intestinal system has become progressively greater and the maintenance of gastro-intestinal adjustment has become increasingly difficult. A psychogenically-determined gastric disturbance represents a failure which most of the human race has been able to overcome in the process of evolution.*

FRANK: There have been certain persistent problems that every group has had to face from the beginning of time. Every generation must face those anew and try not to solve them but to reformulate them in terms of the knowledge and understanding and sensibilities of its group. Now, each child must come into that process.

PARSONS: *He must come into that process and within certain limits he must go through it the hard way. Certain of the great dilemmas of human action have been the major foci of the historical religious systems. Another example: It is inherent in the human situation that honest effort and skill will be rewarded only part of the time, and so every child has to experience frustration and disillusionment. Certain themes such as this run through the whole of human history and could, I think, serve as a focus for looking for certain analogies.*

FRANK: Shall we say that historically what is called religion is a statement of man's relationships to the universe, to his own group or society, or culture, and therefore to himself? Because of the way in which those beliefs, those assumptions were inculcated, the child found in the past a definite pattern of relationships to guide him.

Now, today, we have broken down the old pattern, we are trying to get a new set of consistent, coherent, assumptions, beliefs and patterns. Until we do, there will be disturbed personalities because in our private world we are fighting all the larger conflicts and our own inability to get an integrated coherent unified theory of existence.

KLUCKHOHN: *This takes me back to a question I wanted to ask Ruesch about time concepts. Is your assumption that you see more when you are closer a universal proposition, or are you saying that this is a part of training, too? My own view is that Americans do not want to pay any attention to what has gone on in the past; whereas other people are much more conscious of the past. I am just asking whether we are more trained to look at things that are close to us than we are at things that are back* in time and whether other people may not have more training in that direction.

RUESCH: If you study people who deal with data, you find that they have learned to look at things from a great distance. I have never seen an economist go to town and ask an individual about his economic habits. That is not the way he does things. The economist sits in Washington and determines the purchasing power of the population or something of that order. His procedure is not the result of training in adulthood; it is already the result of training in childhood. There is evidence to believe that the mathematician, the theoretical physicist, or the economist has an entirely different sort of childhood experience as compared to that of the people who go into person-to-person or person-to-animal investigation.

HENRY: But in the nineteenth century we did not think of getting close to the individual and observing him. The development of very close observational techniques is recent.

SHAKOW: This is not dealing with distance. Suppose Emerson could bring back the situation of ten million years ago with all the detail of existence. We would be observing them closely, would we not? Time, as I see it, does not matter really. If you have enough data from a nineteenth century family to study it in all of its closeness and complexity, as if it were a family in the present, it would seem quite different from a nineteenth century family studied from remote acquaintance.

KLUCKHOHN: But I am asking why people disregard this observation.

RUESCH: The problem of distance of observation is related not only to distance but also to the dimension of the thing observed. If you want to look at a tower, for example, there are two alternatives: either you go far away and see the complete tower or you stand close and look first at the point of the tower and then at the base of the tower. In order to get a full view of something big you have to get away from it. When you get away from it, the relationship is called "objective" in science. "Subjective" is the term used in science when the dimension, proportion and time scale of the observer are similar to those of the events under consideration.

HENRY: In the early history of personality and culture theory in anthropology, the results of observation were summed up as if the observer were far away. Now, in contemporary personality and culture theory in anthropology the observations are analyzed as if the observer were very close. This has happened to me in my own anthropological experience. The observations on Pilaga children which I made fourteen years ago, I initially attempted to sum up as if I were far away. But now as I look at the same data I examine it as if I were very close. The difference is that between the position of an observer and as a synthesizer of the same data.

FRANK: The same thing is true in social science. Classical social science looked at these large scale regularities and tried to establish relationships between prices or something else far removed. But today the clinical viewpoint is increasingly emphasized. The analyst or psychologist, the clinical psychologist, or social scientist is giving us a close-up view of persons in transaction.

PARSONS: *But they are not performing the function of improving generalizations about the not-directly observable large scale systems. You cannot get at those generalizations by putting many small things under the microscope.*

SHAKOW: *The over-all, highest level of generalization probably will not come from any of the disciplines represented here. Perhaps it will come from a philosopher or somebody else who sees all the different systems simultaneously. These sciences can probably be arranged in a hierarchy as to their interest in individual events. The more their interest in individual events, the less likely they are to yield broad generalizations.*

FRANK: Everything depends upon the kind of generalizations you want. If you want understanding of a dynamic process, then you have to look for illumination where the process is occurring. The dynamics are located in individuals in interpersonal relationships.

PARSONS: *Dynamic processes are not necessarily at a particular level. The movements of celestial bodies are dynamic processes, just as much as what is happening inside the atom is a dynamic process.*

HENRY: *Now we are beginning to talk as if we wished to establish a hierarchy of generalization. If you generalize about great big things, it is a very important generalization and if about small things, it is not important, implying that celestial mechanics have more prestige than quantum theory, which is not true.*

RUESCH: *It is certainly not true. The whole argument is derived from nineteenth century thinking. Subjectivity, which is pooh-poohed today in scientific circles is really a special case of relationships of distance and dimension.*

RAPOPORT: *Perhaps closeness enhances the importance of the subjective view but I define subjectivity as something else. I would rather define objectivity and picture subjectivity as its complement. Objectivity requires that different people independently come to the same conclusions about some portion of the world, as a physicist working in Chicago and one working in Tokyo. They are very likely to come to the same conclusion because they work with objective matters.*

RUESCH: *You are dealing with a very special case. If your investigation means that you have to be in contact with the thing that you investigate today from April 20, 1952 until October, 1952, then the next observer cannot repeat it.*

RAPOPORT: *That is the point. As you get very close to that which you are observing the difficulty of making objective observations increases.*

PARSONS: *To return to Henry's point: It is not the size of a phenomenon which is relative to generalization; it is the treatment of analytical abstraction relative to what is concretely observed. We have to be in a position to abstract and to relate units of observation in simple ways to units of other observation. From this point of view it does not matter whether they are statistical data about what 200 million different individuals have done or statistical observations about 200 million separate units of action of one individual; they are susceptible to exactly the same kind of analysis. It is not the fact that one observer deals with the large scale society and another deals with a particular individual. The difficulty is the tendency in the clinical method not to segregate things for simple kinds of analysis but to try to deal with 100 variables all at once. As a result, certain kinds of generalizations cannot be reached.*

FRANK: I think, Parsons, what is involved may be illustrated thus: The economist deals with a large array of data on behavior. From that he has developed certain theoretical concepts of the economic system and its operation by giving certain meanings to those observations and data which were consistent with his conception of the system. Now the clinical person is also dealing with persons who are engaged in economic activity but with the same data he gets a different kind of interpretation, a different set of meanings.

PARSONS: *But my quarrel with Frank is with his assumption that what has been done in the human behavior field is essentially the equivalent of what was done by classical physicists in their field and that moving on is now in order. I do not think anything approaching the equivalent has been done.*

SPIEGEL: *Our problem here is to bring all these points of view into one field and therefore I set up a six-sided figure. I still think an important point is how far away or how close you are to what you are observing. Another problem is how to get it all into one field and maintain some kind of distance respective to that one field? I do not think the problem is how far away the observer is when he is making the observation but how far away he wants to get when he synthesizes.*

EMERSON: *Most physical scientists deal with a relatively simple pattern of factors, and often they know all the factors and their quantitative effects that may be arranged in "laws." Therefore physical scientists have a high degree of predictability. But the minute you analyze a biological system you begin to deal with a literally infinite complexity. If all human beings concentrated all of their lives from now until the sun gets cold on the interactions of the protoplasms in the amoeba, I doubt whether they would know the complete story. Because of the tremendous complexity, scientific method has to attack the interaction of factors at a much higher level. At the level of analysis of the gene, which to chemists is a large molecule of nucleic acid with a tremendously complex enzymic effect, a biologist is working with simplicity itself.*

Now to go back to your situation. You reason that a given personality at a given moment is partially to be explained in terms of the time dimension of his life cycle.

Another time dimension is evolutionary time, which is contained in the concept of recapitulation, in contrast to what we might call the life cycle. There is an ontogenetic time dimension—that is the life cycle of the individual. There is also a phylogenetic or evolutionary time and the individual is in part the result of the time dimension of evolution and in part of the time dimension of his life cycle. He is also obviously in part the result of the interactions of the contemporary systems. It seems to me that all of these things are involved and fit in with biological models. In other words, you may say that psychologically we have to do what the physiologist does in looking at the organism. He has to understand its growth processes and development in order to understand the physiological processes. If he does not, he loses perspective on some of the facts that are right before him. In the same way you could write a story of the personality based upon life cycle. I do not think it would be complete, but I do think it would be a good one, better than the one based upon interactions of the given moment.

I have contrasted recapitulation with the life cycle, time in the former being evolutionary time. Recapitulation has been treated as simply a label for certain types of phenomena without looking into its causation. When it was first conceived, the biologists did not have enough information about the possible mechanisms to treat it as anything more than a label for a certain grouping of facts. Now, with the development of the field of physiological genetics in the last twenty years, we know the mechanisms by which the recapitulated phenomena can be explained. Each of these processes, each principle, each factor can be experimentally demonstrated, but you still have to do a bit of imagining in any given case to link all these factors together.

Not everything can be explained by this concept alone. However, we are making a consistent picture out of it and it has been extremely exciting in its practical applications. We can analyze conservatism over millions of years in a way that we were never able to do before. We can understand the process of change in a way that we were never able to do before.

The symbol as a means of communication and continuity presents some suggestive and stimulating comparisons in the dynamics of cultural evolution in contrast to the gene in the dynamics and mechanisms of biological evolution. I think this comparison needs to be carefully investigated down to small details to see whether, for instance, the gene as a system in biological evolution really corresponds in important attributes to the symbol in cultural evolution. I am inclined to believe that it may, but I think it needs very careful investigation.

PARSONS: But what do you consider a symbol in comparing it to a gene? We use the term symbol for a very wide range of different things. If you take the Imperial institution as a symbol of Japan, the comparison might hold. But it you take the letter "t" as a symbol, I would question it.

EMERSON: We had the same difficulty with the gene as an entity. You may be surprised to hear that the gene concept is an analogy of functional units that may have wide differences. One gene and another gene may be biochemically quite different. Not only that but they may have different mechanisms and a different historical origin. It is the way in which they act that gives us the clue for placing them within the same category. The analogy can go all the way from a molecule to a whole chromosome; there has been quite a bit of argument as to whether the chromosome was a gene. It has certain unitary qualities in heredity so that you have a wide range of intercomplexity, which you undoubtedly find in the symbol, too.

PARSONS: I think that the comparable phenomenon is a symbolic complex, which functions as something like a unit in the structure of behavior systems. We have formulations of symbolic complexes from all of the perspectives of the different systems that are involved in culture. Psychologically they are referred to as needs. Sociologically, I think they tend to be formulated as role patterns or role expectation patterns with the *regulatory aspect emphasized. I think on the culture level there is less pinning down as to just what the unit is; the trait is too indefinite a unit. It is a very hctcrogeneous category. Things like value patterns are much closer to what we are talking about.*

EMERSON: *The fundamental logic is this. We understand a good bit about biological heredity and we can build it into the system. Now we have another kind of heredity when you study the socio-cultural system. Heredity can be considered as a culture. It is transmitted from one generation to another. Obviously, the unit cannot be a gene but there must be something analogous to it. Perhaps the symbol is that analogous unit.*

FRANK: The symbol is meaningful only insofar as it is used by people. Would it not be a more effective analogy to say that each *individual* in a society plays somewhat the same role as the gene in the sense that he ensures the perpetuation, with variation of the symbol patterns and practices? The symbol has the disadvantage of being an entity and moreover, it is not acting. I would rather think of the personality as perpetuating symbols and culture patterns from one generation to another and make the analogy between the gene and the person as the dynamic enzymatic system.

EMERSON: *But your person is something like the individual. After all you might also say the individual is perpetuating its traits. But that does not stop you from breaking it down to genes and developmental influences. You have an individual in your cultural pattern, too, and it is a recognizable system, but you can also break it down into lower level systems and those lower level systems may have a certain degree of independence in the individual. In other words, the cultural symbol moves along somewhat independent of the individual.*

FRANK: As long as they are individuals, but we have plenty of archeological evidence of symbols which cannot interpret any more because we have no human beings to put in the meaning.

PARSONS: *You may say that the human germ cell has forty-eight chromosomes, but any statement of the number of genes is arbitrary because it depends on how you break it down. That is a principle of the very greatest importance, running right straight up and down. Any statement of the number of institutions in a society is in that same sense arbitrary or any statement of the number of patterns in a cultural system.*

RAPOPORT: *Not quite. Because it is not only the correlates of the gene which are important. The gene is to a certain degree a locus and legitimately it has a certain minimum size. It makes a certain sense to think of the gene as a real physical particle.*

EMERSON: *There are two characteristics of the interplay between gene and trait or character. At one time in the early stages of genetics the gene was thought of as unitary—one gene, one character. Now we know that this is certainly highly questionable. True, there are certain investigations now in enzymic effects that indicate one gene catalyzes one kind of chemical reaction. But even then, the thing is blown up into multiple effects of the same gene so that we speak now of the pleiotropic effects of the gene. Each gene has multitudinous effects on the organism.*

Symbols build up into patterned systems in development—from symbol to pattern of symbols, to personality characters which you may label schizophrenia, or something like that. The same system of symbols that operates to produce schizophrenia, let us say, is going to operate in all sorts of other character combinations and schizophrenia, itself, is based upon a multiple system. So I say we should use the symbol as the unit to compare with the gene. For there is also a multiple gene effect. In other words, many genes are operating on one character and at the same time influencing many other characters and these characters have an interrelationship in the system.

RUESCH: *I would be happier if you would speak about the parallelism between gene patterns and symbolic systems rather than genes and symbols. Let me give you an example. I am not a mathematician, but I have learned that the Romans did not know the symbol or concept of zero or the symbol or concept of infinity. This deficiency put an end to the development of certain operations that the highly developed technological Romans carried out. The introduction of zero and infinity vastly altered mathematical systems and technological operations.*

PARSONS: *Such concepts as institutionalized value patterns on the sociological level are analogous with the gene. They do not occur at random in the social system and they cannot be related to behavioral trait complexes at random. Certain areas of the order are fairly well understood by sociologists; others are still obscure, but I think the analogy does hold.*

FRANK: But, to repeat, the symbol becomes operational only when people do something about it—act toward it, communicate it, use it as a guiding point.

EMERSON: *That is also true of the gene. It is not there unless it has a function. Its very existence is because it has function.*

PARSONS: *But social scientists are moving toward that idea, too. Instead of treating culture simply as symbol systems in the psychological tradition, we are moving in the direction of motivated symbolic action systems. We are looking at the same phenomena from a different perspective, in terms of the regulatory mechanisms that make the interaction of human beings patterned and orderly within limits, orderly but variable.*

RUESCH: *We have come to a very interesting problem. The gene and the symbol analogy is the organization of evolution, of things that follow each other in time in the biological development of the individual going through a life cycle. It consists of those messages which are not destined for immediate consumption but through a tremendous number of delays are destined to influence the next generation. But where would you look for the central integrative factor? We are kept together somehow; we are not floating in space.*

EMERSON: *The guiding factor leading these systems to integration and adaptive adjustment is natural selection. It chooses which of these variable systems is to survive, and I think that the guiding factor toward socio-cultural adaptation and psychological adaptation even including the learning process is also something like Darwinian natural selection. The body moves to adaptive responses within itself and to its external environment without a mind reasoning and learning to direct it. When the mind comes into this picture, it is capable of performing a circular transaction and the effect will influence the cause. The effect influences the continuous or repeated cause. The process must occur in a time scale for this to happen. It occurs in biology, and I think in the social sciences; I leave the latter in your hands. Philosophers and theologians have sought constantly for this guiding factor. But most natural scientists have fought the idea of any supernatural implication, and we are now discovering scientifically the elements of this basic intuitional awareness of something that is bringing about order, by analyzing it. In the broad analysis natural selection is the guiding factor. Natural selection itself is obviously complex. If we add to that the concept of feedback, circular or spiral influence, the effect influencing the cause, I think we can correlate these concepts with the ability of man to direct not only his own life cycle but his own evolution, provided he recognizes the principles and undertakes to do it. I think he can do it; it is not just all automatic as it was in large part before the advent of intelligent man.*

RAPOPORT: *Take an automatic range finder on a gun. For a naive person on the outside it will seem as if the gun seeks out the target and* behaves purposefully. The projection of the future to the naive had become the causative factor which then determines the behavior of the gun; in similar ways theologians tried to explain purposeful behavior in the individual. It can be stated that a beam of light will follow the path where the action is least. Thus, to follow the path of least action seems to be the "purpose" of a beam of light. You can put it that way if you like, but you don't have to. The equations of light propagation indicate that only the "present" influences the path and all traces of "purpose" have disappeared.

RUESCH: But you cannot explain the death of the biological individual with that theory and that is a crucial point. You cannot put your finger on the central integrative factor which influences life or death.

EMERSON: This brings us to another one of the fundamental points that we have been discussing. If the individual was part of a larger whole that is real and is a unit of selection, then when the individual ceases functioning in relationship to that whole or has passed his optimal function there will be a selection for mechanisms for producing death. You can prove that biologically very easily. If you treat an individual in relationship to the whole, you can utilize the same sort of explanation as that of the death of a cell in the body. The liver phagocytizes 10,000 red blood cells per second. It eats them up, much like an amoeba, reaching out and absorbing the cell. It sends the hemoglobin products on down to the bone marrow where these are used again in the manufacture of new cells. Here is the death of a unit—you can understand that perfectly, but not if you take the individual entity as the ultimate. If you were just thinking about the red blood cells you could not explain it, but if you think about the organism of which they are a part then you can understand it.

Let us look at another example. You would probably say that a unit cannot evolve a system that is sterile if natural selection operates and still maintains its existence. Evolution of sterility seems impossible and yet it has happened several times in the animal kingdom. In one instance the somatic cells of the body are sterile so far as reproduction is concerned. There has been a tremendous evolution of somatic functions at the sacrifice of reproductive functions for those cells, easily understood in terms of the organism. Another instance is the evolution of sterility in the castes of the social insects; workers and soldier ants could not possibly be understood except in terms of the group. Here is the point where you extrapolate from one system to another in order to understand the phenomena. You have to recognize the group as a real entity, and of course you are dealing with the society as a system here.

PARSONS: *There is a direct analogy there in the differentiation of social systems. The primitive society does not differentiate its culturally reproductive activity from the rest. It is organized about kinship groupings almost exclusively. That is very schematic and of course there is enormous variability, but I think we can say that the family as a social structure is a specialization in cultural reproduction. It happens also to be specialization in biological reproduction. In certain respects the family is analogous with the specialization of the germ cell in the organism. You could even suggest that there is an analogy with the bisexuality of the germ cell—that is, with the fact that they must come from different organisms in order to reproduce—and the incest taboo which is one of the striking social universals, and whose function is to require that the new reproductive process for the new family unit bring together elements from two previous families; it may not go on in the same family continuity. Then, on the other hand, we have things like factories and universities and all that sort of thing which look more analogous with the somatic asexual structure of the body, for a university has certain secondary culturally reproductive functions, but what is taught there is not the foundation of the cultural orientation.*

◈◈◈

EDITOR: *In this discussion comparisons were not made, but cultural and social were considered as aspects of the environment or surround. The environment was considered as the dimensions of a field in which individuals and various sized groups transact or communicate in a circular and reciprocal way with each other and the environment. Thereby the field is created and maintained. The transactions involve forms of communication, usually verbal or written or in complex role patterns. The individual from birth on is both affected and affects the field, conforming in part and in some fashion maintaining his individuality. Often his conforming and non-conforming aspects are in conflict with each other, or the latter in conflict with the social-cultural environment, leading either to personal unhappiness or to social change (if there are sufficient or enduring conflicts). It was suggested that such a field theory model could lead to a unifying theory.*

The conference considered again the frame of reference of the observer in respect to time and distance from the object since the discussion of culturalization led into the question of recapitulation of evolutionary processes and ontogenic development. Gene, symbol system and individual were compared in their roles of perpetuation of physical, cultural and social systems.

The second conference focused on comparisons between systems. The principles involved were those of homeostasis, fields composed of and composing transactions, and communication. These were not mutually exclusive but seemed to represent concepts applicable to all systems. They involved purpose and value; relatedness of all systems, organizations or foci in the universe; and the processes transpiring within and among them. There was considerable discussion concerning how and in what way these concepts could be identified in each system, with relative agreement concerning those functions that were to some extent known. Yet the facility of generalization gave one the uneasy feeling that it represented less conceptual abstraction than a cloak for ignorance. Therefore we proposed to discuss homeostasis in its broadest aspects again at the next conference.

THIRD CONFERENCE

Homeostasis Reconsidered

Stability Vs. Adaptation: Some Speculations on the Evolution of Dynamic Reciprocating Mechanisms

Homeostasis in a Special Life Situation

Autonomy and Boundaries According to Communications Theory

Concluding Discussion and an Outline for Future Conference Deliberations

CHAPTER SEVENTEEN

HOMEOSTASIS RECONSIDERED

Presentation by Anatol Rapoport

I SUPPOSE we are all agreed on a working definition of homeostasis as comprising the self-regulating properties of a living process. To trace that notion historically we would have to go back as far as Hippocrates, who called attention to the principle which in Latin was later called "*vis medicatrix naturae*," which says that when an organism is disturbed from its "normal" state it tends to return to it, provided the disturbance is not too great.

Hippocrates thought in terms of agencies that somehow operate in nature to restore the "normal" state of affairs; like guardian angels over the organism. Hippocrates' theory was a tremendous step forward from an older notion that health and disease were in the capricious hands of the gods and without rhyme nor reason. As soon as "health" was thought of as a natural state of affairs, students began seeking the conditions under which the organism is disturbed. Therefore, the way was open for the creation of a natural science.

To be sure, natural science did not emerge exactly at that time; it was some 2,000 years later in coming. Finally, however, it arrived, first as astronomy and physics and chemistry, and later as physiology.

Most promising of various historical approximations of the concept of homeostasis is a statement made by Charles Richet in 1900: "The living being is stable. It must be so in order not to be destroyed, dissolved or disintegrated by the colossal forces, often adverse, which surround it. By an apparent contradiction it maintains its stability only if it is excitable and capable of modifying itself according to external stimuli and adjusting its response to the stimulation. In a sense, it is the necessary condition for the true stability of the organism."

Note the paradox; it is stable and yet it cannot be rigid. It cannot be stable in the same sense as a rock is stable. Its stability is an activity and not a static state of affairs. It is a dynamic state; an open system as opposed to a closed system.

The advance in the point of view of nineteenth century physiology has been in the recognition that restorative forces are inherent in the very construction of the organism. In order to understand how "*vis medicatrix naturae*" operates, one must understand how the organism is constructed.

This outlook, placing the homeostatic activity into the structure of the organism instead of imagining it somewhere out in nature, and thus focusing attention on the construction of the organism itself, has borne fruit. As a turning point in physiology one might take Claude Bernard's famous suggestion that the organism really has two environments, the external and the internal.[1] Claude Bernard focused attention on the *internal environment*, and, as most of you probably know, he first took it to be the plasma of the blood which buffers the organism against the violent changes of the outside—a good first approximation.

Attention was fixed on an identifiable, observable factor, and there developed, toward the end of the nineteenth century, an elaborate physiology of blood circulation and of respiration, of tissue nourishment and waste elimination; and the physical and chemical processes associated with them. Instead of asking, as the old philosophers did, "What are the natural forces responsible for the preservation of balance in living processes?" one asks instead, "Is there anything in the way the organism is put together that insures the preservation of this balance?"

One identified the observables of this balance, largely concentrations of chemicals in the blood, lymph and tissues, but also such things as temperature which is an entirely different kind of concept than, let us say, concentration of a chemical. Temperature is very much more abstract, and a mechanism for the regulation of temperature would be a much more sophisticated mechanism from the point of view of modern technology than a mechanism for regulating concentration. To regulate temperature you would need something like a thermostat, which connects the principle of homeostasis to some very interesting modern technological principles.

[1] *Leçons sur les Phenomenes de la Vie Commune aux Animaux et aux Vegetaux* (Paris: 1878).

The living organism now appeared more like a mechanism than a mysterious carrier of some vital force. The whole science of mechanics was founded on the metaphysical revolutionary principle that one should not consider ultimate causes at all, only the causes here and now, pushing, as it were, instead of pulling from the future, which the teleological explanation assumes. The mechanistic outlook led one to look for states of the organism which more or less automatically drove things in the direction in which they went, without considering what the ultimate outcome of such activity might be.

To be sure, the notion that living organisms are mechanisms is considerably older than physiology; one might trace it to Descartes. He did not dare to assume that human beings were mechanisms, but he did assert that animals are mechanisms. Of course, he could mean by a "mechanism" only what was considered a mechanism in his day, and the "mechanisms" known in the seventeenth century were almost exclusively clockworks.

Now a clockwork is an arrangement whose future course can be predicted by the knowledge of the kinetic energies of its constituent parts, and also such potential energy which results from a deformation against a force. The only idea of potential energy was displacement against a force, as in a pendulum or a watch spring.

In the nineteenth century an entirely new notion of potential energy was introduced and that was the potential energy of a heat source. The scientists of the day first noted the potential energy contained in coal; later on, chemical potential energy or electrical potential energy, and, even more sophisticated, surface tension. As the notion of potential energy became broadened, the notion of mechanisms became broadened.

To give an example of how the explanations of natural phenomena developed as the notion of mechanism broadened: suppose an early natural scientist noted that an organism removes "good air" from its environment and gives off "bad air." He used these naive adjectives because the elementary chemical properties of oxygen and carbon dioxide were not known. How is this purposeful selection of good air, and discarding of bad air, to be explained? It certainly cannot be explained by any clockwork model which does not select but only pushes. However, some quite elementary knowledge of biochemistry puts the phenomenon into an entirely different light.

It is now known that when a red corpuscle passes near the alveoli of the lungs, the concentrations of oxygen are such that oxygen goes from the alveoli into the corpuscle, and when the corpuscle passes the tissues the oxygen goes the other way, again because of the differential in oxygen concentration. That is a mechanism, of course, but not a clockwork, and therefore would not appear comprehensible to a seventeenth century philosopher.

I should say, parenthetically, that by mechanism I mean something one constructs. Descartes would understand a mechanism as something that is constructed by a knowledge of the mechanics of the day, alone. I use the word "mechanism" to include all constructions, machines, engines, and even information-transmission devices.

This example which I have given, the tendency for the oxygen concentration in the blood to be constant and various other concentrations to remain constant, was given the name of homeostasis, I believe, for the first time by Walter B. Cannon.[2] He discusses a number of such homeostatic mechanisms. I call them mechanisms because their construction is fairly well understood, or at least one assumes that by investigating the constituent parts one can understand them as mechanisms.

It is not claimed by Cannon or anybody else, of course, that all these things are perfectly understood in the sense that they can be definitively called mechanisms, but enough is known about them so that they can be assumed to be mechanisms. As soon as enough is known about the constructions, they will be constructed and some have already been constructed. Mechanical hearts and mechanical kidneys, and so on, have been constructed with the gross features of homeostatic devices that we observe physiologically.

The examples by Cannon and other physiologists of homeostatic processes include, *first*, the tendency of blood volume to maintain itself. When a breach is made in the circulatory system, the blood, because of the pressure within the system, has a tendency to escape. A homeostatic mechanism lies in the chemical properties of blood constituents which, upon contact with air, release a series of chemical reactions leading to the coagulation of the blood and sealing of the breach. Thus blood volume is maintained as a mechanism.

Second, the mechanism which keeps the sugar, salt, oxygen and carbon dioxide concentrations in the blood constant, working mostly by the principle of diffusion, osmotic pressure.

Third, mechanisms which keep the body temperature of higher vertebrates constant.

Fourth, mechanisms for the removal of foreign particles and invading organisms from the blood stream, the action of phagocytes, and so on.

The discovery and investigation of these assumed mechanisms constitutes to a certain extent an understanding of the living process, accord-

[2] In *The Wisdom of the Body* (New York: W. W. Norton, 1939).

ing to the views of those physiologists. I understand how a magician performs a trick if I can also perform it, and, similarly, I understand how a given physiological process occurs if I can build a replica or a model of it, and such replicas are in fact continually being built more and more frequently, as I just mentioned mechanical hearts, mechanical kidneys, mechanical lungs, and so on.

The philosophical question is: Has the old Cartesian notion of mechanism been finally vindicated by simply broadening the notion of mechanism sufficiently? Some people say "yes" and some keep saying "no," and still others say both "yes" and "no." Before we examine the question, it is interesting to see why some people keep saying "no," in view of the fact that so many of these things have been duplicated. If asked, "Why does blood coagulate when a blood vessel is breached?" they say, "Well, if it didn't coagulate when a blood vessel is breached it would run out and the organism would die." That focuses the attention on the purposefulness of the phenomenon. There was a time when only this answer could have been given.

But another way to answer is, "It coagulates because when fibrinogen comes in contact with oxygen certain things happen." Then you see the series of events that lead to coagulation of the blood as efficient, not ultimate causes. There is no purpose involved here; events are simply shown to lead from one to another. This is more and more often given as the answer nowadays.

Evolutionary questions can also be answered from two different points of view: from the Lamarckian point of view and from the Darwinian point of view. The former is teleological, the latter mechanistic.

I say "purposefulness" because I am used to this term. You can also consider it as "directiveness." But the question remains: Can the notion of purposefulness be dispensed with in any discussion of any observed behavior of an organism? Can all these processes be explained without any reference to what is going to happen? If we can construct mechanisms that duplicate the behavior of organisms, I think we have dispensed with "purpose" because mechanisms do not have any particular interest in maintaining themselves.

To cite another example: When an animal is thirsty it behaves in a variety of ways, all of which we interpret as "seeking water." Seemingly we cannot simply say that when the humidity of certain mucous membranes falls below a certain level such-and-such events will occur. We cannot say that because the events that occur cannot be unambiguously described. They vary with the circumstance.

If we are dealing with a complicated organism, such as a human being, then the behavior "seeking water" is just the generic name for a lot of different behaviors. The man may turn on a tap, or he may dig a well, or he may step into a bar, or he may say, "Give me some water," all of which we subsume under "seeking water."

But it does not describe what happens when the mucous membranes of his throat become dried up. To do this we have to say what muscles are going to jerk, and in what order. That is not what we observe. We observe a great variety of events which somehow, in our language, because of the teleological notions that we entertain we have subsumed under the term "seeking water"; but we have not actually described what happens.

Certainly the lower down the scale you go the more purely mechanistic are the systems you will find, generally speaking. Yet all of this complicated behavior is certainly a part of homeostasis for it serves ultimately to restore a certain balance. It is because the homeostatic behavior of higher organisms is so varied that one fails to see anything that characterizes all its forms except the ultimate result. One cannot unambiguously describe the process of events. One can, however, say that it leads to the ultimate result. Hence some people persist in the notion of purposefulness and resist explanations in terms of mechanisms.

PARSONS: *Cannot some such concept as goal directiveness, and so on, essentially be used as a way of avoiding these difficulties by focusing on certain problems to the exclusion of others, either because the others are not solved yet or because it would just not be economical to take that enormous detour? When you say the animal seeks a goal, it is an extremely convenient shortening, and it may be a framework in which certain facts can be legitimately and accurately described, even when the mechanisms by which this process goes on are unknown.*

RAPOPORT: Certainly. The objection is that people want to stop with such explanations. In other words, I hold the view, with many others, that behavior is not explained unless you can duplicate it.

SHAKOW: *This is a criterion of understanding; you test out your understanding by being able to reproduce it?*

RAPOPORT: Yes. To go back to my simpler homeostatic processes, for instance, coagulation of the blood: Saying that the salt level is maintained because the organism would die otherwise, that the organism seeks to maintain its salt level in the blood, is not sufficient any longer for a physiologist. He has to know how. He will understand if he can construct a model. By a "model" I mean a description in which each event will appear as the consequence of preceding events. You start with initial conditions and describe what is happening at the moment, and then you give a full description of what is going to happen as far as you can go.

The radical behaviorists will still persist in seeking reproducible models to account for all aspects of the living process, including homeostatic phenomena, in terms of stimulus-response relations. Their opponents maintain that this approach is sterile, and insist that somehow purposefulness should be included in the theory of living processes, particularly of those involving the behavior of higher organisms.

Here you have, then, the two extremes. Those are the people who say "yes" or "no" in answer to the Cartesian question, "Is it true that all living processes can be reduced to mechanisms?" The people who say "yes and no" are those who admit that the purely physiological models dealing with chemical and physical processes may be inadequate for explaining, let us say, complicated forms of behavior, but who recommend the extension of the notion of mechanism so as to permit the construction of models which will account for at least some purposeful behavior.

Some people (and I agree with them) say that these new mechanisms to account for purposeful behavior will have to involve the accumulation, storing, transformation and transmission of another kind of entity which is not force and which is not energy, and this new entity has been recently called information. The most hopeful sign of the possibility of relating this entity to ordinary physical observables seems to be the relation shown to exist between the mathematical expression for this entity and the thermodynamic quantity called "entropy," a physical quantity.

To see how this notion applies in developing a theory of purposeful behavior, consider the following example: Suppose we watch a robot which is simply a device on rollers able to move over a floor in any direction, which changes direction or stops when it receives certain signals from the floor. The floor is marked off in movable squares. One square is marked with one dot, another with two dots, another with three dots, another with four dots, and so on up to twenty-five, in an arbitrary order. This robot keeps rolling along and when it comes to the square with one dot on it, it stops. Then it rolls along again, hits the square with two dots on it, and stops again. Then it stops on the square with three dots, and so on up to twenty-five. Can this robot count? To find out, we shuffle the squares into different positions. But no matter where the squares happen to be the robot seeks out one first, two second, and so on. It seems that here is an example of purposeful behavior, and yet, of course, if you know the construction of robots you need not invoke purpose at all. You can easily construct a robot to do just that. It receives signals from the marked squares, and it is so fixed that when it receives a signal which one dot gives it, it stops. As it stops, automatically the "set" within it changes so that it will not stop until it receives the signal from two dots. When it stops the second time, again the "set" changes and it will not stop again until it receives the three-dot signal, and so on. So, no matter how we arrange these squares, eventually it will hit the square with one dot, and then it will keep rolling along, stopping at all the squares in order as though it were "counting" them.

A robot has certain connections within it to which we can refer, perhaps facetiously, as its nervous system. This nervous system, of course, can be represented by a blueprint, wherein the relays, switches, wires and so on are marked with the conventional diagrammatic notations. We can represent such a nervous system more abstractly. Instead of making a blueprint of it and marking all the connections, we describe such a nervous system by a set of propositions of the following form: "If so, then so, unless so and so, in which case so; but if so or so, then so and so."

These propositions are actually directions for the robot, specifying how it is to behave in any circumstance which may arise during the course of its activity. Once we know how the behavior is prescribed, there is no mystery concerning its behavior because from this set of statements, from this set of logical equations, the robot can be constructed.

Its intelligence then disappears, so to speak. However, here is a very curious thing: If, instead of saying "If so, then so and so," we simply make one proposition, describing the end result only, namely, "Seek out the numbers in their order," then somehow we make the robot again appear to us to be intelligent and purposeful. But when the robot's behavior is stated as a program, it does not appear intelligent.

Behavior appears less and less purposeful the more the detailed aspects of it can be organized under a few rules. Information theory provides a quantitative measure of the state of our knowledge concerning the repertoire of activity of a mechanism. If we ourselves build the mechanism, we know presumably its whole repertoire, and no purpose is included. But if the mechanism is given, and we are trying to infer its repertoire from its behavior, we have what Wiener calls the black box problem.[3] The engineer's problem is to construct a mechanism that will behave in a given way. The black box problem is the inverse, that of inferring the mechanism from the behavior, which is immensely more difficult than the direct problem of construction.

Many mechanisms which achieve an invariant final result under varying conditions have been constructed during the past war. Called servo-

[3] N. Wiener, *Cybernetics* (New York: John Wiley, 1948).

mechanisms, they are target-seeking torpedoes; anti-aircraft guns which correct for altitude, speed and so on; and many other murderous gadgets. We may very well say that the principle of homeostasis is involved in the construction of such devices, namely, the corrective principle, which operates by signals from the environment, by means of which information is transmitted as to the difference between the existing state of affairs and the desired end result.

A torpedo seems to seek its target. We know its construction. It is simply a mechanism which receives signals from the environment, showing how the direction differs from the direction to the target, and thereby the correction is made, and so the torpedo seems to seek the target. One of the simplest homeostatic devices, the thermostat, works on this principle. The thermometer relays information to the furnace as to whether the temperature which it registers is higher or lower than the temperature at which the thermostat is set. If the thermometer is higher than the given temperature, the furnace goes off. If it is lower, the furnace goes on. All the furnace has to do is to choose between two things—off and on. If the decisions are equally likely, the choice involves one unit of information which has been called by theorists "one bit," an abbreviation of "binary unit."

Now to turn to the organism's behavior: An approach to the theory of the nervous system as an organ for transmitting and storing information was initiated by McCulloch and Pitts.[4] They argued as follows: Suppose a nervous system consists of elements called neurons, and the only property of such elements is that they are either firing or not firing.

Suppose we have a network of such neurons connected by axones. McCulloch and Pitts have considered the characteristics of nets composed of such neurons. The behavior of such nets can be best described by reference to a diagram (Figure 9, below).

If the entire blueprint of the nervous system can be given, all its behavior patterns can be inferred. Conversely, given any pattern of behavior, we can also build a blueprint of the neurons such as will duplicate that behavior. It does not mean that we are assuming the historic 1:1 correspondence between stimuli patterns and response patterns, because it is conceivable that certain stimuli will set up certain activities within the net which will continue because of the circular connections which may be in the net. So conditions within the net may be constantly changing and when other stimuli enter different responses may result from the same

[4] W. S. McCulloch and W. Pitts, "A Logical Calculus of the Ideas Immanent in Nervous Activity," *Bulletin of Mathematical Biophysics*, V (1943), 115.

stimuli and vice versa. Learning is included, and even such things as spontaneous responses, because once the activity has set in, neurons can be activated without additional outside stimulation.

McCulloch and Pitts have shown that any kind of behavior process can theoretically be accounted for by some such device as this.[5] But this does not mean that they have offered an acceptable model of the nervous system. When one tries to construct nets to account for complicated be-

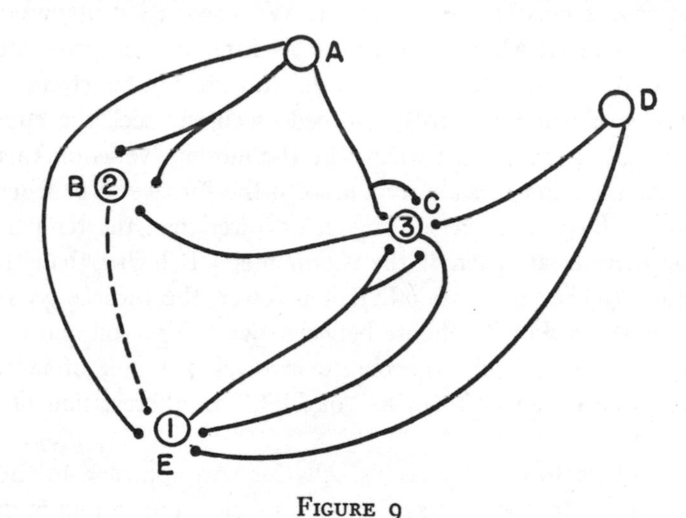

FIGURE 9

SCHEME OF A NEURONAL NET WORK

The circles are neurons. The lines are the axones. The little buttons at the ends of axones are the end bulbs. When a neuron fires, all of the end bulbs at the ends of its axones become "active." They can then make the neurons upon which they impinge fire at the next instant under certain conditions.

One of these conditions is determined by the threshold of the neuron designated by the number inside the circle. Thus, if the threshold is 2, it takes 2 end bulbs, active simultaneously at the instant t, to fire the neuron at the instant t + 1. This is the case with neuron B. Thus if A fires at t, B will fire at t + 1, but if only C fires at t, B will not fire at t + 1, because there is only one end bulb from C impinging on A.

The other condition involves inhibition indicated by the dotted axones, such as from B to E, ending in an "inhibitory" end bulb. Such an end bulb cancels the activity of all other simultaneously active end bulbs. Thus if B fires at t, E will *not* fire at t + 1, regardless of what stimulation it receives from the other end bulbs.

You can now verify that the conditions of firing can be described by statements such as:

"B will fire at t + 1, if A fires at t."

"C will fire at t + 1, if A and D, or A and E, or E and D fire at t."

"E will fire at t + 1, if A or C or D but not B fire at t."

[5] *Ibid.*

havior, one finds so many objections that from a practical point of view the theory is worthless. However, it is extremely important from a conceptual point of view, as I will try to show.

I want to stress once more that the significance of the McCulloch-Pitts theory is in no way dependent upon its applicability in explaining behavior in terms of neural anatomy. For one thing, the behavior of the "neurons" is much too rigid. Secondly, the correspondence between behavior patterns and nets is not one to one. There is always an infinity of possible nets to account for a particular behavior pattern. Third, there is as yet no known way of analyzing actual behavior patterns of organisms into elementary component parts, such as muscle twitchings. If all behavior patterns could be schematized and you could say, "This is what happens in terms of muscle twitchings," then it might be possible to construct a net to account for it. But we do not know how to do it. As I talk now, can you tell me what muscles I move?

The only question I am raising in this presentation is the question of reduction. The question is, can we provide the links? At present we cannot and so must jump. We do not know how to explain the behavior of a human being in terms of the component constituents—muscle twitchings and so on, so we leave the question and say, "Let us take the behavior units themselves for our elements."

PARSONS: *And partly because different physiological processes are often equivalent from the behavior point of view. For example, the physiological process of speaking and of writing is totally different but the information conveyed may be the same.*

RAPOPORT: The worst thing about it is that according to some early estimates the number of neurons required to account for some rather simple behavior patterns probably exceeds the number of neurons available in any nervous system, or perhaps the total number of atoms available in the universe.

In view of all these difficulties the theory is worthless in the sense of immediate application to physiological psychology. However, it is of great importance as a conceptual framework. One can well ask what sort of over-all behavior are the McCulloch-Pitts nets capable of, and what sort of parameters does this behavior depend upon? Perhaps in due time such parameters can be referred to other parameters involving the behavior of organisms, for example, abstracting abilities, conditionality of response, acuity of discrimination, learning, memory capacity, and so on.

In view of this, some of us are studying McCulloch-Pitts nets, but not rigid nets where it is known how every neuron is connected to every other neuron, but starting at the other end where nothing at all is known about how the neurons are connected and trying to derive the over-all properties of such nets. We are trying to see if a net of neurons picked completely at random can possibly give certain characteristics of behavior which are reminiscent of homeostatic phenomena.

I have listed six elements of a homeostatic phenomenon.

First of all, we are looking for a steady state of activity. Such a steady state is not necessarily presented by a constant magnitude, but by an invariant of a function. For example, the amount of water in a vessel can be arbitrarily fixed and will remain constant. You put a gallon of water in a container and it is there.

That is not what we mean by homeostasis. The simplest case of homeostasis would be if we kept pouring water in and water would keep running out. The water would always be changing in the container. But in spite of the change, something about that water would be constant, namely, its volume. However, if a vessel is so constructed that the outflow is some function of the amount of water in it, then the steady state amount will depend both on the rate of inflow and on parameters characteristic of the construction of the vessel.

The *second* is threshold. Up to a certain point an input into the system has no effect, but beyond the critical point it has a pronounced effect, often independent of further influence.

HENRY: *Can one really say it has no effect up to a certain point? The body is so constructed as to have a certain resistance. Actually, is not the body doing something?*

RAPOPORT: The trouble comes if you think of every function as continuous. Then the threshold appears as a contradiction. There are, however, mathematical systems that do show threshold effects. These are systems with several equilibrium points, some unstable. When a disturbance carries the state of the system beyond an unstable equilibrium point, it may very quickly pass to the next equilibrium or "explode" altogether. This multiplicity of equilibria is the *third* characteristic of homeostasis.

The *fourth* characteristic of homeostasis and one of the most distinctive is a pre-set response, exemplified by a cat jumping at a running mouse. The stimuli, instead of eliciting a continuous response, seem to "add up." The cat seems to do nothing but just sit, computing what is going on, and then—bang! the response occurs, and the response is a result of adding up of the stimuli.

SPIEGEL: *Is this different from threshold?*

RAPOPORT: The threshold is different in this case. The response is pre-set. It is calculated in advance, and when the trigger mechanism operates the thing is done. Now, of course, the cat is doing something in one sense, but from another point of view nothing happens until the jump. We are fixing our attention on the jump.

THOMPSON: *Do you mean the jump could have taken place earlier, but for some conditions a summation took place and the range was stretched to the maximum?*

RAPOPORT: Let us say the cat is chasing the mouse. We will say that the stimuli from the mouse would be a feedback to the cat, and the cat would correct its direction of sunning depending on where the mouse was. That would be a continuous response. But when the cat is stalking the mouse, something inside the cat must be determining the future sudden act (the leap). I call this a pre-set response.

The *fifth* characteristic of homeostasis is the filter response, or resonance. If the input varies over a certain set of values, the response occurs only when the impetus uses certain definite discrete values. There is a double threshold, above and below.

An example of that would be the recognizing of a pitch. If somebody strikes a key on the piano, outside of certain limits I will not say it is C, but inside the limits I will say it is C. A physiological example is found in inspiration and expiration, processes associated with different frequencies of stimuli from the medulla impinging on the muscles involved in breathing. At one frequency the stimuli call for inspiration; at another frequency the stimuli elicit expiration. Or take the ordinary phenomenon of recognition. How do we recognize a word or a face or anything else? You can certainly distort it to a great degree, but it has to be within a certain range to be recognized.

Finally, the *sixth* characteristic of homeostasis is learning and feedback. The functional relationship between an input and an output is itself modified as a result of the output. We have shown how that operates in the case of a robot, where each successive act of the robot changes the set inside it so that the next response will be not to the same stimulus but to a different stimulus.

SPIEGEL: *Is it a combination of all these elements that describes what we ordinarily call compensatory mechanisms in the homeostatic system? Are these all changes in the external environment? If so, then the system itself does something in order to restore the change. Do we need something other than what you have described?*

RAPOPORT: Homeostasis can be looked at in these terms. I have not considered whether they are all unified about the idea of restoration. All these other things, such as filter response and pre-set response that appear to be elements of purposefulness have to be discussed in relation to homeostasis.

I would now like to go into the mathematics of the elements of homeostasis, and point out some of the difficulties involved.

Take the threshold notion first. A threshold involves a discontinuity. On the other hand, the mathematics underlying physiological theory is largely a mathematics of continuous properties. In such theories the threshold has to be introduced as a special assumption. To take an early example, the following equation has been proposed to underlie the excitation of a peripheral nerve by an electric current.[6]

$$\frac{d\epsilon}{dt} = AI - a\epsilon$$

Here ϵ is the concentration of an excitatory substance supposed to accumulate at the cathode when a current, I, is applied to the nerve, while A and a are constants characteristic of the nerve. The crucial thing in this situation is that when a constant current of a certain magnitude is applied for a certain time, the so-called "spike potential," the excitation of the nerve proper, appears at the cathode and propagates along the nerve. However, this phenomenon, being essentially a discontinuous event, cannot be obtained as a consequence of that equation alone—an additional assumption must be added, namely, that when ϵ reaches a certain critical value, h, excitation occurs and is propagated. The equation and the assumption *together* can then account for a number of observed quantitative relations, such as that between strength of current and time of excitation.

The ad-hoc character of the threshold assumption is unsatisfactory, of course, from the theoretical point of view. One is motivated to seek a mechanism underlying it. G. Karreman has postulated such a mechanism, involving ionic equilibria, membrane permeabilities of nerve fibers, transport of potassium across membrances, etc., and on the basis of the chemical kinetics of this mechanism has *derived* a discontinuity in the process, that is, a threshold effect.[7]

The method is typical in the theoretico-mathematical approach. One asks what sort of assumptions will lead through mathematical derivation

[6] H. A. Blair, "On the Intensity-Time Relation for Stimulation by Electric Current," *Journal of General Physiology*, XV (1932), 709.

[7] "Contribution to the Mathematical Biology of Excitation with Particular Emphasis on Changes in Membrane Permeability and on Threshold Phenomena," *Bulletin of Mathematical Biophysics*, XIII (1951), 189.

to the kinds of results observed (in our case a sharp discontinuity in the time course of the potential across the nerve membrane). If one has found a set of such assumptions, one then asks what *further* consequences can be deduced from them. If these consequences agree with other seemingly unrelated phenomena or (in some fortunate cases) if they actually predict results observed in specially constructed experiments, the mathematical model is considered a good one. It yields dividends, so to speak.

Karreman has derived the threshold effect from physico-chemical considerations. Such effects can also be derived from purely mathematical considerations applied to the structure of neural nets, thus relating threshold not only to the behavior of a single nerve but also to the over-all behavior of an idealized nervous system. An example of such a model is given in the so-called random net. A random net consists of neurons of the McCulloch-Pitts type, which I discussed earlier, where nothing is known about how the neurons are connected. In fact, it is assumed that complete chaos reigns, that the probability of a direct connection between any two neurons is the same for all pairs. If, now, h is the *individual* neuron threshold in the McCulloch-Pitts sense, the random net *as a whole* exhibits a threshold effect, that is to say, if a certain fraction of its neurons chosen at random is stimulated from the outside, then the excitation will spread to a much larger fraction or, on the contrary, will die out, depending on the size of the fraction initially stimulated. There is thus a *critical* fraction such that if you excite less than it, the excitation will die down, and if you excite more than it, the excitation will spread. This situation certainly illustrates threshold and other homeostatic elements besides, for example, different equilibrium states. The random net can be shown to have both stable and unstable equilibrium states of excitation. If it is a stable state, then small fluctuations from that state will tend to be restored, while large fluctuations, which carry the excitation beyond an unstable equilibrium point, will generally not be restored but will carry the excitation into the next stable state.

Similarly pre-set responses can be accounted for in a random net, if it is supposed that certain subthreshold stimuli feed into it during the presetting. They will not be observed by themselves but will play a part in determining the equilibrium at which excitation will be established when a super-threshold stimulation occurs.

To summarize the problem of relating structure to function of a nervous system (of which the homeostatic problems are special cases): Given a time series of inputs to be mapped on a corresponding time series of outputs, construct a net of neurons which will make the mapping.

McCulloch and Pitts attempted to solve the problem exactly. The inputs and outputs were defined in terms of the firing patterns described by specifying the state of each neuron. Their nets, accordingly, were blueprints, where connections are exactly specified. The random net approach is an attempt to solve the problem only for certain over-all features thought to be characteristic of nervous systems—threshold effects, equilibrium states, pre-set responses, etc. The nets are not described by detailed blueprints but only by over-all parameters—number of axones per neuron, distribution of individual thresholds, connection biases, if any, etc.

We have shown in particular cases that such problems can be solved. If more involved input-output mappings are given, the hope is that such mappings can be analyzed into components of simple functions which would allow the construction of more or less random nets to realize these functions. Such an approach seems promising because it would obviate the necessity of minute construction of the mechanism. The nets would have a certain amount of leeway. There would always be errors in it, but within a certain tolerance, one could have approximately what one wants. One could save an enormous amount of theorizing (or engineering, if the nets should be actually constructed) by not specifying which neurons go to which but only specifying the connection biases and the distributions of the various parameters.

PARSONS: *That is what the sciences of behavior are trying to do, physiologically.*

RAPOPORT: That's right. They throw away specifications, ignoring which muscle jerks after which other muscle. You don't want the behavior to be rigid, because if you prescribe it once and for all, and prescribe also the sort of things we have been able to learn, you may not have foreseen certain other things. But the random net approach fits that requirement, because all you are demanding is that output be a certain function of the input within a certain tolerance. Occasionally it may hit on something which is different. Randomness implies a certain flexibility. This is about the state of the study of homeostasis among the mathematical biologists at the present time.

EMERSON: *This is a remarkably clear and concise presentation of homeostasis. I would emphasize a few principles that I think will supplement and help the concept.*

First, the directive principle is contained in evolutionary selection, and this in large measure resolves our problem of teleology.

Second, I would stress convergence. The mechanisms that produce similar effects may be various.

Third, *circular causation or feedback*, which Rapoport also emphasized—simply stated, the effect may influence continued or repeated causes.

Fourth, *disequilibrium may be homeostatic*. Asymmetries may be necessary for action, inhibition or maintenance.

Fifth, *individual and group homeostasis* may be contrasted. The external environment of one unit becomes the internal environment of the more inclusive unit. This emphasizes one of the main considerations in relating, let us say, a physiological system to a behavior system, because protoplasmic integration within a protoplasmically contiguous organism may switch to behavior integration in a protoplasmically discontinuous system—that is, a group. Therefore, behavior becomes homeostatic in a group system, as contrasted to physiological homeostasis.

PARSONS: This last named is particularly interesting to me because in some of our work we are phrasing the principle problem, that of the orderly statement of the less and more inclusive systems and their relations to each other, exactly in the terms you state—that what is internal environment to one is external to another in the behavior field.

The process I am working on now is that of child development. The child at birth is not really integrated in any system of social interaction. It then becomes integrated closely in a mother-child system, which is a subsystem of the family, a larger system. He then becomes more fully integrated in the family as the larger system, and less exclusively with the mother. Finally, the family is a subsystem of a larger system that we might call residual community system, and the last major transition the child has to make is integration in the community independent of family orientation.

So we are analyzing a process which includes transitions through a series of such lesser or more inclusive systems, each of which is homeostatic in certain respects.

SPIEGEL: I would like to use your case to clarify this very abstract model. As I see it, it describes a situation entirely from within. This model does not say anything about the characteristics of the external or environmental or larger system; is that correct?

RAPOPORT: The thing to which the model refers need not be specified at all. It may be a nervous system and it also may be a clock. I asked this question: What are the mathematical characteristics of homeostatic phenomena? Here are some simple ones. Can we, without too much specification, by making random connections between elements, by imposing certain over-all characteristics, approach such a state of affairs? To a certain extent we can.

The next logical question is: To make for more specificity, what do we introduce? The community is a community, no matter how things are connected. In other words, one community may be entirely different from others as to who knows whom, but there will be, nevertheless, certain general characteristics. For one thing, on the average each person knows so many people. Secondly, there will be a certain bias of personal relationships. If A and B both know C, the chances that A knows C will be better than average. Thirdly, there will be a certain symmetry. If I talk to you, the chances that you talk to me will be better than average.

By these statistical parameters one can perhaps describe a system. Having described the system, one then tries to describe a process within it. What will happen to a piece of information through a community? How will it spread? If the general statistical parameters of a community or a neural net are given, how will an activity spread through it? How will it die down or be stopped? What has to be imposed on the system for the responses to the information to be integrated so that events happen in a certain order?

You start from the completely random process, instead of trying as McCulloch-Pitts have tried and the engineers are trying, to describe the thing in all details as if you are constructing the mechanism.

EMERSON: *What is called structure process is in part the common phenomenon of* division of labor *that is involved in more complex systems. A part of the division of labor may be a function of a homeostatic mechanism itself. As a structure is formed a function is delegated to one portion as contrasted to another portion. This structure may not be anatomical only, but for the time being a psychological function may be associated with a formed concept.*

One individual may delegate a function to another individual in the group. All of this is certainly incorporated within our concept of levels of integration plus homeostasis.

GRINKER: *As Rapoport brought out, it is not easy to explain division of labor, but it is the change in the whole system which is effected by development, by growth, by evolution, in which the equilibrium changes along with it, but nevertheless the system itself changes. Therefore, in terms of learning and evolution, there is something expansive. Are you contending that that is a form of homeostasis in that it is a response to the stimulus, or is it an internal process?*

EMERSON: *No; it is a little different. The course of evolution at any given level is in the direction of an increased homeostatic control. In other* words, it is the operation of homeostatic mechanisms in all their infinite complexities that produces the directive selection principle or choice of surviving systems. An organism or group survives that solves its problems of homeostatic control better than its forebears or its competitors.

DEUTSCH: You would say process A is more homeostatic than process B if the average deviations from the level to be maintained are smaller. In this case, homeostasis is related to the amplitude of the deviations. The second would be that a process is "more homeostatic" if the range of loads which will not throw it out of gear is larger. Finally, of course, you could think of a learning process that is increasingly capable of dealing with one range of loads, but becomes increasingly sensitive or increasingly easily destroyed by other ranges of loads.

I am not sure, therefore, whether there is a measurable general homeostasis. I cannot easily imagine a measure of over-all learning capacity or "all-over" feedback performances.

I think homeostasis was originally a qualitative concept in the days of Bernard and Cannon. In this original image you do not separate the notion of an equilibrium (which we may or may not have) from the load put on the system from the outside, the gain in the response of the system for restoring some original state, and the lag which this response may have in it. The result may be that in this interplay of load, lag, gain and lead the system never gets back to its earlier state. It actually may end up with mapping out a time pattern. The national economy may never get back to normal—whatever "normal" is supposed to be. Is this still homeostasis?

EMERSON: To answer that I would say that there are almost an infinite number of phenomena that could be brought under the concept, but that they have a certain degree of independence of each other so that the concept of homeostasis does not mean unity of phenomena but rather multiplicity of phenomena, and our task is to investigate. Our present knowledge indicates that wide periodic and non-periodic fluctuations may be maintained by homeostatic mechanisms, providing these fluctuations are functional and they often are.

At the present time, at least, homeostasis is a remarkably adequate concept for quantitative measurement. Through this concept we can make comparisons between phenomena that, without it, are very hard to compare, because we don't have a quantitative relationship in quantitative terms that is applicable to the different phenomena.

For instance, behavior is contrasted to a physiological mechanism. Those are very difficult to compare unless you have a concept like homeostasis that can be quantified and the quantifications compared.

MORRIS: *Can you indicate what type of quantification you mean?*

EMERSON: *This equilibrium, so-called, may be a control or maintenance of disequilibrium, if disequilibrium has a function.*

RAPOPORT: The difference between steady state and equilibrium can be pointed out.

EMERSON: *That's right. You mentioned dynamic equilibrium. Dynamics may be the maintenance and control of an asymmetry in the system, rather than a static equilibrium.*

RAPOPORT: There are numerous examples of quantification. The last system I talked about gives definitely the threshold beyond which it cannot be disturbed without going into another steady state. To the extent the organism is capable of withstanding outside temperature, it has a temperature control; the temperature may vary so much but not more.

Even behavior may be in dynamic equilibrium. We might ask: "To what extent can a person stand hardship?" Or, to make it more precise, "How much does it take to make him go crazy?" "How much does it take to make him behave aggressively?"

SPIEGEL: *A question about Rapoport's model: Does this conceptual model allow for internal differentiation and the establishment, let's say, of a smaller circular system if, somehow, the input load should become greater?*

RAPOPORT: I started with the random net because it was the pole opposite to where McCulloch-Pitts started. Even with the completely random net you can get homeostatic behavior.

TOMAN: *The importance of Anatol Rapoport's formulation was not that he took the conception of homeostasis in its original classic physiological form and forced it on all kinds of phenomena, but rather that in trying to arrive at a suitable model for a system which showed the optical illusion of a stationary state, he also arrived at some rules that had to do with shifts in state.*

A certain confusion rises in the discussion about evolution, learning and irreversibility, between the state of a system and the information in the system. Information does not have the same kind of reversibility as over-all states. For example, you can set up a system which has a number of alternative states, so that it can be kicked from one to the other, and it can be reversed. But this is not a property of the differentiation or adaptation of the system which is irreversible.

RAPOPORT: Reversibility and irreversibility, if it applies in this case, will mean: A disturbance which results in the restoring of the original state, that state of affairs we call reversible; if the disturbance causes the system to move to another state, then it is irreversible.

EMERSON: *The well known phenomenon of regressive evolution may clarify this. It is a universal principle that every organism has once had adaptations in its ancestry that are now lost. Involved in this phenomenon is evolution toward ecological position. The species may have moved to what we call a favorable environment, where it may not have to control its physiological activities in certain respects as it had to in the earlier environment. So it regresses, losing some of the adaptations necessary in the more widely fluctuating environment. Homeostasis may be more easily maintained by ecological position in a little-fluctuating environment than by elaborate homeostatic mechanisms in a widely fluctuating environment, so there may be an evolutionary advance by means of a loss or regression of needless homeostatic adaptations.*

Or it may move toward a greater control but it may share this control with other organisms. For instance, the species may have the necessity, in one environment, of synthesizing an amino acid; but if it moves into association with other organisms that synthesize the amino acid for it, and to which it has a food relationship, it may lose this genetic ability to synthesize that particular amino acid.

A much more obvious case of regressive evolution is that seen in the evolution of animals. All animals have lost their ability to carry on photosynthesis possessed by their plant ancestors. They are able to do this by living with and depending upon plants that did carry on photosynthesis. Therefore, part of the picture of increasing homeostatic control is division of labor, which may not only be within the organism or the species but it may be between individuals in the interspecies system, or it may be between species in the ecological system, where often an increase in general homeostatic control may involve a decrease in the homeostatic control of an individual or a species.

I am almost certain, but I will leave it to the rest of you, that these phenomena will show relationship to the social behavior of humans. There will be regressions of former adjustments as the individual becomes incorporated into a more inclusive unit where these functions are taken care of by others—division of labor among humans. You may also find that the regression of a former individual adaptation is made possible by a greater homeostatic control by a group.

So it really is progressive evolution, but the level of integration is changed. Evolution may be aimed at a higher or more inclusive system of homeostasis with an increase in optimal conditions of existence and survival. The concept of the optimum means that we can come back to a quantitative measurement, and that is our big task in fact-finding—to discover these optima and their relationships.

EDITOR: *Homeostasis was reconsidered from a mathematical point of view exemplified by the analysis of random nets. If one can construct mechanisms demonstrating behavior, "purpose" may be dispensed with. Behavior is truly explained when it can be duplicated, for if one can build a mechanism whose repertoire is known, purpose can be unimportant. However, to infer possible behavior from an already built, unknown mechanism is difficult. Rapoport discussed the mathematics of six characteristics of homeostasis which can be built into a mechanism. There followed a discussion by Emerson, dealing with homeostasis in living organisms and bring out supplementary concepts.*

CHAPTER EIGHTEEN

STABILITY VS. ADAPTATION: SOME SPECULATIONS ON THE EVOLUTION OF DYNAMIC RECIPROCATING MECHANISMS

Presentation by James E. P. Toman

TRANSLATING Claude Bernard literally, "The fixity of the internal environment is the condition of the free life," [1] I shall analyze this concept and then consider some of the levels of biological organization where there is an apparent contradiction between the tendencies toward maintenance of stability and toward permanent alteration.

The fixity of the internal environment has preoccupied classical and modern physiologists; fixity in the sense of maintenance of those processes in the internal environment which seem to remain stable over a long period of time—fixity of oxygen and carbon dioxide tensions, of fluid and salt balance, of levels of important metabolites, and so on. But as pointed out by Rapoport, there is also the possibility of alternative states of fixity.

In the mammalian organism, stabilities of the sort I have just mentioned are ordinarily maintained within relatively narrow limits. It is equally true that as between the resting state and the state of rather vigorous exercise, many of these values are changed. There is a very intricate set of mechanisms for the poising of the values at new optimal levels for

[1] *Leçons sur les Phenomenes de la Vie Commune aux Animaux et aux Vegetaux* (Paris: 1878).

different states of activity. Therefore, I think we must broaden the conception of homeostasis to include the possibility of maintenance of different levels of regulation.

In the internal milieu, what is fixed is not only a set of properties that seem to guarantee survival but also something of the external environment itself. Claude Bernard thought of the mammalian organism, and the multicellular organism in general, as containing within itself a portion of the primordial sea, which it maintains in some past historical optimum condition.

The organism also contains a continually increasing quantity of information about its environment. Here I am thinking not just of conditioning in those animals which have complex nervous systems but also about chemical conditioning in the simplest kinds of organisms. Furthermore, it could be said that organisms contain, in their genetic make-up, past experience as part of their internal environment. Here we are no longer concerned with the steady state of the organism over a brief period of a lifetime, but with its stability over generations.

Claude Bernard spoke of the fixity of the internal environment as being the condition of the free life. Not only physiologists but, to a considerable extent, psychologists, psychiatrists and others, think of this word "free" as if the major consideration were the avoidance of hostile changes in the external environment, that is, freedom from fluctuations. But freedom has positive connotations also, among them the freedom to utilize, which is a major basis of change in the organism.

Let us approach the apparent paradox between homeostasis and adaptation by asking: What is the simplest form of life which we can visualize at all? At what stage of complexity were the self-restoring mechanisms built in? In the primordial seas there were probably a great many simple molecular species. We surmise that over a long period in history, fairly large polymers were temporarily formed. For the most part, the history of such polymers must have been that over a long time many were both formed and disintegrated, and there was no growth, nothing but the accidental association of random molecular species.

It takes something more to introduce growth. We doubt that one of these polymers hit upon a direct scheme for utilizing other molecules and reproducing itself in a direct way. But with the development of many kinds of polymers accidentally, by the very nature of things, their surfaces in turn became potential enzymes or frameworks or templates for the deposition and organization of other molecular species, forming new molecules not identical with the original polymers, but in a sense their mirror image.

Assuming that these new structures could split from the old, at some stage there must have developed a possibility that each one of the new molecules in turn could serve as the framework for a mirror image of itself. This is the beginning of a chemical feedback system, with the possibility of true growth. Figure 10 shows such a hypothetical system. A and B are polymers. Both of these may be a polysaccharides—they need not be proteins. If A can last long enough to produce more than one B, and B can last

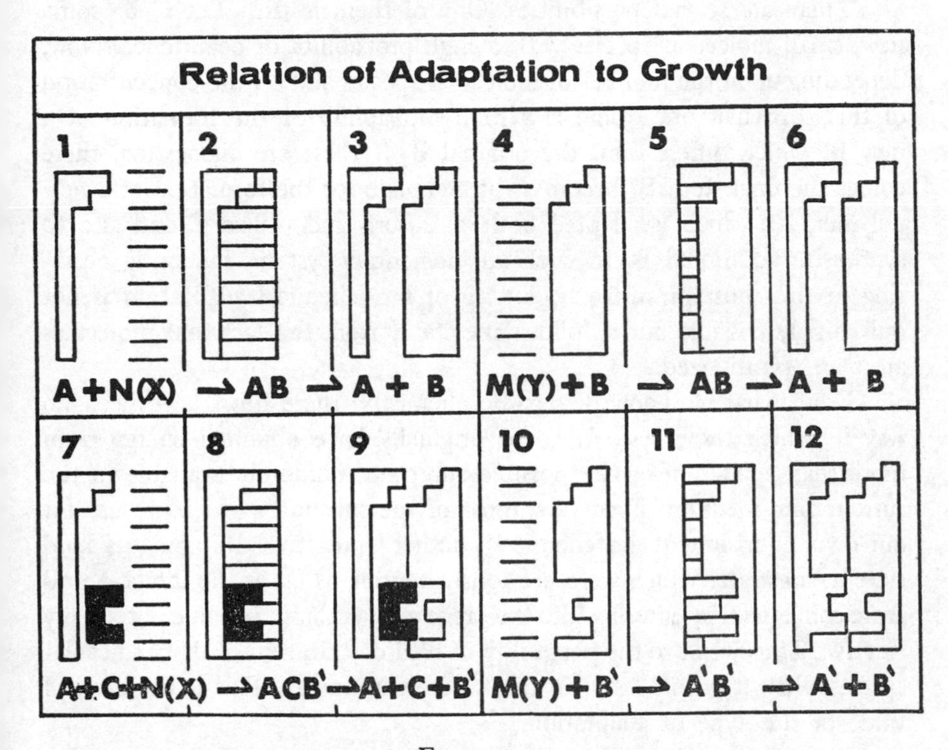

FIGURE 10

DEPENDENCE OF ADAPTATION ON GROWTH

This schema shows a hypothetical complex A acting as an organizing surface for synthesis of n molecules of substrate X into a complex AB, which then splits into its components A and B. Complex B can now serve as a template for synthesis of n molecules of substrate Y into a new molecule of A, and the reciprocal progress may now go on stably in the presence of sufficient substrate.

If a new complex, C, becomes trapped in the process of synthesis of B, a different template, B^1, will be formed. Therefore, a new form of A, A^1, will result. Both of the new components, A^1 and B^1, have been "adapted" by C and in effect perpetuate a "chemical memory" of C.

long enough to produce more than one A, then it is possible to have a reproducing reciprocating template system. The gain may be greater than one, and depends upon the stability of each of the two systems and on the probability of formation of more than one product of each template. The turnover rate for the number of B's produced, with A as the enzyme, has to be greater than one B per unit lifetime of A. Another property of this feedback system poses, at the lowest possible level, the question of memory, of adaptation or of the carrying along of environmental changes. What happens when some smaller, new molecular species intervenes, at the time the synthesis of B is taking place?

There are several possibilities. One of them is this: Let C be some new, small molecular species with a high probability of occurrence. Now, depending upon the number of molecular species and on the concentration of this particular one, there is a high probability of the formation of a new B_1 which differs from the original B. If these are dissociated, there comes the final step: B_1 becomes the template for the formation of a new polymer, A_1, which is adapted both to adsorb and utilize C and also to synthesize additional B. In such an elementary system, randomly occurring in this most primitive beginning of life, chemical adaptation is not only highly possible but it follows inevitably from the fact that molecules are being synthesized.

From what we know of organic chemistry, there must have been no way in which these systems could originally have obtained energy from more than a fraction of the possible substrates randomly available in the surrounding medium. Even now most of the substrates which we use for our own nourishment are chemically rather unreactive. But by this kind system, substrates which were previously neutral, as far as the intact A and B are concerned, by entering into the process of synthesis, become potentially reactive. Thus we have the possibility of future utilization of that molecular species when it occurs again in the fluid environment. This is the survival value of this type of adaptation.

It also brings with it certain disadvantages. Since substrate C now becomes reactive with respect to the enzyme upon which it can be adsorbed, large concentrations may swamp the system, an eventuality which would not have happened originally when the same molecules were presented to the neutrally responding material for the first time.

The next evolutionary step in this system is simply the cohesion of the system itself; that is, a strong tendency among the polymers, whether polysaccharide or protein or other, to band together. When this is the case, you have the beginning of a system with an interior and an exterior.

If cohesion and growth of mass take place, certain new solutions to the problem of stability become possible. In the first place, there will be the tendency, obviously, for all utilizable molecules to be already handled before they penetrate to the interior. Therefore, the interior is less exposed, potentially, to the swamping effect of large changes in concentration of the utilizable substrates. That means a greater tendency toward continuity of the same molecular species at the interior than at the exterior.

However, there is still the possibility of continued chemical adaptation. Although the concentration of the utilizable species tends to fall off toward the interior, the completely new and neutral substrates would do so only on the basis of diffusion gradient and not on the basis of their utilization. Thus both the adaptive and stabilizing functions are favored at the interior, while energy-yielding reactions predominate toward the surface.

I would be inclined to believe that we are seeing at this level the first examples of homeostasis in the more classical sense, that is, the setting up of a system that tends to maintain the stability of the organism. We know of no such primitive organisms at the present time. A virus is not an organism since it is not a self-producing system. It reproduces in reciprocity with constituents of the bodies of other animals or plants. Some of the viruses themselves, if one can call a bacteriophage a virus, already begin to show a duplex structure, but apparently insufficient for their independent propagation.

We now have started thc process of differentiation with the beginning of a more continuous, more conservative and stable germ plasm internally, and a more metabolically reactive system externally. The unity of the contradictory properties of stability and adaptation lies in the interaction between the interior and exterior of the differentiated cell. And still this elementary cell carries with it the possibility of considerable chemical adaptation.

Whatever the mechanism of cell division may be, the dispersion of cells tends to work against continuity of species, since no two cells can have identical environments. The next step in the stabilization of species is the fusion of two organisms under conditions of stress, which is the very basis of the system of sexual reproduction. One does not see this in bacterial species but in a great many other unicellular forms. It is common to find that under unfavorable environmental conditions there occurs a fusion (even when recognizable stable sexes are not yet determined) of like organisms which are not really alike but which have somewhat different paths, somewhat different chemical memories. The conception of sexual reproduction as a pooling of information may not be current, but it seems to me to be an important step in homeostasis, at least in the simplest organisms. In much more highly differentiated organisms where the sexual process of reproduction has become the only means of continuity of species, it also becomes a factor for variation as well as stability. But at the most elementary level, where it began, it must have been a means of pooling chemical experience which had survival value because it was the ultimate combined chemical utilization potential of the combining organisms. The reciprocity between sexual and asexual reproduction represents a new level of integration between stability and adaptation.

This is not intended to be a complete picture of evolution from the primordial slime up to man, but only of some elementary levels at which the beginnings of homeostatic mechanisms may be imagined.

EMERSON: *I might make one or two remarks briefly at this point. There is some confusion in your use of the word "adaptation." It might be wise to separate the concept of variability, which you postulated through your diagrams, as contrasted to adaptation related to function. Variability might be non-functional. A mutation is much less likely to be an adaptation than to be deleterious and hence to be eliminated because non-adapted. On the other hand, adaptation requires a selective process operating within a degree of variability, and you used these two terms as if they were interrelated.*

I agree with you that sex is a mechanism involving homeostasis. It might clarify the issue to put it this way: There is the function of maintaining and replicating the system, which I would call the function of heredity. It is a conservative function. It keeps that which has already been acquired. Then there is also the function of creating a change toward producing new potentialities. Sex in part is a balance between these. In large measure (and we can actually measure this), it is a conservative hereditary system. Over 99% of the total function of sex is that of heredity as contrasted with creativity. Too much conservativism would not allow for evolution. Too much variability would destroy accumulated adaptation, so it has to acquire a balance, and the fact of this balance is certainly being demonstrated by modern genetic experimentation. The balance is the homeostatic function of sexual reproduction.

TOMAN: If we wanted to develop the evolutionary picture a little further, a new move in the direction of conservatism of species and of maintaining the chemical memory against the eventuality of future fluctuation is provided by the tendency of dividing cells to hang together in groups. That is the beginning of the multicellular organism.

To the extent cellular elements can be relatively removed from the buffeting of the environment, a new measure of stability is introduced. The cells in the center of the mass are interacting only with part of the interior, and not with the exterior.

For an organism to grow till its size becomes a useful means of stabilization, function must now become specialized in such a way as to provide an internal environment. There would have to develop specialization in particular of a vascular system so that portions of the organism could

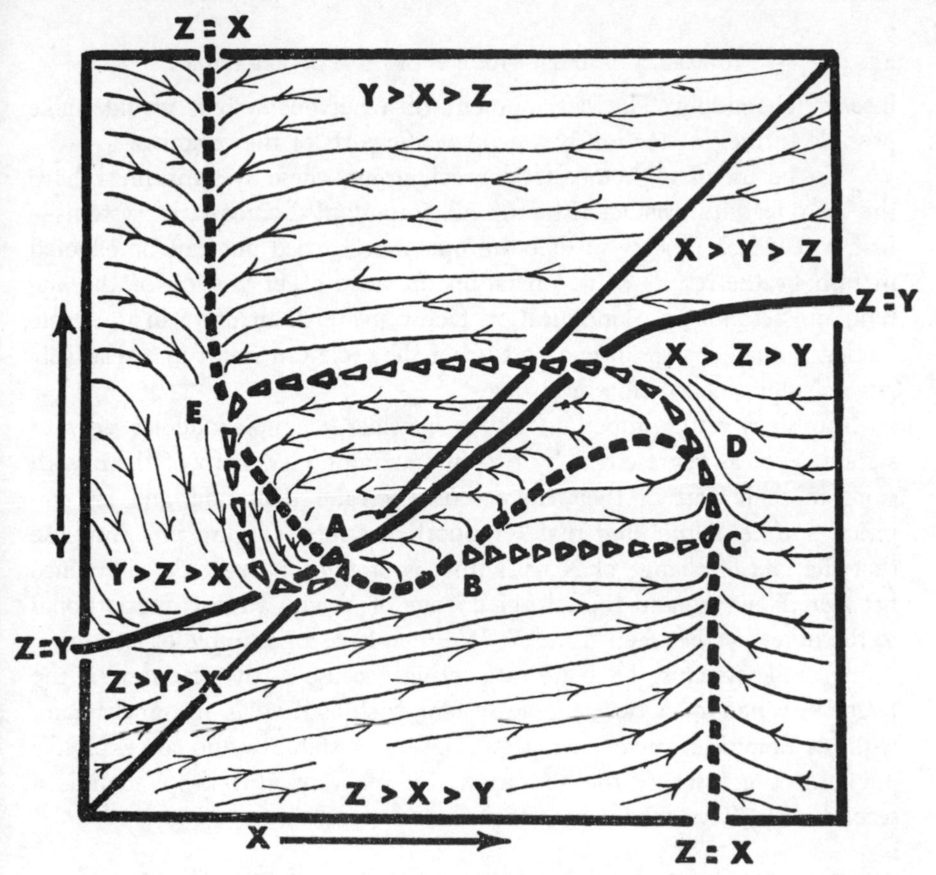

FIGURE 11. TWO-CYCLE INTERACTION SYSTEM

This schema shows a hypothetical excitable system based on two interacting cyclic processes and having the property of spontaneous recovery. The X ordinate gives the direction in which the system may be moved by stimulation. The Y ordinate gives the direction in which accommodation to displacement occurs. The Z ordinate is at right angles to the page and gives a surface representing the size of response (for example the amplitude of a nerve action potential). The following rules of cyclic interaction are postulated and determine the movement of a point on the Z surface:

1. $dX/dt = K_X(Z - X)$ 2. $dY/dt = K_Y(Z - Y)$

where t is time and K_X and K_Y are velocity constants. For convenience it is assumed that $K_X = K_Y$. The empirical Z surface would in practice be mapped by experiment.

Given these postulates, a point on the Z surface representing the momentary state of the system must move in the directions indicated by the arrows on the various segments of the surface. As drawn, the only stable position of rest is at A where all coordinates are equal. If, by stimulation, the state is brought to point B (detonation point or threshold), it will proceed spontaneously to the next position of pseudo-stability at C. It will then move slowly along the path C–D until stability becomes impossible, following which it will recover rapidly from D to E and then more slowly from E to the resting point A.

interact chemically. The development of a nervous system would make possible further interaction between specific parts of the organism.

To be useful as homeostatic mechanisms, these systems must have the two features characteristic of all important homeostatic systems—first, a feedback process so that the operation carried out can be effected in turn by the results of its operation on some other portion of the system; and secondly, an amplification factor greater than unity in the cycle so that a small change in one portion of the cycle can result in a relatively large change somewhere else.

To show both properties, let us consider a simple circular nervous system. We can represent it by two interacting cycles, both of them with gains in some part of their characteristic greater than one, and an empirical surface of the kind that Rapoport described (Figure 11). Suppose that the rate of change of X with time is proportionate to the difference between Z and X, and the rate of change of Y with time is proportional to the difference between Z and Y. We then have an example of two interacting cyclic systems. They are interacting because Z, the response, is the factor in common. A two-variable system, such as Z vs. X in our diagram, with an empirical curve having two levels of stability and an explosive point, does not satisfy the conditions for recovery. But if we include a second cycle, Z vs. Y, we may then describe recovery.

RAPOPORT: *There is a well known theory of Rashevsky* [2] *that if you put in the threshold artificially you must say that when the excitation reaches a certain level and then goes off on its own accord, then it is excited, which provides for restoration (Figure 12, below).*

TOMAN: In my formulation it is obvious that the response and the threshold and other excitation parameters are all tied together. Its importance for us here is in showing how one can design, with a fairly simple two-cycle theory, a relatively complex set of properties, as long as one provides an empirical surface.

A theory is important to us, anyway, as a framework for handling the observed facts. The empirical surface can be determined by experimentation; without doing all of the conceivable experiments one can arrive at those that will describe this surface. What I want to do, however, is to pass from the study of the peripheral nerve into some similar considerations in the central nervous system.

Let me go now to some questions concerning states of regulation in

[2] N. Rashevsky, *Mathematical Biology of Social Behavior* (Chicago: University of Chicago Press, 1948).

complex nervous systems. The minimal number of states found by direct observation of the electrical activity of the mammalian brain includes at least two waking levels in which conditioning can occur—one relatively at rest and the other disturbed or excited. There are also several stages of sleep in which conditioning, if it occurs at all, certainly does not occur very effectively. There is a state of drowsing and a state of deep sleep, and even below that the states obtained in deep anesthesia—one can go all the way to complete silence, for example, in fourth-stage anesthesia—without permanently disrupting the brain or the information it contains.

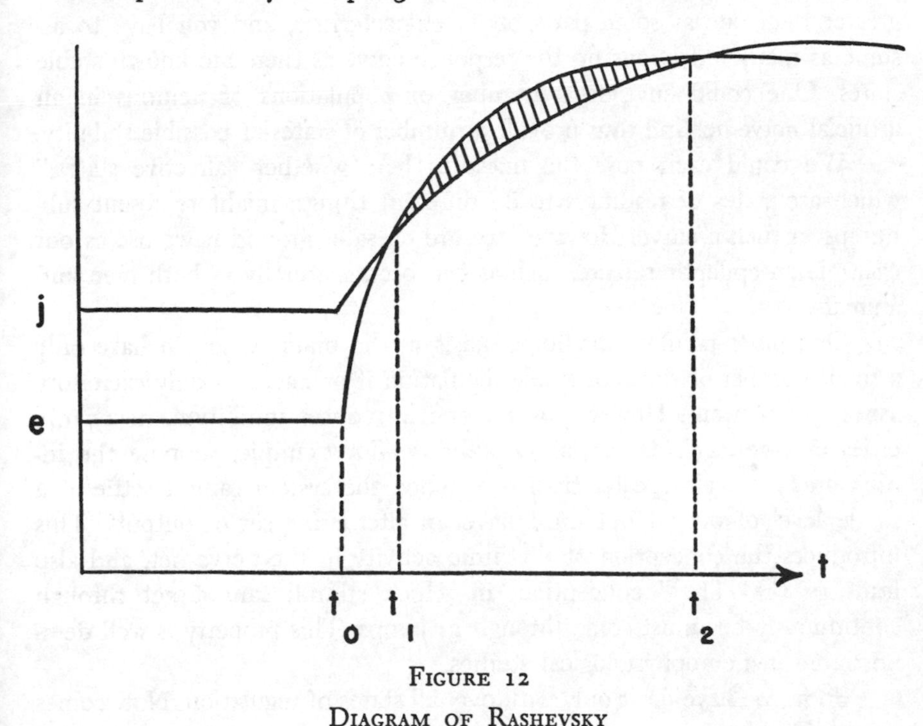

FIGURE 12
DIAGRAM OF RASHEVSKY

Rashevsky, generalizing Blair's theory on the intensity-time relation for stimulation by electric current, postulates two differential equations, one for an excitatory substance e and one for an inhibitory substance J:

$$\frac{de}{dt} = KL - ke; \frac{dj}{dt} = MI - mj$$

where it is expressly assumed that $k = M$ and $k = m$. The time courses of e and j are shown in the figure. The current I is applied at $t = t_0$. Excitation occurs when e becomes larger than j, hence between the instants $t = t_1$ and $t = t_2$. The weakness of this model is the same as that of Blair's in that the threshold is introduced *ad hoc*. But again a detailed analysis of the events accompanying excitation has provided a theoretical basis for deriving just such an effect.

At the opposite extreme, there are also states of excessive activity which can be obtained by excessive chemical or electrical stimulation of the brain, namely, partial seizures and major complete seizures involving the entire brain.

Working with experimental animals, one finds as one puts the animal under stress, either with depressing drugs or with exciting agents, that there is not a smooth transition through all of these states, but instead there are definite jumps. How does one account for these jumps? Again I think you have to consider, at the simplest, a feedback system with gain greater than one at some parts of its characteristic, and you have to assume as many inflections on the response curve as there are known stable states. One could envision a number of populations of neurons in an artificial nerve net and thus provide a number of states of possible stability.

We could even pose the question here whether "affective states," which are states of readiness to do different things, might represent subhumps in such a curve. However, we are on safer ground if we use as our example an epileptic seizure, such as can occur naturally in both men and animals.

One more point about homeostasis in the brain: One can have only a small number of states of stable regulation if one accepts only excitatory aspects of neurons. However, when one introduces inhibition, new properties emerge, such as oscillatory stability. For example, suppose the inhibition has a gain greater than one. Then the system cannot settle at a single level of output but must have an alternating set of outputs. This introduces the conception of rhythmic activity in the nerve net, and also leads to the "filter" conception, in which stimuli cannot get through continuously but must come through in jumps. This property is well demonstrated in neurophysiological studies.

So far we have dealt only with over-all states of regulation. Now comes the problem. How is new information permanently stored in the brain? Again we must deal with contradictory tendencies toward both stability and adaptation.

Many experiments point to the fact that the pattern of sensory information must reverberate for some period of time before it becomes structurally fixed. Conversely, it must eventually become structurally fixed or it would not be capable of surviving complete electrical inactivity of the brain during coma, or very deep anesthesia. Therefore, the question would arise: Is there something in the brain analogous to chemical conditioning? What is the nature of the interplay between the electrical activity produced by patterned stimulation, which in some manner can reproduce itself for a period of time, and the permanent change in brain cells, such that the information pattern becomes anatomically fixed? Here there is practically nothing we can say in the way of mechanism. By analogy with our earlier concept of primitive adaptation, there must be some reciprocating process by which these patterns multiply within the brain. But no one is in a position to say whether a particular structural pattern is repeated many times anatomically over the surface of the brain, or whether there is one single mosaic which is laid down over the entire surface of the brain.

PARSONS: *I suggest an analogy with written language, which is a kind of extraorganic memory. The importance of the analogy might lie in the fact that here is some kind of anatomical residuum, whatever it may be, analogous to a linguistic symbol. It can be scanned like a page of writing, and it is a pattern which is put together but need not in any way resemble the original objects any more than the letters on a page resemble the meanings of the words.*

TOMAN: What the cerebral scanning mechanism may be I do not know.

EMERSON: *Doesn't the phenomenon of attention to a certain degree involve scanning? You look at one section of the memory at one time, and at another section at another time.*

TOMAN: We have to talk about scanning in discussing many phenomena, but we are certainly in no position to say how the scanning is done, nor what is being scanned.

DEUTSCH: *Can we say that this involves in any case a very high degree of concentration, or condensation of information? That is to say, we have at this stage something like a rapid calculator by which the thing can give the answers in a curve. The "whirlwind" calculator at M.I.T. can even be made to photograph some of the curves which it projects on a screen in the course of its calculations. I do not know whether it has a device for reading its own photographs, but what is actually deeply recorded is in any case only a small abstraction of the total information which it processed in producing the curves. Similarly, in written language, the thing written down is a fraction of the information which spoken words convey. You always need this steep condensation factor from the current memory to the deep memory.*

TOMAN: Now to summarize my presentation: First of all, just as the most primitive system of chemical memory becomes perpetuated as the heredity of the organism, by adaptations that occur in a cyclic way with feedback greater than one, and become permanent in a new kind of molecular structure, so also during the lifetime of the individual with a complex central nervous system there must occur, by grossly similar methods of interplay and reproduction of cyclic systems, patterned jumps—one step at a time—which become permanent as experience differentiated somewhere in the structure of the brain in a still unknown manner.

To make this story complete, I would point out that we attained socially at some time in the history of man an amplification greater than one in the interaction between individuals, and between individuals and their products which outlast them. At this point a new and definite direction occurred in history, where we were no longer dependent on our germ plasm alone, or on our immediate life-span memories alone. We have been developing in an accelerating way for several thousands of years this new cycle of social interaction, which is interaction between things created and the viable organisms creating them.

PARSONS: *It seems to me that these things are extraordinarily suggestive of two basic considerations that bear on our bigger problem of unified behavior. One is analogy. I think there is more than analogy; it is a hierarchy of systems. For one thing, in sociology and psychology we are coming rapidly to pay more explicit attention to the problem of the differentiation of internal and external.*

Freud's anatomy of the personality is very clearly built on the postulate that the ego is the part of the personality most directly oriented to the external world. But, interestingly enough, he has two internal components, both id and superego. The other point about the analogies is with respect to sexual reproduction. Both personality and social system with their special kind of interlocking have taken up the biological mechanisms of sex differentiation and sexual reproduction, and in a sense repeated them but with a difference on the level not of biological heredity but of cultural heredity. The family, which is built around sexual differentiation, is the primary mechanism of social heredity.

There is a very important analogy between the germ plasm and the family for the latter is a specially segregated and protected environment, and it is organized around sex. Moreover, the anatomical differentiation of sex is organized on the social level into the first fundamental qualitative differential in the social development of children.

The other interesting thing is that the principle of segregation enters into the social level again, in the new factor of the incest taboo, which is not found in pre-social and pre-cultural life. On the earlier biological levels the basic phenomenon is that the same organism shall not be the sole source of reproduction. Correspondingly, on the social level the incest taboo prevents any one family from being the source of socialization. Each new family formed by marriage has to be compounded out of two whole families. The same relation controls variation.

This suggests that the principle of hierarchy of systems involves increasing extensiveness. Chemical systems become units in organisms. The organisms become units in sexual reproduction and species evolution, but then also in social systems, and thereafter there is the same order of hierarchy of systems within systems on the social level, but always with certain of these basic reference points.

Finally, Toman's point about the whole nervous system is tremendously suggestive to the social scientist because of its obvious connection with symbolic process, which is the focus of culture.

HENRY: *How would we apply the amplification or "gain" concept to changes in society?*

RAPOPORT: *For example, the birth of a fad, or the spread of a panic, or the birth of an idea—any sort of contagious process in society—may settle on an equilibrium or die out or explode like a bomb. One can put down the conditions for equilibrium, for threshold, for explosion, and so on. There are very nice analogies. "Gain" means whether it will multiply or not.*

GRINKER: *Toman, your concept is that these gains represent jumps and discount continuities in change, and that there are threshold values that demarcate rather sharply these jumps and gains?*

TOMAN: The levels of stability are discontinuous, but there is a continuous path of transition from one to another.

RAPOPORT: A good example is the election. *The voting habits may be continuous, but the administration changes are discontinuous. If you look only at the administration you think it is a discontinuous change, from Democrat to Republican, and vice versa.*

EMERSON: You do not mean to exclude the possibility of a gradation or gradual change in a straight line relationship, do you, especially if you had multiple cycles that balanced each other out to a certain degree? If there are gradual changes, the effect might be like a straight line, although actually gradation is likely to be the result of multiple tiny jumps.

TOMAN: These are not instantaneous processes. Our society did not suddenly develop an excess of our products and our interactions and our written symbols over what we need to maintain equilibrium in one generation. But now, having made this step back in history some place, we are not all in equilibrium but are going toward some unknown equilibrium point.

GRINKER: *Can you not tell when irreversibility develops?*

TOMAN: No. All we can tell about society is that it is in a certain direction. But if we reach an equilibrium point, presumably we would know it by the fact of stability over a number of generations.

THOMPSON: *I do not see why the whole process you are describing is not irreversible. If you are talking about, say, Midwest culture or any other particular culture in a particular point in space and in time, why isn't the process you are describing irreversible? Some societies at least in the past have had a process of equilibrium which is irreversible.*

RAPOPORT: *One might think of culture changes in this way: Little stresses can somehow be taken care of. The homeostatic process sets in, and the old norms are re-established. If disturbances are so great that certain structures within the society are ruptured, the society may go into a different configuration entirely, and that is what we would call an irreversible change.*

DEUTSCH: *There is a relation between information storage, condensation, and a possible definition of irreversibility. In the description of the first "life" between the enzyme pairs, which we heard earlier, the typical phrase used again and again was "mirror image," meaning that most of the points in one molecular structure have their counterparts in the other. The amount of variation is very small, and the amount of repetition, even bona fide repetition, is very large.*

In society and culture it turns out that in order to have deep memories, one has to use a very high degree of either abstraction or condensation. Incidentally, if one can give a definition of the difference between the two, one can condense a sequence of one million digits, such as, for instance, one million even numbers, by giving the statement, "Begin with zero and add two." In that way you can give all information to generate the whole sequence. On the other hand, if you give a formula that will approximately summarize it, such a formula might be not generative but selective.

In either case, in order to learn and remember and teach, both the individual and the society have to throw away fantastic amounts of detail.

You remember by flattening and sharpening images, patterns, rumors and the like. If this is so, then there comes a stage where we have thrown away so much detail, and simplified so much, that we can no longer reconstruct the earlier ensemble from which the latter patterns were generated. Irreversibility thus would occur where generative combinatorial universes have become critically modified or depleted by selection.

Social development, in particular, always involves stages of great simplification. It must be irreversible because very soon the information needed for retracing the intermediate steps is lost. Irreversibility, in other words, is the opposite of novelty, and novelty is the opposite of the economy of recording facilities.

RAPOPORT: In the development of the individual, the process is an irreversible one in which equilibrium is reached for a very short period, and any kind of reversibility amounts to regression. But I disagree with Deutsch that, either in thinking or in biological development, much is "thrown away." If regression takes place, much is recovered which seemed totally thrown away. So it was never really lost.

EMERSON: In biological processes, particularly in ontogeny, rejuvenescence occurs even if you have irreversibility in the individual during a growth process. Rejuvenescence occurs with the production of a new individual in the reproductive process. So in the new individual the reproductive process does not carry with it the irreversible aging that the parent individual may already have had.

You could also find this occurring to a certain extent in phylogeny, in the time dimension of the species, where Dollo's rule of irreversibility in evolution is fairly well substantiated. But evolution, however, in this respect differs markedly from ontogeny. You do not get clear senescence in phylogeny, which in ontogeny is the ultimate of irreversibility. So I doubt the existence of a senescent process, in let us say a species, because in the process of reproduction it is always rejuvenating itself and losing the senescent qualities of the individual. If an innate directing influence, such as is assumed in orthogenesis, could be demonstrated, the concept of increasing homeostasis as the direction of organic and human evolution would break down.

You can find irreversible processes, and you can also find reversible processes even in such things as mutations. We have cases of mutations where your analogy with your template system occurs; you may also get reversed mutations that go back to the original, probably for some biochemical reason, although we haven't worked those out in complex nucleo-

protein substances. The conclusion is not either/or, but includes both processes and they may occur together, sometimes in combination with various other phenomena.

TOMAN: A one-cycle system is truly reversible in the sense that it can be made to retrace a path which it has originally taken. But most living processes do not simply retrace their steps. They come back by circuitous pathways even in the sort of homeostatic systems we usually talk about. Furthermore, even a small dislodgement in state will give a circular pathway, a hysteresis, even if there is no qualitative change in state. Finally, if other cycles are involved, such that the empirical structure of the system changes as a result of a change in state, then you can have true irreversibility.

PARSONS: *There was a very major disturbance of the social equilibrium in homeostasis in Russia which reached a crisis in 1917, under the aegis of an ideology which has not been officially overthrown. Part of the ideology called for the abolition of a whole series of traditional institutions which have played a very important part not only in so-called Western capitalistic civilization, but much more widely, notably, the family. Also abolished were the differentiations of authority in the every-day business of life, differential reward in the occupational system, and finally, law as independent of governmental administration.*

It is one of the most striking phenomena of modern history that, to be sure, not capitalism but every one of those fundamental institutions has come back in Soviet Russia, and in many cases in quite glaring contradiction to the most solemn official pronouncements of Lenin. Whereas the family in Marxian tradition was declared to be essentially a bourgeois prejudice, Stalin has decreed that it is the pillar of the Soviet state, and nobody challenges what Stalin said.

The ideology has shifted. There was a violent disturbance of equilibrium and then a return in certain respects. Not that Soviet society is just like Czarist society, but it is somewhere between what Czarist society might have entered into without Marxist intervention and the Communist ideal.

◇◇◇

EDITOR: *Toman showed how the most primitive systems of chemical memory, perhaps even related to the origin of life, become perpetuated in the heredity of the organism. Certain cycles may feed back processes which* accrete to the organism's structure rather than simply reproduce it, thus a "gain greater than one." Similar interplay of cyclic systems may produce such gains within the nervous system and in interpersonal behavior. Thus social systems have developed and are continually changing in accelerated fashion.

CHAPTER NINETEEN

HOMEOSTASIS IN A SPECIAL LIFE SITUATION

Presentation by Jules Henry

I AM going to tackle some of the problems of our last two sessions. One of them is how one handles the problem of homeostasis in a particular situation, and the second is how one passes from the individual to the group; finally, how one can bring some of the things together in a unified system. I will read what one of my students observed, standing by the bedside with a stopwatch, studying a mother and baby in interaction on the third day after birth.

"The mother was lying on her back in a lightly raised position when the nurse carried the baby in and laid it on the bed beside the mother. The mother took the bottle and put the nipple to the baby's mouth and said, 'Every time he comes in here he is asleep.' The baby moved its arms. The mother took the nipple out in five seconds. The mother rubbed the baby's mouth with the nipple, patted the baby's buttocks and shook him vigorously.

"Baby moved its arms near its face. The mother pulled the baby's hand away from its face. After two attempts the nipple was successfully inserted after forty-seven seconds had elapsed of the nursing period. The mother said, 'He is not doing anything. Can they when they are asleep?' The observer replied, 'Not very well.'

"As the baby started sucking the mother said, 'There he goes.' The baby sucked for four seconds. The mother jiggled the nipple and patted the baby's buttocks. The baby moved its arms and the mother said, 'Oh, sleepyhead.' The mother jiggled the nipple and the baby moved its arms again, and the mother said, 'Come on!' The mother laughed. The mother patted the baby's back and pulled the baby's arm away from its face. The mother patted the baby's head and said, 'Come on,' and shook the baby and said, 'He just doesn't want to wake up.' The mother rolled the baby from side to side.

"The baby moved his hands around over the top of the bottle. The mother twirled the nipple. The mother rolled over farther on her side. The baby sucked for two seconds. The baby made a wry face and the mother said, 'Hey, wake up!' The mother jiggled the nipple again and said, 'He's having a hard time making out.' The mother jiggled the baby's arms and said, 'Come on, sleepyhead!' To the observer she said, 'I never see him with his eyes open, hardly.'

"Mother rolled the baby from side to side, jiggled the nipple and said, 'Come on, come on.' Baby moved its arms and the mother said, 'You never get any water down you, you sleep so much.'

"The mother pulled the baby's arm and said, 'Come on!' Baby moved arm. Six minutes after the beginning of the forty-five-minute nursing period the mother pulled the nipple out."

The question now arises, who is being kept in a steady state by this procedure—the baby, the mother, the hospital, American society as a whole or the world?

The baby would eat when hungry and sleep when sleepy if permitted, so pediatricians tell me. Its own physiological self-regulatory mechanisms would take care of this. In the hospital, the baby drifts off to sleep repeatedly, but is awakened and obliged to eat. *In social interaction the baby's own self-regulatory mechanisms are ignored.* If homeostasis occurs at all, it has little to do with baby's self-regulating system. Maybe the mother is maintaining the steady state. If so, what is non-regulatory for baby is regulatory for mother. Hence, within this biosocial system the homeostatic mechanisms of mother and baby are opposed.

Since most of the eighteen babies in our sample are bottle-fed, physiological homeostasis of the mothers cannot be in question. Since, as we have seen, the baby's physiological homeostasis is not either, we must search within our very general handling of the homeostasis hypothesis for some other explanation of the behavior just described.

Cannon's argument that infants have no self-regulatory processes [1] looks more like a socially than a scientifically determined position. When the mother feeds the baby as stipulated, of what homeostatic system is she

[1] W. W. Cannon, *The Wisdom of the Body* (New York: W. W. Norton, 1939).

a part? Why does the hospital run baby feeding in this way? When we ask this question we must change our position of observers to find the answer, no longer in mother-baby as a mutually interacting pair, but in a system of mother-hospital-baby, a more complex interacting system.

A modern hospital in a large city is itself a complex social system which is but part of a larger and even more complex system. Thus full understanding of the mother-baby system involves us in a study of interrelationships which expand rapidly outward. This maternity hospital, for example, is but part of a large medical center which must be run according to a plan. Furthermore, a baby in our culture is a biosocial nonentity. The hospital expresses a tradition of efficiency, one important component of which is routine. This hospital is insufficient for the needs of the surrounding population, a condition characteristic of the nation as a whole at the present time. Finally, babies cannot leave this hospital until they have gained back to their birth weight.

Thus *in controlling baby's self-regulatory mechanisms,* society *regulates itself. The baby is not allowed to indulge its own self-regulatory tendencies as this would upset the hospital schedule.* If the schedule is upset, it thwarts the employees (meaning everyone from director to the orderlies) in their efforts at simplifying their functions. Of course, were the birth rate to decline sharply, pressure on hospital facilities would diminish, and insistence on rigid routine might be less urgent, for it always seems that as anxiety diminishes rigidity decreases also.

Baby's inherent homeostasis thus appears to be distorted and sacrificed to the maintenance of society in its present state, not in a state of maximal efficiency but in a state in which it is at the moment.

Homeostasis when used to refer to the body involves two ideas: One is the normal state, and the other is the state of maximum efficiency, which two, Cannon implies are the same.[2] In society, however, we know that the normal state can often be far more efficient or optimal. I have written a book about one tribe whose normal trait was self-destruction, and several papers about another whose normal state was one of great tension that revolved around one of the primary factors in physiological homeostasis, that is, food. The beautiful expression of the American soldier, "Snafu," more closely approximates social reality than any theory of social homeostasis.

One aspect of Cannon's theory of homeostasis applies to society; in all societies there are devices that resist change. In the hospital just discussed, baby's inherent physiological process is a menace to the social order. Hence, the hospital must do everything to alter the baby's way of life.

[2] *Ibid.*

We now perhaps can bring the concept of physiological homeostasis into line with what we know about resistance to social change. This is possible through suggestions coming from psychosomatic medicine.

Life stress conditions the autonomic and other bodily systems, but what these life stresses shall be is determined by culture and society. Hence, a particular combination of social and cultural conditions determines how the nervous system shall be conditioned. This conditioning is such, for example, that a particular stress configuration, A, produces in the autonomic nervous system in time a particular readiness to respond, a. The stress configuration, A, plus the response, a, may be thought of as representing a homeostatic complementarity, which seems to correspond structually to the kind of complementarity postulated by Cannon. If now A changes to B, which is a different stress configuration but somewhat like A, the autonomic nervous system has no b with which to match it. The result is malaise. Behind the resistance to social change probably lies a whole network of such complementary nervous systems. Not only does a no longer satisfy b, but a, which is a certain readiness to respond, cannot be called forth. Hence, a second source of malaise; the body cannot utilize the responses which it already has.

To bring the matter down to the present case, albeit in a somewhat over-simplified way: Behind the hospital's resistance to change is the conditioning of the autonomic and other systems of the employees to respond to certain fixed sequences of events which we may call "routine." It is easier to force baby into similar responses than to change the hospital.

This hypothesis may be made somewhat more explicit through this model (Figure 13). We will assume that in a relatively homogeneous social system, such as that of the Eskimo or a group of Ona wandering over Tierra del Fuego, there is a constant ratio, A, between rewards, R, and punishments, P, operating on the organism over time, and that A pro-

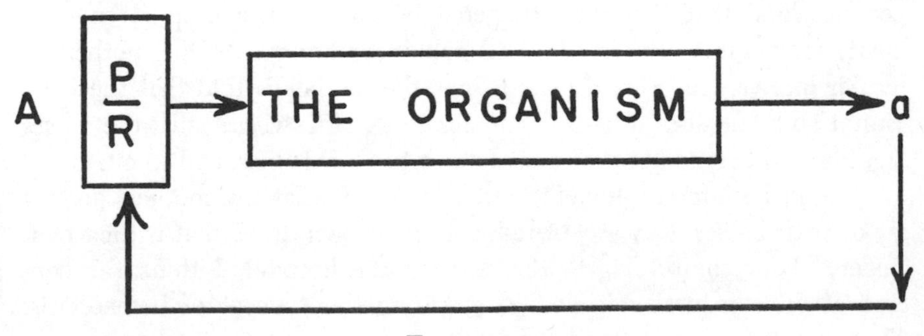

FIGURE 13
A MODEL OF SOCIAL CONDITIONING

duces a certain readiness to respond which we call a. Now a acts like negative feedback to maintain the configuration $\frac{P}{R}$ relatively unchanged. Should something then happen to $\frac{P}{R}$ to change it to B, which would then be $\frac{P_1}{R_1}$, the population still has only a to deal with the new condition.

At this point a non-exhaustive catalog of the possible happenings in the system would include the following: First, a changes promptly to b, and the system is maintained under the new conditions. The second possibility is that a does not change, and thus tends to force B back to A.

The third possibility then is that a and the new condition B interact in such a way that they drive each other to ever wider and wider divergence. This would occur, for example, where under one set of conditions a relatively weak attack at A would elicit a relatively weak but successful self-assertion at a. Change in circumstance now brings a heavier attack, which we call B, which produces not a but b, which is submission. Submission now provokes a still heavier attack, C, which results in c, which is still greater submission. Continuation of the process forces the attacked organism from the field.

Now I would like to examine some of the responses of the mothers within this child-mother-hospital system. The thing they say most often to the baby is "come on." Next in order is "wake up," or some related phrase; next in order are utterances pertaining to speed or quantity of intake; next in frequency are utterances in which adult wishes are opposed to baby's wishes. The frequency of utterances pertaining to achievement, work, failure or success of the baby or the mother is smallest. (There are also some "miscellaneous" remarks.)

Since these utterances are relatively uniform, I conclude that they were determined by certain uniformities in the mothers in previous experience, and that they were triggered by cues in the hospital environment: for example, the fact that all babies are brought to the mothers at regular intervals for a fixed period; that the mother is told that the baby cannot go home until it has gained back to its birth weight; that the nurses urge the mothers to get food and water into their babies, and so on.

It can be inferred, therefore, that much of what the mothers do and say to their *babies* is by way of reducing their *own* drive, that is their own anxiety about conforming to the rules of the hospital. I think the concept of drive reduction is closely related to the concept of homeostasis. Thus, the *baby's* physiologically determined homeostatic mechanisms are altered by way of drive reduction, that is, maintenance of homeostasis, *in the mother*. The mother's drive in turn originates in the conditions of the hospital.

The matter is still more complicated. The utterances of the mother revolve around certain ideo-emotional elements—emphasis on achievement, work, dominance, quantity, the importance of minutia, and success. These are related to the importance of an expanding industrial order.

Thus, in a hospital, which is a cultural institution, the environment of the baby is such as to oblige the mother literally to shove the cultural ideals down the baby's throat. When this is done the hospital and American society as a whole are enabled to go on being what they have always been.

This circumstance might conceivably be brought analogically within the conception of homeostatic control, but whether it has any relation to optimal function, maximum human happiness, or even to survival of the commonwealth is open to question.

The crucial difference between animal (particularly insect) societies and human ones is that while the former are organized to achieve homeostasis, the organization of the latter seems to guarantee instability—and this is the hub of the matter, as I see it, from the standpoint of human evolution. Life stresses bring about important changes in the human organism. These changes can become hereditary through selective processes, for only organisms that can adapt to the stresses and to the ensuing changes will survive; but since *human society and culture determine the nature of the stresses*, and since human society is unstable, the stresses on the organism are always changing and different. Hence, biological selection is always taking place in terms of the changing stresses produced by the perpetual instability of human social systems.

Thus I suggest that man evolves physically in terms of a perpetually unstable social life, and perhaps this suggestion may help to bring sociological, biological and psychological theory together into a common frame of reference.

EMERSON: *I think there is a danger of imputing perfection to the concept of homeostasis. With numerous factors and numerous responses, many of which could be in conflict one with the other, one could never expect perfection of adjustment, either physiologically or behavioristically. If we discovered an optimum for a certain process, we could, I am sure, easily discover in the same system a different optimum of the same factor for another process. Therefore, there has to be compromise.*

Also, efficiency may be relative. There may be short-term efficiencies that are selected, which to a certain degree are in conflict with long-term efficiencies. To resolve these differences in temporal optima one has to assume time dimensions to the system, which I maintain are realities. So you may imagine positive selection for a gene that assists the organism to adjust to a certain temperature in the summer and negative selection in the winter for the same gene, all in the same organism.

Turning now to the baby: So far as we can tell, the primitive reptilian mammal was egg-laying and probably paid very little attention to the egg. Certainly in the reptilian ancestor the egg may not be cared for at all, and must be entirely self-regulating without any parental attention or care.

In the marsupial stage very little attention is paid by the mother to the off-spring, at least at the time the young migrates to the marsupium, or pouch, and attaches itself. The milk is squirted into the attached young without nursing behavior by the parent or young. The young migrate to the pouch without any parental help. A remarkable set of mechanisms is involved. In the placental stage of mammalian evolution the mother physiologically takes care of the young through the placental membranes and adaptations.

In some mammals when the young are born they are relatively independent. A young horse can run quite well a few hours after being born. The human infant is relatively helpless, but the family system intervenes; and of course the family system, characterized by the development of the mammary gland itself, provides parental care and homeostasis of food supply for the benefit of the baby. The baby adjusts to that, and the parent adjusts even through hormone regulation and behavior responses to this family system. Ultimately we have the growth of the family into the human system that you are describing.

Infant mortality statistics might indicate that there is a certain cultural level of the social system where the relation of mother to baby is better regulated. There is here an indication of improvement in the complex combination of homeostatic mechanisms and your illustration does not controvert the concept of homeostasis, but rather gives data to verify the concept.

Grinker: Why the term "improvement," and why get angry at the hospital? It is a problem of change. We can see the change from the laissez-faire attitude of our great-grandmothers and grandmothers to the rigid scheduling of mothers in some of our own families, followed now by a change to the self-demand schedule, which already is being supplanted as a result of certain problems arising in children developed in that way. The problem of homeostasis should not be sought in the struggle between the child and its mother, but in the delayed feedback that would occur *decades later. Whether one direction or another direction is improvement has to be judged by the long-term results.*

HENRY: I find it difficult to visualize a base line from which to judge whether a social system is out of kilter or not. In society this, to me, is the issue. The other problem is the difficulty, as Emerson mentioned, of evaluating the homeostatic significance of any particular act in society. We are never sure that we have considered all the pertinent circumstances.

DEUTSCH: *Didn't you present only half of the baby's needs? He also needs to be protected against cold, hunger and infection. Therefore, he has to be protected against physical exertion, and this has to be done in a servantless society in which personal services are at a premium. The babies are uncomfortable under the speed-up system, but most of them survive. It might well be that the self-demand system, under which mothers cannot be hospitalized, or the old plantation system in which there were colored nurses to look after everybody's needs except their own, would be more expensive in terms of human life.*

A more important matter is the difference between mechanical or zoological feedback on the one hand and social feedback on the other hand. In an organismic or a mechanical system, you usually seek for the most efficient feedback by simplifying the components, by cutting out degrees of freedom in the components, and trying to solve for maximum determination in the component so as to get maximum complete efficiency. Unless Emerson corrects me, an ant hill runs on the basis of getting simplicity in the components as a means for getting efficiency.

In society, by contrast, we find something for which I don't know of any counterpart outside society; that is, we have autonomous feedback-steering in the components, and we usually have multiple solutions.

One class of solution involves reducing the autonomy of the components, such as making people into the nearest equivalent of machines and treating the baby in the way Henry described. The other class of solution consists in working with these autonomous processes instead of against them. Usually this class of solution requires more intelligence, and their introduction therefore is often slow. A parallel to the problem which Henry described here is now being dealt with in labor relations departments at some of our universities—the passing from the speed-up idea to the cooperation idea; that is, to the idea of evoking more rather than less spontaneity from the man in the factory. Similarly, the rooming in method in the hospital might be shaped to correspond more closely to the self-demand schedule in home nursing, and this might be in line with the second class of solutions.

HENRY: How the system may be most efficiently run is often determined by historical circumstances. It is true, for example, that a more efficient management of babies and society as a whole is made possible by being more permissive? Or is the doctrine of permissiveness a function of this particular historical period?

SPIEGEL: *May I say something about the position of the observer here? An observer focusing primarily upon the system could argue that this early system puts great emphasis upon achievement, planning, and so on. To create of the baby an individual who will function maximally or optimally as an adult in this society, one might very well introduce such training procedures at the earliest possible moment. Then you set up no conflict or antagonism between the hospital and the mother, because her values are the same as the hospital's, as the society's, and they are the values this child is going to have.*

But, if you are looking at the strains that the individual baby may have to suffer as a result of this training, then you may see a difficulty in integration, because this early pressure may result later in difficulties in the autonomic system in the form, say, of peptic ulcer.

If, on the other hand, you try to step outside of this system into larger time and space, and notice then the laxity of the system itself—that there are within it conflicts of values as to planning, achievement—then the individual organism and its autonomy or spontaneity may be seen in a different perspective. If you take 100 years as the time segment, this lack of integration seems to be getting settled by an evolutionary change. For homeostasis is not bad or inefficient. The way it looks depends on the position from which you are observing.

If you look at most hospital systems you will discover that within them exists the same type of conflict that exists within the social system. The hospital administrators have meetings among themselves to inquire into the question of how we can give the patient more individual attention, how we can pay more respect to the autonomous and spontaneous needs of the individual. There is more interactive process than you represent.

HENRY: But one could turn the whole argument around and say that every change, every provision that is made in society provides for malaise in the future, and does not provide for balance.

Let me give a demonstration of a social system characterized by what I have called multiple subordination. It is that of a hospital I have been studying for the past year and a half. This hospital has four divisions which we will call nursing service, nursing education, administration and the department of neuropsychiatry. In the psychiatric wards there is a supervisor who receives orders (let us call them informational impulses) from these four departments, which she must transmit to all her subordinates. This means she must transmit four different kinds of information to each one of her subordinates.

It is obvious that this is theoretically an unworkable system, because it depends upon *complete* consensus among the four departments. It means then that the supervisor receives contradictory information which she must then transmit to the people under her, who then become still further confused. As a result, naturally, no supervisor could function in this system. By firing the supervisor, the hospital hoped to guarantee that the system would limp along in the same way as it had gone before. Is this homeostasis? No. It seems to me a guarantee that the system shall continue to be malfunctioning. Two supervisors have been fired in the past two years. Now they do without one.

EMERSON: *I might point out that there is survival of the entire unit. If this hospital continues to function inefficiently in (let us say) competition with other hospitals, it will ultimately go out of existence, and a new system, which may function better, will come in. I think there would be a slow automatic evolution by a natural selection, even at a cultural level. But after all, unlike animals human beings do not have to wait for automatic selection but can make an intelligent selection.*

FRANK: *In most human organizations, such as a hospital, a factory or a social order, we find that certain practices and relationships become established as customary and are accepted not only without question but with little or no concern for evidence that those practices are valid or desirable. But when someone attempts to introduce a new practice, they are met with an insistent demand for the most conclusive evidence in support of the proposed new practice. For example, those who have advocated a change from the four hour feeding schedule for infants to a more flexible so-called self-demand feeding and those who have advocated "rooming in"—keeping the mother and newborn baby together—have encountered the most determined opposition and a demand for evidence in favor of these practices, while calmly accepting the existing patterns as if they had been scientifically validated and experimentally demonstrated. Needless to say, no such evidence for the existing practices is available, but they are maintained as the only valid and correct ways of doing things. This seems to emphasize Spiegel's point about remembering the position of the observer and also what has been said about the maintenance of systems against any outside impacts or proposed changes. The crucial question in all these situations, and especially in the often heated controversies they engender, is the question of what criteria are to be used in evaluating a situation or an established practice. To formulate a theory of human behavior, we must resolve, if possible, the many conflicting criteria which the different disciplines adhere to not only in their own scientific work, but in their acceptance or rejection of the work of other disciplines.*

HENRY: If society always provides for instability, this compels evolution, because the system must constantly adjust and select so as to perpetuate this continued instability.

PARSONS: *I do not think that is in contradiction to the theory of homeostasis in the least. You are mixing an empirical question of degrees of instability, which is a perfectly legitimate and open empirical question, with the theoretical question of whether the idea of system, which has regulatory mechanisms, is theoretically a useful idea. The two are linked if you say this is a type of phenomenon in which this kind of regulatory process, which is empirically drastically irrelevant, exists. The day-to-day weather is extremely unstable. It does not mean that the idea of system in meteorology is no good. There are a lot of classes of unstable phenomena, especially in short-time perspectives. But that is not the basic issue.*

RAPOPORT: *Coming back to the question of homeostasis, it is most relevant to ask, first of all, homeostasis with respect to what? What is it that is being maintained? Henry brought forward a very pertinent critique: Is this maintenance of a status quo? If so, let us examine the status quo. Is it the maintenance of something that one might consider a description, but from another point of view it might not be considered desirable at all?*

Usually these various points of view are not explicitly stated. One preserves a status quo without knowing it. In his own mind, he is not preserving the status quo, but preserving some ultimate morality. If one has stated sufficiently clearly that if we preserve this system then this is what will happen, we then have the liberty of making another choice. The trouble is that one does not have a clear picture of the consequences of preserving the status quo.

DEUTSCH: *Aren't there usually a number of aims in practice? If we want to reduce mortality, reduce learning, reduce habit-changing, reduce expenses, reduce the need for new ideas in establishing the hospital, we must try to find a strategy to meet a number of different conditions. But all the time, too, our weighting of the different criteria is likely to change. At one time we do not care whether the babies get complexes, and at another time we begin to be aware of the psychological consequences of our* hospital schedules for mother and child as distinct from the goal of economizing nurses' time.

In terms of these multiple goals, you are looking for some optimum strategy of behavior, or at least for a better strategy or policy than the one you had before. This is similar to seeking a better or a best solution in the theory of games. What then happens frequently is that, first, you find only some very obvious and trite solutions. At a later stage you begin to discover what damage to some of your less conspicuous goals is being caused by behavior based on these superficial solutions. Yet a report such as Henry's on the hospital routine for instance often will not even then shake the monumental calm of the hospital administration. The forces for change are not sufficient to shake the over-all feedback that restores the system year after year.

Then something happens in the environment, or in competing organizations, that changes the entire scale of the picture—and suddenly the objections which for 100 years were perfectly sufficient to prevent change seem dwarfed. Then everybody says, "Why didn't we think of this long ago?" Suddenly states federate which never wanted to federate before, or a reform gets through which seemed impossible before.

RUESCH: *I don't think we are dealing with the same phenomenon, when we talk about homeostasis in individuals and when we talk about homeostasis in society. In the individual the envelope is given. You have two eyes, one nose, two ears, and so on. If an ear is cut off, it is gone. You might replace it by an artificial ear, but if two eyes are gone so far we cannot replace them.*

In society a matter such as this can be handled. We can postulate, for example, that one day hospitals will not be needed any more because preventive medicine will have taken care of disease. Or people invent firearms and then the crossbow and the arbalest become obsolete. The basic difference is that in society, by and large, we handle situations by creating machines and institutions which will handle the situation. When they become obsolete, we remove them. Within the individual, we have to operate with the organs we have. Society cannot be compared to the individual.

HENRY: In reporting on the hospital I wanted to see what we could do with the analogies that have been drawn between homeostasis in the body and in insect and human societies. I thoroughly agree with you that we are dealing with very different things.

RAPAPORT: *While I think it is very good to deal with society and individual society as two different things, the point Ruesch makes does not impress me. While man has only two arms and does not discard them like old tank models are being discarded, man certainly has what you usually call habits—motor patterns. He changes his cars, puts them on the junk heap, revamps them, and does it exactly like the old tank models or the ancient form of atom bomb, or something like that. Usually he keeps it in reserve still.*

RUESCH: *But what you can do with the organism is predetermined and limited. You can calculate the probabilities of what you can do with it. But the probabilities of what you can do with the machine, I think, have not been exhausted at this point.*

PARSONS: *I think you are drawing a false analogy there. You are talking about so-called material culture, but that is not the analogue of the organs of the body. If you are looking at a social system as a system then the analogue of the organs of the body is systems of roles, and you cannot shuffle and reshuffle systems and roles at will without reference to their interdependence in systems. There are similarities between the social system and the organism. There are differences also. Our task is to discover both the nature of the differences and the reasons for them, and the nature of the similarities and the reasons for them. Analogy is fruitful if the differences and similarities are real.*

Our tendency as scientists is to over-simplify. And yet we have to handle our concepts by over-simplifications, because they are in reality so complex. But if we over-simplify and add a bias to it, we may deviate from a real analysis of reality.

MORRIS: *I would like to make two points. One is on the matter of value that I find dogging this discussion. On the first point there may be a sense in which there is an over-all notion of system, whether characterized by homeostasis or some other way, but nevertheless there are sub-classes of systems that have certain properties in common with all systems and yet that have differential features. We are not yet spelling out in sufficient detail these differential features which characterize the human social systems, the biological systems and certain other kinds of systems.*

My other point concerns the notion of progressive evolution. We are living in a culture in which "progress" is a sacred word, and I think the question of how far this is an evaluative term, and how far it is a scientific term, is a point we ought to be clear on. I think you cannot just equate it with homeostasis and the development of homeostasis.

When it comes to problems of value, we must ask what is the system which is taken as the point of reference. The human set of values or the human evolutionary process may itself be within some larger system which will require in time the extermination of the living system as we now know it. You might still say that is progressive evolution in the sense that it increases the range of homeostatic process, but the characteristic of the larger systems is that they require the using of the subsystems as phases in certain stages of their development. What is progress from the point of view of a large system need not be progress from the point of view of a subsystem.

And so I think we have to separate the question of the place of homeostasis as a theoretical concept in the theory of systems, from the question whether the way human civilization is going is necessary, in a value sense of the term, better or worse.

EDITOR: From a discussion of the homeostatic regulatory systems of mother and neonate in the field of a modern lying-in hospital, we were led into a discussion of optimal function, "happiness" and other values such as "progress" and "improvement." Morris called attention to the use of such evaluative terms as not scientific and not to be equated with homeostasis.

CHAPTER TWENTY

AUTONOMY AND BOUNDARIES ACCORDING TO COMMUNICATIONS THEORY

Presentation by Karl Deutsch

I SHALL try to state notions of autonomy, as found in control or communication theory. The organization of the contact points of our special fields might be best explained by way of some of the notions of communication theory, because that is where the idea of these contact points between our various specialties developed. I begin with a group of concepts, then structures, then processes, as found in communication theory.

First, what are the *units* around which we organize our knowledge? There are certain obvious units, such as the single individual organism, and such obvious social groups as the family or the village or the state. What in this connection is a "level of organization"? Are there hierarchical levels? What are our criteria for speaking of a higher level? Is this a static judgment, or can we set up some tests for levels? The notion of "level" is possibly connected with the notion of "scale." How are our notions of "level" and "scale" connected with our notions of relevance and importance in each field?

Secondly, from the concepts we would go to a closer look at the structures we are dealing with. Our first question again, in each of our fields, might be this: What are the *boundaries* of a structure? Are there operational tests for boundaries?

In particular, are there boundaries which are confirmed by a multiplicity of tests? That is to say, do boundaries come in bundles, such as "the edge of a woods," ecologically speaking. I say "in bundles" because from one point of view it might be the region of where there are no trees beyond a certain height. But from another, woods stop where the trees are no longer close enough together to resist deformation by wind. A third test of the edge of a woods would be where the trees are no longer close enough together to prevent the growth of the lower branches. A fourth would be the cutting out of the underbrush. All these tests would give you a coincidence in the middle of a forest, but each of these would possibly give you slightly different boundary zones—a timber line, for instance. Practically, we use a word such as "woods" or "forest" in every-day language because the different operational boundaries are close enough together so that we have an ensemble that will serve most of our purposes.

Do we find in social systems, or in the field of human behavior, boundaries that reinforce each other and are close enough together so that a definite unit is delimited? Does not only the one particular test we happen to pick on, but do a multiplicity of tests give a roughly coinciding boundary for the units?

If any one test is not very well related with any other test, it would be very hard to find any units. Otherwise, we could find certain units which are indicated or confirmed by many tests, and then state the significant exceptions. This is a boundary-mapping problem.

At the other side of this undertaking would be a search for causes, or better, for *critical components* or conditions. Can we state that within a unit there are particular parts which are the more important? I might divide a unit into a large number of subregions, and say, "Is there any one *critical* subregion here in which a small change will lead to a bigger change in behavior of the whole than an equally small change in any other subregion?" —in the same way that an injury to the heart and brain of an animal has greater effect than an injury at the periphery of the body. One test of importance would be this: Which part of the system gives you the maximum over-all change in system performance for the least change or smallest change in the subassembly structure?

If we find that certain subassemblies give a wide variety of system changes for a wide variety of small disturbances, we may speak of them as "causes" or "control points" or "centers": for example, genes.

The *third* point about structures: Do we find that there are structures which carry a high statistical *frequency of interaction* or transaction? We can call them nodes. We speak of "communication nodes." They are like the intersection of roads, or a switchboard in operation. To some extent nodes may become "causes," but there may be nodes that are not "causes."

The *fourth* point is: Are there *memory pools?* By memory pools I mean facilities where information is stored in the form of physical traces, to be recalled by some physical process and applied to a current input, so that the output of the system or of the organization is a function not merely of the input. A system or organization with a memory pool is not a "penny-in-the-slot-and-out-comes-a-chocolate-bar" affair, for to some extent it can be predicted not by knowing the input but by knowing what is stored inside.

The *fifth* thing to be looked for are *decision points.* Decision points in an organism, as well as in a social organization, are the points or the couplings where recalled data from the past are fed into the stream of current decisions about current inputs and outputs.

There are two kinds of such decision points. First, a decision point could occur in any organism or organization without a memory, so long as an input could give rise to two trains of responses, two outputs. There would then be a gate that goes one way or another. In the second place, if you have a memory feeding into the process of responding to external inputs, you are likely to get something like a three-way decision point where the input signal, the information recalled from memory, and the alternative output pathways all meet together. This is a higher order decision point. We might get comparable information from the behavior of many different things—the behavior of cultures or tribes, or of political organizations, or of individuals by asking where their memories are brought into the process of deciding about their reactions to the outside world, or into their internal choices of initiative.

We can explain constant bias in these terms, too, as follows: In the typical memory more information is stored than you can feed into any one decision at any one time; consequently, you have to select. Usually it is a selection of memory traces, and often a decision must be made about what is being recalled. When something is selected out of a whole pool of memories, behavior is very close to autonomous. The system itself, or the individual himself, may not know what he is going to do or what his decision is going to be. There may be, as it were, a number of degrees of freedom in the output-input sense of relationship to the outside world, and another number of degrees of freedom in what is going to be recalled from within, from memory. Free will or autonomous decision is related to this pattern.

Now, if you can predict a relatively invariant reaction, you have essentially a built-in bias. The individual with a bias has by-passed his memory, closed the library, and built himself a simple, low-order decision point which says, "If you come to the intersection, go to the left—one way only." No decision is necessary any more, and no memory.

RAPAPORT: *If I understand you correctly, this was not included in your earlier definition of the decision point. You mentioned two sorts of decision points, both organically pre-channeled. One, where an input has the opportunity for two outputs, and the choice between them might be exemplified as follows: A man can go into an action on a certain stimulation and can react with affection or can react with sorrow. These are built-in possibilities. You describe that with a decision point.*

The other sort of decision point mentioned by you was the point where actual memory is fed into and is joined with the input before output comes about. In this case, something was added that was not given with the organization originally. That means that either you want to add a certain subitem to your decisions, or you want to add to your list of structural issues a built-in bias, or whatever term you choose.

DEUTSCH: It is an instance of one of two things: If the bias is complete so that the probability equals one, then essentially we do not even have a decision point any more, but only a simple channel. We have closed down the decision point and replaced it by a rigidly determined pathway. The other possibility arises when the bias poses a high probability but where the bias is less than one. The result is then a decision point and its order depends on what other pathways and probabilities come to meet at this location.

The *sixth* point about structures would be: Are there structural facilities for *high-order feedbacks,* that is, feedbacks which abstract information either from the memory or from current decisions or current inputs, and which permit the simultaneous impact of several sets of the stored data?

This is not far from what we sometimes think of as *consciousness.* Do we get any signals? If a librarian is asked, "How strong is our collection of Slavic books?" he can answer it by making himself aware of the index cards and titles, very roughly, of a fair part of this collection, at least; and then, by comparing this with his idea of what a strong collection in this field would be, he can answer "yes" or "no." He does not do this by reading all of the Slavic books in the library. His is second-order information, involving a feedback process where second-order information is condensed or abstracted, and where the abstracted data are inspected simultaneously.

I asked the question, "Are there any high-order feedbacks which abstract information and permit the simultaneous inspection of several sets of stored data?" These data are stored in the organization. Either they are stored fairly steadily in some memory facilities, or they may be data about something that is moving currently through the organization, as a college administration is aware of the students by keeping track of all sorts of forms.

HENRY: *What is the difference between high-order feedback and memory?*

DEUTSCH: The high-order feedback may be wiped out immediately after it has been used. That is one difference between it and memory. The other difference is that items or traces in a memory pool can be kept there for long periods without interacting with each other, just as books in a library do not disturb each other; even though written by controversial authors, books peacefully sit side by side on the shelves. On the other hand, in a consciousness type of feedback it is of the essence that you *inspect* your abstract information for things such as consistency. The man who directs from the landing tower at the airport the incoming airplanes must be aware of whether there are two airplanes heading for the same runway or not.

I have suggested that we look at six aspects of structure: units; boundaries and critical components; frequencies of transition; memory pools; decision points; and high-order feedback processes. The purpose of this suggestion was that each of us could ask, concerning structures: "Are there any structural facilities in my field corresponding to the points raised thus far?" If they are not there, we could ask, "Are there corresponding gaps in the behavior of the organization?"

Now, I come to the third element in communication theory, the processes. Here we test performances. One class of process would be homeostatic. We could use feedback analogies here and ask some quantitative questions: With what differences in loads can homeostasis be maintained? How quickly is it recovered after a disturbance? How large an amount of facilities must be devoted to it? How big a rudder do you need to give a ship of a given size and speed a turning radius? How much money do you have to have available for counter-speculation in the market, to prevent fluctuations beyond a certain level? Such quantitative questions might go well beyond the classic concept of mechanical equilibrium and might give us new insights into problems of freedom and control in political and social situations.

The feedback concept, unlike that of classic equilibrium, permits us to ask quantitative questions about time and timing. How soon must a reaction come to be "in time" within a feedback process? How fast do you have to make the reaction speed of a greyhound to keep up with the zigzagging rabbit? How fast a reaction speed would a schoolteacher need to keep up with the lively class of nine-year-olds? (It might turn out that disciplinary problems are partly problems of reaction speed, as well as many other things.)

If Parsons asks, "What is a society without tensions?" that question can be restated: Let food scarcity be a load condition of a certain type, and a culture such that behavior is stable provided there is a certain input of food. Then, if the input of food declines, you might try to find out where and how soon breakdowns or other changes occur. This somewhat resembles the problem of certain thermostats which will work reasonably well even in a cold wave in contrast to other thermostatic systems which will work well in moderate climates but will break down in a New England January. A similar question about overload conditions could be asked about homeostatic processes that involve largely the handling of information.

Another class of problems involving load conditions and response speeds and amounts are the processes of metabolism; which means the actual taking in of physical goods of some sort—of physical material and equipment—such as occur in physiology, in the chemical industry, in logistics and in ecology. In all these cases, limited amounts of tangible objects are moved and processed in ways which require the feedback of information if the system is to be preserved.

Rapaport: *I understood you earlier to say that these issues of homeostasis pertain to quantitative questions, the rudder of the ship, and so on. It sounds to me as though you say now that this is handling of information. Is that consistent, or have I misunderstood you?*

Deutsch: You must handle information in order to steer physical behavior. To some extent I think the *behavior* of the cycle: information, steering orders, rudder positions, changed course of the ship—is different from the *cycle:* coal input, steam under kettles, coal used, miles traveled. Possibly we might end up by saying this is an artificial distinction, but since I want to make the thing look no simpler than it is, I have listed them separately.

Rapaport: *There may be a connection between energy and entropy. Those two problems are distinctly different in the analysis of the problems of metabolism and information, metabolism being analogous to the energy problems and information being analogous to the entropy. The principle of the conservation of energy is qualitative. It goes both ways. We can account for all the energy. However entropy cannot increase, but always de-*

creases in an energy system. It may be fruitful to argue by analysis that the information will always decrease by becoming degraded. Those are quite distinct concepts. Although one likes to think that, of course, they are connected conceptually, this connection is by no means obvious, and perhaps it is fruitful to treat them separately.

DEUTSCH: I would agree with that. I have a suspicion that it might be possible to treat metabolic processes as a subclass of homeostatic processes, but not vice versa.

PARSONS: *You spoke of the physical intake of physical materials. Can it be stated in a little more general sense? In a social system there is a metabolism of memberships. In a social group there are new members coming in and old members dropping out, and yet it is stretching a point to say that this is an intake of physical material. Instead, it is participation in many roles at once. The students in a college have not ceased to be members of their families. You can't say that above the neck belongs to college, and below the neck belongs to the family. Actually, "physical" parts of the organism or biochemical entity are not the units of a social system. It is that which is metabolized.*

DEUTSCH: It might be safe to say, possibly, that we should head this group under some such words as "metabolism and quasi-metabolism." That would include either the physical membership of people who bodily move into an organization, as the extreme cases of soldiers in the army who have to give it almost their entire time. Otherwise, one could break it down in terms of time and attention. The notion of an organization is the coordination of the activities rather than the bodies of the participants.

PARSONS: *For theoretical purposes I think the bodies become involved insofar as certain somatic processes have to be involved in activities.*

DEUTSCH: I agree, and it seems to me that our views are in harmony on this point. We shall pass from the homeostatic and metabolic processes to the third type of processes. These processes seem to occur in all of the systems, for they concern performance. They cover such questions as these: (1) How much information is transmitted; (2) What fraction is it of the information received; (3) What is the *fidelity?* You speak of high fidelity equipment in sound reproduction, meaning how many overtones are reproduced? It is the inverse of the overtones lost—of the information that is lost.

The fourth is self-steering or *goal-changing*. Is there correlation between the fidelity with which the information is transmitted and other performance characteristics of an organization of human beings?

RUESCH: *"Goal" is a term derived from a special theoretical concept, and whether it has any meaning outside of that is very questionable.*

DEUTSCH: This came out of the problem of guided missiles design. You build a system in which a certain equilibrium is produced if the homing missile brings itself into a certain relationship with the outside world. The relationship with the outside world at which the inner disequilibrium of the system—in this case, of the missile—is at a minimum is a *goal situation,* that is, an objective physical situation. If the system has been given suitable effectors it may approach this goal situation, and in this sense the word "goal-seeking" can be applied to the performance of a collection of copper wires and assorted equipment. In biology you speak sometimes of tropism.

I used the term "goal" here in order to get another distinction. If you see a physical object which seems to correct its course, and if its mistakes are getting smaller, and it seems to steer toward a certain state or goal, then I can ask, "What 'goal' is this system approaching?" Then I can ask the second question, "What 'goal' was it supposed to be approaching, according either to the idea held by its designers (if it is something made in a factory) or (if it is a manned ship) according to the images held in the heads of the crew?"

Henry asked: "What do the people in the hospital think they are doing to the babies, and what are they in fact doing?" [1] This distinction between the goal and the *goal image* is of major importance in political science. What statesmen have done has often been strikingly different from what they thought they were doing.

Then one could put in here another process characteristic—number five in this enumeration—and that we could call "noise and error." That is to say, there are scattered errors. There is a difference between a multiplicity of scattered errors and a steady bias, of which we have spoken, which may be built into the system and which is predictable to the outside observer but which may not be recognizable to the person observed. *Noise* is any message that is not relevant in terms of the original message, and which interferes with communication. It may actually convey very important information if you turn aside and look for it. A preconception may occasion noise, or mere mishearing. Noise may arise at either or both ends of the transmitting system, and also in the channel.

[1] Cf. Chapter Eighteen.

The question is commonly asked, "How much noise is there?" Rather than seek a noiseless system it is more rewarding, for social systems, to ask what is likely to be the general level of random activity or disturbance. A very valuable concept in engineering is the *signal-to-noise ratio:* Given a certain level of noise, how much stronger must be the particular signal to be heard over it?

As an organization gets more complex, the probability of noise may increase and the question would be: Are there specific organizations or devices or processes set up to reduce noise, or else is specific machinery set up to insure that a signal will be transmitted clearly above the noise level?

The sixth group of processes deals with filtering and *recognition* performance. That is, how do you pick out particular types of input from other types of input? How does a society recognize, or how does an individual, or an organization recognize a particular pattern of information among others? I can imagine that in the case of a visual type you test for structural correspondence in the sight patterns. You could probably do the same for sound patterns and other types of patterns. Recognition of style in art could be dealt with in this way. To recognize style would mean, from this viewpoint, to recognize a probability of partial recurrence or recursion. You can recognize that after another six yards another Gothic gird is going to come, and another arch will be so-and-so far away.

RAPAPORT: *The whole issue of anticipation, not in the scientific sense but in the sense of the subjective psychological process, or unconscious psychological process, involves recognition. It reminds me of what happens when you listen to a lecture, then read it. Even if the transcription is absolutely correct, the difference is amazing between reading and hearing it spoken. I would not call it "filtering." There are additional signals beside the words which make the speech understandable; the visual context is clear and the emotional context is clear.*

Besides filtering and besides the major context of the signals there is a secondary signal system given with every signal system. I believe it is true not only for individual but for social institutional contacts, that such a signal is accompanied by individual or authority signals, meaning that there is not just a field question here but a higher clearing of signals.

RUESCH: *We have called it "instructions about communication" or "metacommunication." The filter refers to the fact that any information is unintelligible unless it is accompanied by the things which do refer to the message itself, yet are not content. But the filtering also applies to the second thing: Not only can you filter out messages about messages, but also messages about messages about messages, of any kind of order. But the filter is a different quality or dimension.*

PARSONS: *I think there is a difference between the mechanical communications systems and human systems. In human social life the sender and the receiver are not determinate apart from the interaction process itself. There have to be messages that have to do with how the sender and the receiver are to be defined relative to each other, and not merely the independent content of cognitive communication.*

DEUTSCH: I agree with you, but this is often true of mechanical transmission as well. That is to say, high fidelity transmission is only possible by means of an appropriate state or appropriate equipment mobilized at the receiving end. You cannot say whether a gramophone record has a certain mood music on it or not, unless the record tells you what speed to play it at. Without the speed constructions you are not even in a position to find out what music there is.

To revert to the example of a spoken and a written communication: The participants around this table, being experienced conference participants, have mobilized a good many memories on short notice, and in his circulating memory each of us is now and can recall quite easily a large number of associations and connotations which very informal speech will activate. You can trigger these memories quite easily. But if the transcript were then read back to us, or even if the recording were played back, with all the inflections of our voices, or if you made a sound movie with stereoprojection and played it back to us, or to any other group of people who do not have these memories at their fingertips at that time, communication might easily fail. Thus recognition requires not only the signalled detail that comes to the receiver, but also a signal about the detail that is to be recalled for its interpretation. All messages which carry explicit ideas must also carry a second message with them, specifying the communication equipment by which they have to be received.

The seventh group of processes involve *prediction*. You know certain things happened several times before. You have recorded these repeated happenings, and from their stored traces you create expectations. From such memories, or series of traces over time, you abstract the prediction that the sun will rise tomorrow—which is a very simple prediction. Of course, we can think of very complicated ones. The ability to predict and the accuracy of prediction and the use made of such prediction would be of interest in any organization we study.

The eighth group deals with *consciousness* and identification. Consciousness may involve the assigning of symbols to itself or the system.

Does the system have self-reference, i.e., does it have symbols for its own behavior? Does it do anything in response to such self-referent symbols? Does their use lead to a change in behavior?

Group number nine is *restructuring*, which might be one of the results of consciousness. It is the changing of channel configurations within the system.

The tenth group would be *learning*. Possibly it might be better to put "learning" first and "restructuring" as a special case of learning.

PARSONS: *Isn't "restructuring" a certain case of "learning"? It is internal learning, as it were.*

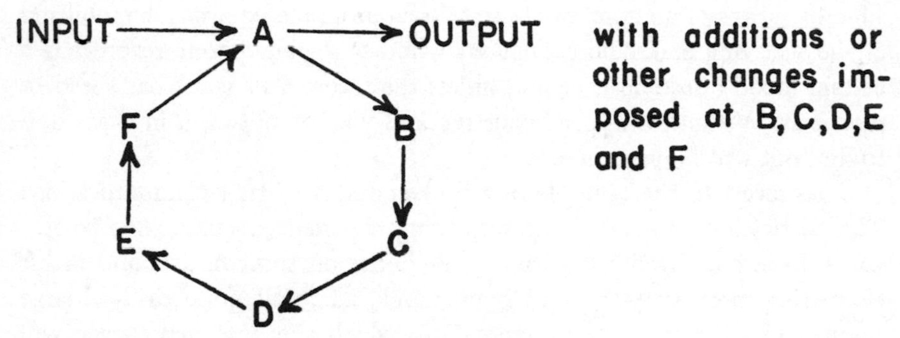

FIGURE 14. INTEGRATION

DEUTSCH: Yes; it is deeper permanent learning. I mean fundamental or broad restructuring. You can learn to play the piano, or you can have a fundamental personality change and be "born again," as the Apostle Paul put it. It might be worthwhile, for practical purposes, to keep apart the restructuring of some minor detail, such as a going concern which merely requires one new skill from a major process of restructuring where a great deal of the entire system is changed in terms of many performance characteristics.

Eleven is "*delegation*." You can say that after delegation, when the thing splits entirely, we get twelve, "*secession*."

Thirteen is "*integration*." Say you have a sequence of stages, A, B, C, D, E and F. F feeds back into A and there is a gain at the cycle. There is an input coming in and modified output going out (Figure 14). If you had secession you might possibly get a situation where you have an A-B-C loop and a D-E-F loop. Then you have complete secession or complete separation between the two (Figure 15, below).

On the other hand, if you have "delegation," you have a single output-input channel, and the loop through A-B-C, but at B there might be a superior loop, and on this higher order loop only might be D, E and F. The only effect of the outcome of D-E-F would be to make a slight difference in B (Figure 16).

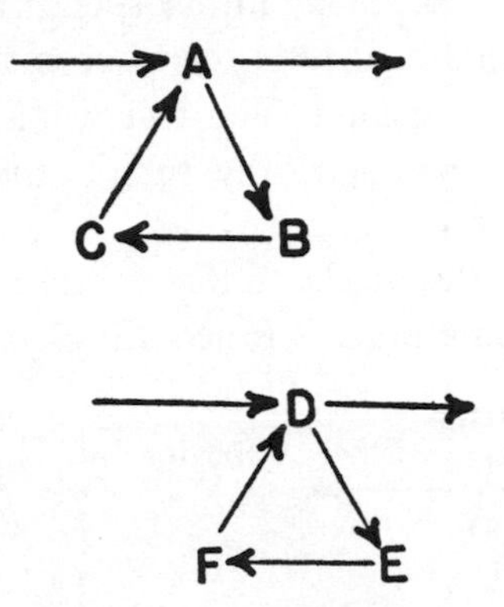

FIGURE 15. SECESSION

In this last case, that of delegation, the effect B has would then have, in its turn, an effect on the performance of D, E and F. Now let us say that F is to be kept at a steady function. For instance, I have a notion of what I consider a comfortable temperature in my room. Therefore, from time to

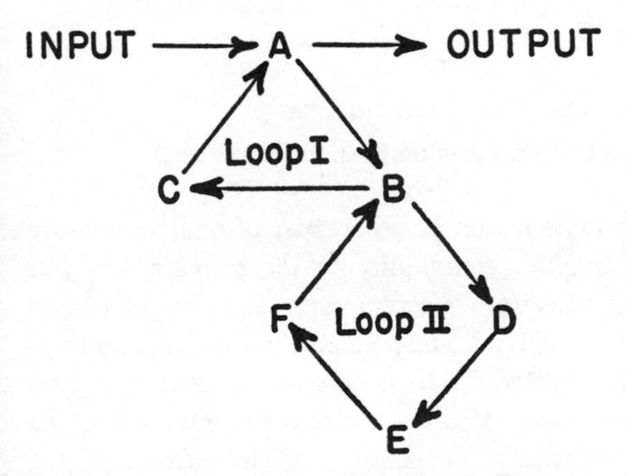

FIGURE 16. DELEGATION

time I will reach out from my chair at A to the thermostat B and set it to turn on the furnace at C whenever the thermometer reading at E drops below a certain value. The entire loop then, from the temperature of the room, D, and its reading at E, to the furnace at C, and back, is no longer in the feedback that has something to do with my behavior at A. I have delegated this to a subordinate feedback—B, C, D, E, B; but this subordinate feedback has one control point coupled at B into my own behavior feedback, A, B, C, D, A, in such a way that what I do to the control at B makes a big difference in the behavior of this feedback (Figure 17). For our studies of communication loops in our special fields we might be very interested in getting operational tests for what is subordinate, what is co-ordinate, what is entirely separate. The test would be which feedback is coupled to the other one asymmetrically, such as the coupling from A to B.

THOMPSON: *A good example of that is the community organization of the Hopi. Where a community is functioning typically it has a complete*

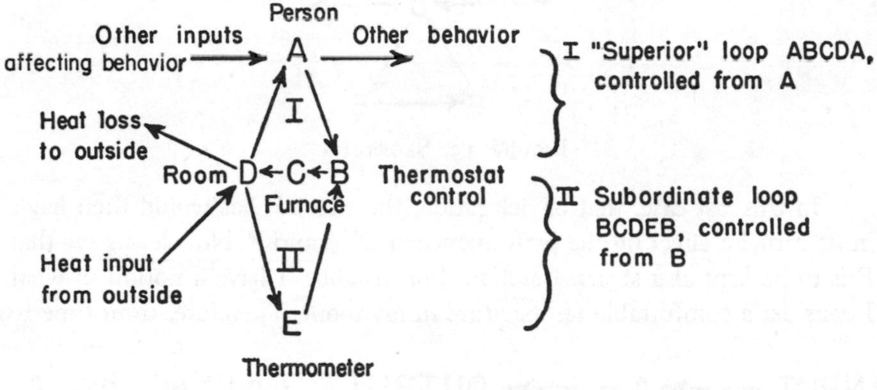

FIGURE 17

DELEGATION: THE THERMOSTATIC EXAMPLE

The Sequence BCD is common to both loops.

ceremonial cycle. Then, for some reason or other, part of one community may split off and form a daughter community to the primary one, but remain dependent on the mother for its ceremonies. The daughter community would represent the second type. The members of the daughter community return to the mother village for their ceremonies, and at a later stage the daughter community may separate entirely and may set up its own ceremonial cycle and be totally independent of the mother. If the daughter community then comes under stress because of a Christian missionary, for instance, the daughter might be influenced to change, and therefore you would have the other type.

DEUTSCH: That is a good example. If we go back to the illustration of the thermostat in Figure 17; the input to the thermostat comes from the room temperature and the output comes through the furnace. Originally, I say, I am in control of this delegated feedback because I am setting the thermostat; or because, in another but analogous situation, I, as an officer, am giving orders to the sentry. But it may happen that the strength of this coupling may change, and the sentry gets insubordinate, or the thermostat gets stuck, or the room gets cold because the windows are broken. In that case I might end up with a secession stage. Or it might happen that in the end I come to the conclusion that B cannot be reset or changed by me and I will change my input-output behavior in accordance with the assumption that there is nothing in the world I can do about B. In this case the coupling has been reversed.

If the probability is that A and B-C system are stronger, given a state of A, B and C, then I can predict with high probability where B will be set. But given a state of D and E, I cannot say what will happen at A and B-C. If you know the temperature at D-E is 65, you don't know what the owner of the house will do. Then, the owner of the house controls the thermostat. On the other hand, if you know the thermometer reading is going to stay in a certain position, and that that position is 95, you probably can predict what the owner of the house will do. He will get out or he will open the window. In this case it is the room temperature controlling him. It is the strength of the couplings at points B and D which controls the relationship "who-whom."

PARSONS: *A subordinate system, or, as you call it, a subsystem in this sense, has to be a subsystem of the personality, and not the whole personality, in this very narrow sense. A man may have essentially a robot function, and do nothing but follow certain very specific instructions; yet he has a whole system of personality needs that inevitably impinge somewhat upon the relationship. It can never be only delegating; there will be other more general relationships between the two systems in which he moves.*

DEUTSCH: If you speak of "subordinate" you mean essentially which feedback governs largely the behavior of the other. Which circular cyclical process governs the other?

EMERSON: *In biology we speak of "dominance subordination." It is coupled with the concept of leadership. The two systems might change ontogenetically: An individual who at one stage in his life cycle was dominant might become subordinate when senile, or he might be subordinate when he is young. So you have shifts in the system in time sequence.*

THOMPSON: *But you don't have to have the phenomenon of dominance. In the acculturation process there are often two groups with different cultures coming into contact, neither dominating the other. You have a transacting process. They influence each other.*

EMERSON: *Cooperation without dominance is found in social insects. But among vertebrates, organization commonly involves a dominance-subordination relationship, although this is not the only type of group system.*

There are times when equality occurs. In the social hierarchy of chickens triangles develop. However, those are usually successional stages, and they end in a strict linear order of dominance. Dominance at the feeding site may not be the same as the roosting site, however. And there is much variation in the hierarchical arrangements among various species.

DEUTSCH: We are looking for the mechanisms leading to secession, or for mechanisms which lead to delegation or dominance relationships, and for mechanisms which lead to integration relationships. We will say, then, that integration is thirteen and "differentiation and coordination" is fourteen. If differentiation is not coordinated the result will be either secession or dominance.

EMERSON: *Integration is not a contradiction of the division of labor of parts, and the two processes are not separate. They are reciprocal and complementary. You cannot have parts functioning unless they are integrated. Some of the parts specialize toward integration, so that part of the division of labor is in terms of integration.*

DEUTSCH: By "integration" I did not mean the dissolution of all smaller loops or patterns of autonomy, but the stress was on the big loop, and I abstracted from the autonomy of the little loops in it. In coordination, differentiation or cooperation, on the other hand, the stress is on the degree of autonomy that stays in the little loops.

HENRY: *If you assume that systems A-B-C and B-D-E-F in Figure 16 represent systems of delegation in a small task-performing organization—our own society—then in a sense B-D-E-F is contained in A-B-C, because the individual at A, who is the director, delegates part of his function to the smaller system, which carries it out.*

DEUTSCH: Yes, but not necessarily. You have brought out a very nice ambiguity in the model which needs resolving, and it is this: If the A-B-C loop has the property of setting B, and if B, once set, controls the performance, you have delegation—you have the thermostat or the sentry, the subordinate. But if it happens that the stage in the feedback loop which has the greatest effect on the performance of the loop is not at B but at E or F, then you have genuine autonomy. Then you have the situation, for instance, of the President and his advisers nominating a man for Cabinet rank, and the Senate, with their own considerations in mind, choosing to confirm or withhold confirmation of the appointment.

If it turns out that the most important stage in a feedback loop can be set from the outside, then the feedback has little autonomy, although there is some in the other stages, assuming the other stages are meaningful. If the strongest stages are set not from the outside but from some of their own resources, e.g., their own effectors and memories, then there is more autonomy in the feedback loop.

RAPAPORT: *I think that poses a very interesting problem, namely, that with systems which I could call autonomy, it seems that the least predictable point is steadily shifting. It is the rare system in which it is fixed once and for all, and is not a variable of time—an independent variable of time. Actually, autonomy would better be bracketed as a relative autonomy in general, because of the condition that this so-called autonomous system is itself part of other systems, and therefore its autonomy or lack of autonomy is an independent variable of time.*

DEUTSCH: You could then say that at any one time probably not all the over-all feedbacks and not all of the memory pools will be of the same importance. Therefore, you ask in, analyzing a particular organization: Is this a feedback where all stages are equally important? If not, where are the most important stages at the moment, bearing in mind that there is a probability that this control may shift to another stage?

FRANK: *This participation in other feedbacks may introduce what from one point is wholly irrelevant but nevertheless obstructive or facilitative reinforcements. That is where the complexity of the social situation arises. It may be something irrelevant to the decision process, perhaps noise, that comes in because of this participation in other feedbacks.*

RAPAPORT: *Possibly this implies the problem of transition from energy engineering to signal engineering. E, F and G's dominance or lack of it may depend on quantitative conditions present.*

To go back to your example of the United States Senate: Whether the Senate will pass or not pass over a veto depends on the forces that stand behind the government at the moment, and the force distribution behind the Senate itself. The point is that the shift of dominance between E, F and G in this case may depend upon purely quantitative conditions. Whether I will see Deutsch here as he looks now, or leering or angry, depends upon a certain kind of quantitative condition within me. It does not depend alone on a stable dominance of my perceptual system, which is supposed to be photographically highly accomplished.

DEUTSCH: To my mind it is of tremendous fundamental importance, for the understanding of processes in human society, to realize that human society consists of putting together relatively simple large feedback cycles by means of fantastically complicated components. For society is primitive compared to the resources and the arrangements of re-combinations available to the individual for short times. In the long run, society can mobilize more people, but in some ways this is different.

EMERSON: *That is extremely well verified in the insect society. The society is very much less complicated in its relationships than the individuals are in systems within the society.*

THOMPSON: *Does that also apply to a natural ecological society—the whole life web and its relationships?*

EMERSON: *Yes. the climax ecological community is much more loosely knit than the intraspecies systems within it, and the intraspecies systems are very much more loosely knit than the organismic systems of which they are composed. So there is a certain trend toward relative simplicity, the higher and more inclusive systems. Thus the personality as such will be very much more complex in its integration than, let us say, the relationship between nations.*

PARSONS: *But whether they are closely knit is a function of the number of units on a given level. Neurons are not units in a society. They are units in an organism which is a substratum which has to operate as a unit in social relationships: One neuron cannot act independently of other neurons in social relationships. Here size of the population is significant. The population of neurons in the human organism is many times the population of the United States, which is one of the most complex societies known.*

DEUTSCH: The amount of excitation among the neurons in the body in a given time is higher than that which we get among a large number of individuals at the present time, as found, say, in a public opinion poll. Again, something relatively simple, within one level and within a given unit of time, is made up of something that is much more complex. The society-to-neuron coupling is stronger than the other way. Possibly one of the most interesting things in the theory of human behavior is to find those patterns of organization which use the complexity of the individual resources as an asset. The obvious shortcut—the army way—is to try to simplify the neuron net in order to keep out of the way of the big simple social nets which get a priority.

EMERSON: *I wish to emphasize that although we get a simplicity of relationships in higher-level organizations, as we have mentioned, never-*

theless the science of society is far more complex than the science of an individual, and the study of the individual multicellular unit is far more complex a study, with many more factors involved, than the study of a cell. And a cell is far more complex than the study of a gene, and so on. In other words, we find a higher category of complexity or multiplicity of factors, and the necessity of getting quantitative data on many more factors as we go up from the physical sciences to the social sciences.

PARSONS: *Predicting the outcome of an election, the specific outcome, let us say, is like predicting whether a patient critically ill with pneumonia is going to recover or not. It may be a very evenly balanced matter, and the fact that you can't predict the specific outcome in this case with any accuracy has no bearing on the reliability of mortality statistics.*

DEUTSCH: Evaluating the performance of these larger social systems leads us to our fifteenth and last concept. It is the group of processes which we call *growth.* Can we get dimensions of social development?

Growth may be built out of the other processes. Thus, one dimension of growth would be sheer size or number. A second dimension, which the biologists have stressed, is independence from a wide range of environments. A third, which Toynbee has stressed, is increase in self-determination. That is, you could say that a system grows if it shows great improvement in autonomy and in its steering performance, which in turn involves coordination and reaction speeds. A fourth dimension might be an increase in the ability not merely to pursue given goals but to change goals; that is, in the range of goal-changing and learning. All these processes may play a role in growth.

EMERSON: *You might make a fundamental separation in your idea of growth or change, between what I would call the ontogenetic growth, similar to the life cycle of an individual, and phylogenetic changes that are similar to the evolution of the race. In biology the development of the individual is without genetic change. In phylogeny there is always genetic change, so we link up a whole series of phenomena with one or the other of the two dimensions.*

In evolutionary change toward urbanization we find a consolidation of pattern, which is a different phenomenon than that which we detect in, let us say, just the growth of a city as a replicated system having certain resemblances to other cities.

THOMPSON: *This may be applied to culture. In island communities that have been isolated for a thousand years or more, with practically no new genes coming in, there may be a phylogenetic change in physical type. An integrated culture may be carried by an integrated psychosomatic type, but also an integrated culture may be carried by a physical type that is not that way.*

DEUTSCH: That is a good point. One could think of the Greek slave economy as a culture which was ontogenetically self-destructive, but phylogenetically it was extremely productive in contributing to cultures which came after it.

Could one then generally include in the process of growth such things as the capacity for mutation or change, innovation and creativity, and, if you wish, the capacity for *self-transcendence?* That is, the capacity to transmit significant patterns beyond the physical existence of the channel system involved, just as parents do for the children who will live after they are gone.

A culture can do that kind of thing. The question came up: Why should human beings make provision for events after they are dead? Obviously, there is a reward for this behavior on the part of natural selection; but why should we care to be rewarded then?

One of the answers was this: If you build a network that handles information and extrapolates data and makes predictions, there is no reason in the world why this network should have an automatic cut-off device in it, saying, "Stop all predictions beyond the probable date of your own physical dissolution." In other words, it would be much more expensive to build a computer that is afraid of its own rusting, or that cuts off all predictions beyond the date of its own obsolescence. It is much more economical and simpler to build something that would cheerfully work and extrapolate things into the future beyond its own death.

There is thus a possible reward from the economy of design. I might call it an elegance of mind and body which might function as a biological reward. It is not only more pleasant but more natural for us to think beyond our own death, in other words, to think in terms of self-transcendence.

EMERSON: *We are integrated with our past generations. What we are now is in part from past generations. We are, moreover, moving as the organism does in its development—toward a future function as a population system. In other words, we have sort of a teleology, just as the eye develops in an embryo toward a future function. Biological data show over and over again that population life cycles are being selected as systems in distinction from individual life cycles.*

PARSONS: *We have a dramatic example of the same thing in the conditions of human socialization. The only basis on which it is possible* for parents to produce acceptable adults in their children, is to produce a wish to be parents themselves in turn, or to produce the motivational system which makes it a fulfillment for them to be parents in turn. The whole thing is so set up that the contemporary functions cannot be performed without providing for the future functions.

RAPAPORT: *I would like to comment on that point. It seems to me this happens only in economies of plenty. In concentration camp stories, records of concentration camp experiences and other conditions under the Nazis, it is a rather rude exception that the parents sacrificed the child for their own survival. There were exceptions to that. There were heroic stories, but the rule was the other. I believe animal and plant society would show such concern for the future. Human society does not seem to have many examples.*

DEUTSCH: I am not sure here whether we have a real parallel. In a concentration camp the parents would expect that the child would have no chance to survive at all, once the parents are gone. Therefore, what they were actually doing was making a decision between two of the family surviving or none surviving. Very few children did survive who lost their parents, particularly if they were small children.

CHAPTER TWENTY-ONE

CONCLUDING DISCUSSION AND AN OUTLINE FOR FUTURE CONFERENCE DELIBERATIONS

RUESCH: Let us try to establish on an intermediate level of abstraction some criteria for the construction of a unitary theory and perhaps we can utilize such an outline as a program for our future talks.

In the last few days we had discussions about boundaries. These discussions about boundaries can occur in several terms. They may occur in terms of membranes, of definition of mathematical systems, of social delineation, of communities, etc. The boundaries, because they are system-attributed, are boundaries in nature and not so much boundaries selected by the observer.

Next, we have been talking about the internal structuring of the events outlined by a boundary, dealing with the problem of organization, differentiation, specialization, etc.

Then we have been talking about the maintenance of the system outlined by natural boundaries. Under "maintenance" may be included such things as upkeep in the metabolic sense, the maintenance in terms of reversible changes, homeostasis, etc. The irreversible changes bring about an alteration of the system, irreversible changes in steady states, and changes in boundaries.

We also have been talking about relationships of one system to another system. Apparently the relationships of systems to other systems of the same order (person to person, nation to nation) have to be distinguished from the relationships of a system to systems of a different order. We have been talking about the relationship of the individual to the group, or we have been talking about the relationship of the liver or any other physiological part-function to the organism. Or we have been talking about the relationship of America to the United Nations. In other words, we have been talking about relationships which pertain to jumps in the order of time-space scales, organization scales, etc.

So much for system characteristics. At the same time we have been talking about things which were attributable to the human observer. The things attributable to the system and the things attributable to the observer stand in a relationship of complementarity. This means that if you talk about things that you attribute more to the system, then you lose information referable to the observer. When you concentrate on information referable to the observer, you lose somewhat information pertinent to the system.

The position of the observer was mentioned when we talked about whether the observer was within the system delineated by these boundaries or whether he looked from outside of the system at these boundaries.

The next problem which occupied previous meetings, more so than today, was the problem of the distance of the observer from the thing observed. As Eddington says, the dimensions of man are halfway between the dimensions of the stars and the dimensions of the molecules.[1] This also applies to the time scale of the observer, meaning that our human brain is equipped to deal with certain time scales and not with others, and that all the scientific reports we make are bound by these times scales of the observer in relationship to the time scales of the observed. This relationship of the two time scales influences our conclusions.

Finally we talked about the personal characteristics of the observer —his permanent bias, blind spots, purposes, methods and his denotation system.

DEUTSCH: Would you put "goal-seeking" between "maintenance" and "change"? "Maintenance" means that you maintain the physical channel system. "Change" means it would have to drift somewhere else. But "goal-seeking" means that a system in organization moves in search of certain things which are not directly related to its maintenance.

PARSONS: That is precisely the kind of trans-system question that I think can be most useful to discuss. I would say without any question that the concept of goal-seeking was essential to what I would call systems of action. The question here essentially is, in the organizational scale order:

[1] A. Eddington, "The Nature of the Physical World" (Gifford Lectures, Edinborough, 1927).

Does this go all the way down to what Toman was discussing—the molecular life system—or is this a point at which you can say there is a transition from a property of that character? Therefore, adding the heading "goal-seeking."

EMERSON: There are interrelationships between these, obviously, and really "goal-seeking" is an indication of an interrelationship between "maintenance" and "change." It is reasonable to assume it is part of both.

DEUTSCH: There are three things involved: external goal-seeking, self-maintenance, and goal changing through self-transformation. You have a given structure that is capable of receiving signals from the outside and reacting to them. This structure, if it is capable of reacting for a long period of time, has to be maintained. The process by which it is maintained may be entirely different from the process by which it gets information. Again, the way the structure behaves may be repetitive, or it may change its goals or its structure. That is the "change" category. These are three different things.

GRINKER: Yesterday we took up the word "purposefulness," and we got involved in a discussion of directiveness. Now we are using the word "goal," which is "need" in another frame of reference. Are these three words and these three concepts necessary in this particular group. Can we talk about action patterns without describing the need or the goal?

TOMAN: I would like to make a point about our own "need." We are a group working in various fields that have to do with man, where we are both participants and manipulators as well as observers. There is a wide discrepancy in the group as to what we think the problems are, where we think the shoe pinches, what we think the needs are. Our need for a theory is a sort of composite of these assorted feelings that something ought to be done about something. Of course, a great many of the things we discuss here are common denominators, ideas we take for granted. But there are also areas of contradiction where we do not seem to be able to make progress even in our individual fields. These areas demand theory. If there is any way of posing some of these problems and seeing what the blocks are, we could narrow down the field in which it is necessary to develop a theoretical framework. I still preserve a certain pessimism about the development of a theory that would simultaneously give indications of everything concerning human behavior.

THOMPSON: If we would agree that we were looking for a heuristic theory of human behavior, we would cover that point—a theory which leads to discovery and not just "any" theory.

SPIEGEL: It seems to me when we escaped the term "need" by describing the state of the system, it was a great advantage. It got us away from a system of terminology that would have brought us face to face with old philosophical problems, which was a happy thing. But if we treat the whole thing really in transactional terms or in terms of feedback loops, then is it really necessary to speak of "goals," or could some other system of description be found which involved a "focal point" or a "node" or an "intersection," with which this particular system happens to be in transaction? We do not need to use the term "goal."

RAPAPORT: But if it is clear that speaking in terms of "goals" is simply a way of speaking—if it is clear to the person who insists that its explanation shall be in terms of "efficient causes" rather than "ultimate causes," then there is no particular reason why he should not use the word "goal" or the word "purpose."

PARSONS: We can distinguish maintenance and goal as follows: A goal state is simply a state which is differentiated from another state in the relation of system and environment, a state which is defined as the minimum of certain forces, or the maximum or the optimum. In action systems a very important consideration indeed is that since there are rhythmic and cyclical processes (that is, maintenance) just looking at the interchange without reference to change of state between the system and the environment system (goal) is not adequate, and so a goal state phase in a cyclical process is a very important phase to consider.

MORRIS: I think something like "goal" ought to be kept in our terminology. We might use the word "orientation" or a term like "direction." It is just a question of what label to use. Although the term "need" has become largely an operational term for many persons, if it is to be used it must be done with care. In any case, we want terms that are general enough and yet neutral enough so that each of us, in our own particular subject matter, can specify how we use them.

HENRY: I would like to suggest that the term itself be left in abeyance, and that we discuss how various kinds of organizations or systems refer to terminal points. Having clarified that, we can decide what term we are going to use. Instead of regarding the "goal" as being in the front and "need" in the back, we need a position of orientation in time and space, but we will not specify whether the position be the terminal point or the beginning.

EMERSON: I suggest that this is another one of these circular feedback systems, and that if you try to arrange it in a linear order you are going to get into trouble.

HENRY: Then we can discuss the mechanisms in terms of which an organism will follow for a certain path, and this eliminates the notion of "beginning" and "ending."

TOMAN: This question of "need" and its ultimate conversion into more objective laws of motion is, of course, something that occurs at all levels of science. But until you have those laws you must have some kind of Anglo-Saxon word to indicate that the thing is moving. I still feel a need for "need" in relation to some of the laws of human behavior.

SPIEGEL: Parsons, where social systems are concerned, is it true that you can get away from talking about needs if you use the term "functional prerequisite," that is, the conditions under which the social system functions?

PARSONS: I don't think that is quite the same level. A need—both biological and psychological—constitutes a structure, for it is an aspect of the system which is organized in the sense so that, with respect to a static or more frequently to dynamic reference, if a certain trend of process in the system is blocked, that blocking will have traceable consequences. Wherever a system has features which meet that order of specifications, there is a "need." But a "functional prerequisite" seems to me to be on a little different level. It refers to the set of conditions under which the stable state is maintained.

EDITOR: *After the second conference Ruesch circulated an outline to all the members indicating matters relevant to systems of relationships in a unified theory of behavior. In it were two major headings: one concerned with relationships attributed to systems, the other to the observer. Statements referring to the observer were in complementary relationship to these referring to the systems. During the last session this outline, reproduced below, was discussed. It was decided to take up each heading in turn and to devote the fourth conference to Boundaries.*

TABLE 5

SYSTEM OF RELATIONSHIPS RELEVANT IN A UNIFIED THEORY OF BEHAVIOR

I. *Statement of relationships attributed to the naturally existing systems:*

1. *Boundaries:*
   (a) Surface characteristics, openings, filters, inner and outer surface.
   (b) Mathematical and statistical definition of the boundary.
   (c) Function of the boundary.
   (d) Energy dispersion across boundaries and interpenetration of boundaries.
   (e) Individual, ecological, social boundaries.
2. *Internal structure and function of the organization surrounded by a boundary:*
   (a) The relatively time resistant, anatomical, geographical and architectural structures.
   (b) Hierarchy and priority systems.
   (c) Specialization and differentiation.
   (d) Storage and memory.
3. *Maintenance processes involving reversible changes in support of the existing structures and functions:*
   (a) Energy sources of the system: metabolism, catabolism.
   (b) Activity periods and refractory periods.
   (c) Reproduction systems.
   (d) Storage devices.
4. *Irreversible changes in existing systems:*
   (a) Irreversible changes in boundaries.
   (b) Irreversible changes in structure.
   (c) Conditions which force change.
   (d) Emergency measures provided for in case of irreversible change.
5. *Growth and evolution in time:*
   (a) Goal seeking devices.
   (b) Goal changing devices.
   (c) The age and the past of the system.
   (d) Direction of development.
   (e) Transformation of structure.
6. *Relationship of system to other systems of the same order:*
   (a) Sex differentiation.
   (b) Autonomy and interdependence.
   (c) Permanent couplings.
7. *Relationship of system to systems of a different order:*
   (a) Autonomy and interdependence.

II. *Statement of relationships attributed to the characteristics of the observer and to his way of reporting scientific information:*

8. *The position of the observer:*
   (a) Inside or outside of the system.
   (b) Static position or changeable position.
   (c) Role of the observer within the system.
9. *The time and space scales of the observer relevant to the scales of the system:*
   (a) Distance to the observed: identified or unidentified particles.
   (b) Cross-sectional study or longitudinal study.
10. *The theoretical system of the observer:*
   (a) Closed or open systems.
   (b) Lineal or more complex systems.
11. *The methods and instruments of the observer:*
   (a) Reliability.
   (b) Validity.
   (c) Relevance.
   (d) Single versus repeated observation.
   (e) Recording machinery; errors.
   (f) Maximization and minimization of certain observations.
12. *The purpose of the observer:*
   (a) Observations in the service of an immediate purpose: status, financial rewards, manipulation of the system in terms of destruction or extension of the system.
   (b) Observations in the service of a remote purpose: extension beyond death of an observer.
13. *Experimental bias of the observer:*
   (a) Loyalties to one kind of observation or system.
   (b) The closed boxes of the observer.

FOURTH CONFERENCE

Statistical Boundaries

Boundary Relations Between Sociocultural and Personality Systems

Analysis of Various Types of Boundaries

CHAPTER TWENTY-TWO

STATISTICAL BOUNDARIES

Presentation by Anatol Rapoport

THE notion of a boundary is one of those notions which are difficult to discuss because of their fundamental simplicity. It is all but impossible, outside of mathematical context, to give a satisfactory definition of a boundary which would not in itself contain an equivalent notion. Yet in topology, for example, such a definition is implicit in the famous theorem of Jordan: That any closed curve drawn on a plane divides the plane into two regions, so that one cannot cross from one to the other without crossing the curve.

It is difficult for a mathematically unsophisticated individual to see the point to the theorem, precisely because its truth seems so evident that we rebel at the very idea of "proof." Only when one becomes familiar with the strange world of topological manifolds, where one discusses such things as one-sided surfaces and bottles without edges which nevertheless will not hold water, that one begins to realize there there may be something more to self-evident notions than meets the eye.

The notion of a boundary is difficult to analyze, because it is sometimes confused with the notion of distinguishability, which is truly a rock-bottom notion, not further analyzable. If, however, it is defined in terms of distinguishability (as a derived notion), we see at once that important generalizations suggest themselves.

Let us first define an unambiguous boundary in such a way as to make it independent of the existence of any physical barriers. We shall say that *if two classes of things are completely distinguishable, they are separated by a boundary.*

Such a boundary is a notion, not a physical thing. The surface of an ocean is such a boundary, if we assume that we can completely distinguish water from air or vapor, although the surface of the ocean is certainly not a material thing and is not fixed in space. Such a boundary is merely a "state of affairs," where the goings-on on one side of it are markedly different from the goings-on on the other.

To take a more abstract example, if a society consists of two or more sharply distinguishable classes they can be said to be separated by a boundary. This boundary has nothing to do with geometry, not even with the geometric outlines of the individuals. For one may have class mobility, where individuals cross from one class to another. If this transition is instantaneous, we still can speak of a sharp boundary between the classes, since at each instant of time each individual is recognizable as a member of one class or another.

The passage of individuals from one class to another can be called the flow across the boundary. The rate of flow is usually called "flux" in physics. In many situations this rate of flow is the center of interest, the boundary itself being important only to the extent that its characteristics or parameters determine the flux.

If the distinguishability between the classes is not perfect, one may speak of a statistical boundary. What shall we call the edge of a forest? Obviously, what we agree to call by a given name is a matter of agreement. If it is observed, for instance, that the density of trees in a certain area can be expressed as a continuous function on the surface where trees grow, we may agree to call the "edge" or the timber line, any imaginary curve such that the density of trees is above a certain specified value on one side of it and below on the other. Similarly, we can call the boundary of cloud an imaginary surface where the density of condensed water vapor particles on one side is greater than some specified value, and less on the other. Similarly, if a social class in a society is characterized by the response which its members make in a particular situation, then unambiguous membership in a class is determined by the exclusive occurrence of a particular response. Those people who respond sometimes in one way and sometimes in another can be said to be in the *statistical boundary*, which can be more precisely defined by specifying the particular probability of response which is to be considered as the threshold of membership.

As an example, consider adolescence as a boundary between childhood and maturity. For legal purposes, and generally in situations where agreement is required, it is desirable to fix an age as an objectively verifiable boundary. Biologically, puberty may be taken as the event which separates the two states. But the age of puberty varies, and is thus impractical. One procedure is to determine the age at which 50% of individuals have gone through puberty. In practice, of course, legal ages are rather arbitrarily chosen; but the choice of a legal age can be justified by such probabilistic considerations: It is the age at which the probability that a person will behave in a certain way reaches a certain value.

Some workers in mathematical biology have utilized this statistical notion for rather fruitful quantitative investigations, notably in psychology. I will present one such example here: A subject is presented with two stimuli, say two different weights, and is asked which is the greater. Suppose one weight is always greater than 100 grams and the other always less. Essentially, then, the subject is asked to draw the boundary between all weights less than 100 grams and all those greater than 100 grams. Obviously, the difference can be perceived only if it exceeds a certain value. Then, if the subject does not wish to make mistakes, he will put all weights which are considerably greater than 100 grams into one class, all those which are less into another class, and the rest into a band which will form an ambiguous "don't know" region.

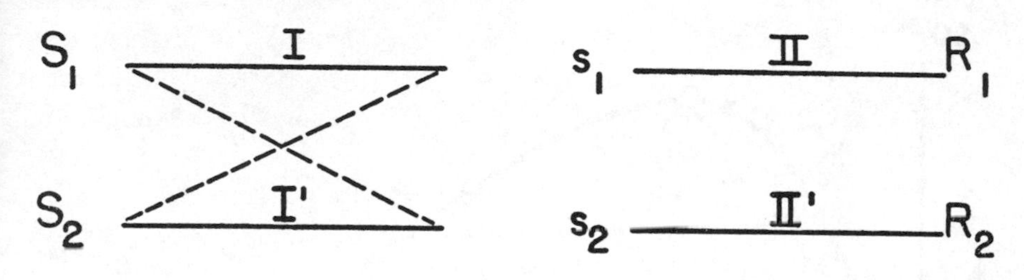

FIGURE 18

A MODEL OF BOUNDARIES BETWEEN EXCITATION AND INHIBITION

Stimuli S_1 and S_2 initiate excitation along the pathways I and I′ respectively, which in turn excite pathways II and II′ leading to responses R_1 and R_2. The dotted lines represent inhibitory tracts. Thus, an excitation of a certain strength in I is accompanied by an inhibition at synapse s_2.

If, however, the subject is directed to make a decision in every case, the ambiguous region becomes a "statistical boundary," in which the answers are sometimes right and sometimes wrong. By making rather simple assumptions concerning the dependence of the response on certain neural events, the parameters of this statistical boundary can be determined, and through them some parameters of neural action can be inferred (Figure 18).

According to this scheme, only the larger stimulus (due to the heavier weight) will elicit the corresponding response. By a slight modification of the scheme, a response will be elicited only if the difference between the two stimuli exceeds a threshold value. The "statistical boundary" is now brought into the picture by supposing random fluctuations of the thresholds at the synapses s_1 and s_2. Now when we apply the equations of nerve excitation and the distribution of threshold fluctuations, we deduce a quantitative relation among the frequencies of correct, wrong and "don't know" responses as a function of the weight differences. Experimental data agree with almost embarrassing exactness with the predicted curve, as shown in Figure 19.

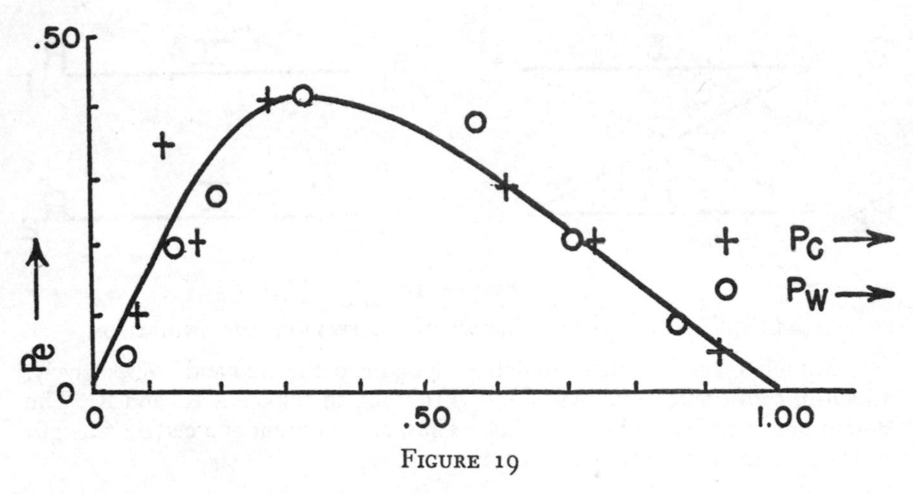

FIGURE 19

Correct and wrong responses (P_c and P_w) are plotted on the horizontal axis and the "don't know" responses on the vertical (P_e). (A. S. Householder and H. D. Landahl, *Mathematical Biophysics of the Central Nervous System* [Bloomington: Principia Press, 1945]; J. P. Guilford, *Psychometric Methods* [New York: McGraw-Hill, 1936].) The asymmetry is only apparent. The maximum of "don't know" responses (about 40%) are correlated with about 30% each of correct and wrong responses. The equality of the latter shows that no bias is operating.

Here, then, is a mathematical model utilizing the notion of a statistical boundary, which accounts quantitatively for certain experimental data. The importance of such models is in that they imply certain values of certain biological parameters. If now an experiment can be designed to calculate these parameters independently, the value of the model is greatly enhanced.

In both biological and social phenomena we are often faced with very similar situations. To make a few wild guesses: Is it conceivable, one may ask, whether hermaphrodism, for example, is an instance of a statistical boundary? Is schizophrenia a statistical boundary between two or more "organizations" of a personality? Can the statistical methods similar to the ones cited be applied in an analysis of opinion polls or other records of mass behavior?

Another statistical aspect of a boundary is seen in a physical barrier, which, however, is not "absolute." As an example, consider the "potential well," a concept often invoked in physics, which can be most simply illustrated by a valley, one of whose banks is higher than the other. Suppose there are marbles rolling over a frictionless surface toward this valley from the left. It is clear that only the marbles having a kinetic energy above a certain value will be able to pass across the valley. If this kinetic energy is distributed in some way among the particles, the flux across this barrier will be a "functional" of this distribution—in fact will equal $\int \frac{P}{k^*} p(k) dk$, where $p(k)$ is the frequency distribution of the kinetic energies and k^* is the critical kinetic energy which just carries a particle across the well.

We are therefore again dealing with a statistical boundary. An analogous biological situation was suggested by Shimbel. Suppose there are two niches in a given environment, one able to accommodate animals of sizes ranging within certain limits and another able to hold similar animals of sizes in a different range, not contiguous on the first. Suppose now there is a mutation of size whose magnitude is distributed with a certain frequency. Then only those mutants which jump from one range to the other will be viable.

We are again dealing with a "statistical barrier," but of course not a "physical" one. This picture can be still further generalized if the survival probabilities for the sizes between the two optima are finite, and if we suppose that several successive mutations can carry an organism from one flourishing species to the other. A possible illustration of this situation may be seen in the amphibians, the "poor relations" of the vertebrate subphylum, which are the transitional forms between the prosperous fishes and the prosperous land forms.

In making decisions, of course, we are really estimating probabilities. We do it in a rough and ready way, but sometimes this estimate becomes quite precise. For example, in business and warfare, and so on, the staffs actually calculate to a certain extent the probability of the result of various actions.

SHIMBEL: *Frequently you find that one person may be in some psychological state, and then for several days at a time he may appear entirely different. One naive person might say it is entirely normal. The same naive* person at another time will say, "He doesn't look right at all." It seems there are two stable states here, in a sense, and at times the transition occurs from one to the other.

GRINKER: That is correct. He passes, as Rapoport said, across the boundary. Regardless of what our particular concept of schizophrenia may be today or was twenty years ago or will be twenty years from now, we will still be involved in the same problem of the observer making these decisions; so the definition of schizophrenia does not mean anything in these terms. You are now talking about the observer and his way of estimating probability.

MORRIS: This forces us to investigate whether there are boundaries or not and suggests that there are problems of determining them. It also raises the question of what degree of probability we are willing to accept. These become matters of relative tightness and looseness of boundaries in terms of probability relations, and it would seem to me that whether we settle on ordinary statistical levels of significance or not, the real test is what we can do with it after we have accepted a boundary. If we do take this as a boundary, then what sort of predictions and other kinds of evidence can we get? I think this question of how much it is in the system and how much in the observer, and so on, must be confronted.

GRINKER: Morris, weren't you trying to raise the question of whether there really are boundaries, and doesn't all this discussion of psychiatric entities bring up the question as to whether these are continuants and whether there are any real boundaries?

MORRIS: Yes. The real point is that we have methods by which we can get answers.

EDITOR: Shimbel next presented examples of boundaries of cells and in particular the membranes of neurons and their processes. Living membranes do not have constant permeability but show large temporal and directional variabilities under different conditions. One theory considers the membrane to possess lipoid solvents, another suggests that the membrane is porous. Such pores or holes would be of different size and capable of being filled up or blocked by certain ions. Perturbation of the membrane could inhibit or increase the passage of ions by closing or opening more *pores. Furthermore, interaction of ions with other ions would influence its size and affect its permeability. Such membrances constitute statistical barriers because they depend on the size of the ions, their concentration in the medium, the oscillation of the membrane and the distribution of the number of pores.*

◇◇◇

TOMAN: *In neurophysiology, as elsewhere, there has been a great deal of energy devoted to the construction of models based on relatively static membranes, except insofar as there is thermal agitation or some other simple type of motion—in other words, a swinging door kind of model, such as we have seen here.*

But some of the phenomena which these models set out to explain may not really exist: for example, the apparent impermeability of cells to sodium and potassium. This issue was forced, originally, by the realization that there is a difference between the inside and the outside of many cells, including nerve cells, insofar as the common electrolytes are concerned. Recently, however, most of the work which has been done with tracer sodium and potassium indicates a fairly high rate of penetration of both, a high rate of exchange across the hypothetical membrane.

In erythrocytes, although superficially it is difficult to change the sodium and potassium concentrations, the actual transfer rates are very rapid. Krogh showed that by the simple expedient of cooling the cells to the point where the metabolic rate is sufficiently lowered, the distribution approaches that of the external solution.[1] *We have shown that one can change the internal concentration of phosphate ion more easily than that of sodium and potassium with peripheral nerve fibers, yet the exchange rate across the membrane for sodium and potassium seems to be higher than that for phosphate.*

Phosphate as it enters the cell appears first to attach to a protein constituent, subsequently to appear as relatively free phosphate, and lastly to become incorporated chemically in the liquid fraction. This is almost the opposite of a physical diffusion sequence.

Furthermore, the rates of uptake are dependent on temperature in a way that very strongly suggests that metabolic work must be done, and

[1] A. Krogh, "The Active and Passive Exchange of Inorganic Ions Through the Surfaces of Living Cells and Through Living Membranes Generally" (Croonian Lectures, Procedures of the Royal Society [London, 1946]), Vol. B 133.

that there is a set of chemical reactions going on rather than a dependence on relatively simple physical diffusion processes with factors for thermal agitation.

Taking all these facts into account—and we could find many more examples—I think we would go further in the study of many of these boundary problems if we did not think of them as merely passive and static.

GRINKER: *The three theories that have been given, that is, the chemical, the electrical changes and the physical diffusion, are not mutually exclusive, nor do they indicate a static state of the membrane. But are they not all necessary at one time or other? Are not all these concepts necessary?*

TOMAN: *Yes, you cannot proceed to the study of biochemical interactions without also considering how two substances can get together in a particular phase in the first place—their solubility. So the physical rules are not contradictory to the chemical rules, and one has to understand both. However, I still feel justified in pointing out some of the dangers of static conceptions which keep recurring in our own field of neurophysiology.*

For example, Ling recently has tried to devise a model of nerve based largely on the properties of sodium and potassium, and avoiding the question of the metabolic work of the system,[2] *just as Conway tried to do for other cell types some years ago.*[3] *This seems to me to put too much emphasis on the passive aspects and too little on those active properties which tend to maintain a self-perpetuating steady state.*

RUESCH: *In social science we are concerned with the "perhaps" more than with the "yes" and "no," which seem to present no difficulty. For example, if you have an army at war, there are people who are alive and people who are dead; you bury the dead and you let the healthy fight. What do you do with the wounded? Do you shoot them or nurse them back to health? Genghis Khan and other Mongol rulers decided that all the wounded and prisoners were to be shot. We decide that all are to be nursed back to health. But there were reactions against both kinds of decision. In social science we always deal with decision-making, meaning that we behave as though we had freedom to choose when actually we do not. When a decision is made toward the "yes" side, something happens pretty soon to reverse it.*

[2] G. Ling, "Role of Phosphorous in the Maintenance of the Resting Potential and Selective Ionic Accumulation in Frog Muscle Cells," in McElroy and Glass, *Symposium on Phosphorus Metabolism* (Baltimore: Johns Hopkins Press, 1952).

[3] E. J. Conway, "Exchanges of K, Na and H Ions Between the Cell and Its Environment," *Irish Journal of Medical Science*, October, 1947, pp. 593–609; November, 1947, pp. 654–80.

RAPOPORT: There are any number of ways you can look at it if you simply imagine that the influences impinging on the individual in his decision-making functions are similar to physical forces, or something like that. Then, what you are actually asking is how the equilibrium position of that person is to be determined. Is that what you are asking?

RUESCH: *What I am really saying is that "perhaps" does not stay a perhaps. In retrospect it proves not to have been a "perhaps" at all.*

RAPOPORT: I will take another crude example. A man is torn between the desire to make money and the desire to conform to certain standards of honesty. He can do it one of two ways: He can either decide in advance, in which case he is going to behave one way, that is, he can choose a boundary. Or he makes no such decision, which I believe is the more realistic case, and sometimes behaves one way and sometimes another.

If you count a great many instances, you will see that there is a certain distribution, which brings us back to the question of the statistical boundary. In other words, the inconsistency of behavior of human beings in various situations, which seem the same, may be attributed to these probabilistic random influences that may inpinge at one time or another.

PARSONS: *Boundaries don't need to be completely fixed and static. They may be. There may be various kinds of oscillatory processes or cyclical processes. I think what Toman was saying indicates that the probability is that there are a great many of these processes which involve relations to the central intrasystem phenomenon, so that the boundary is not stable, independent of the state of those intrasystem processes.*

RAPOPORT: There are two different aspects of the statistical notion of boundary. One is this: You have a hazy region in which things are not decided. Sometimes things go one way and sometimes another.

Another aspect of a statistical boundary is that you do have a barrier, whether physical or any other kind doesn't matter, and you are measuring the flux against this barrier. The flux is determined by the characteristics of the entities which come at it, as, for example, in the case of jumping over the fence. Then the statistics are not in the boundary but in the particles crossing it. The boundary has perfectly definite characteristics, as, for example, the height of a fence. The statistics are there in the entities that are going to cross the boundary. In a steeplechase you have a certain percentage of the horses falling, and a certain percentage of the horses going across. The height of the fence is fixed.

THOMPSON: *May I qualify what Ruesch just said? Some social scientists, on the basis of certain assumptions, study these boundary phe-*

nomena and not the "yes" and "no" phenomenon. Those social scientists, I think, are the groups which operate on the basis of certain premises which they have stated explicitly. But there are other groups of social scientists who have no such fixed categories on which they operate, and therefore they find that they have to investigate not only the boundary phenomena but also what you call the "yes" and "no" phenomena.

SPIEGEL: *I wonder about freedom of direction as far as boundaries are concerned. Even in an idealized model of a membrane, you would have to put into it the fact that even if it is kept at a purely physical level—disregarding what possible chemical events occur—things are going to move in the other direction. Ions are not going to be just coming in from the outside, but I would assume the ions on the inside have to go through those spaces, too. If they do, there must come a time when they meet each other, or crash. What happens then?*

RAPOPORT: You are faced with certain facts. First, in a resting state there is a well-defined difference of the concentrations of sodium and potassium inside and outside the nerve cell. Second, in an excited state there are certain processes which have been well recorded—the inflow of sodium in certain stages, and the outflow of potassium in other stages.

Now, you can explain these facts in different ways. For example, you can say that the difference in concentration is kept in a resting state by reason of a physical barrier. The tracer studies belie that, because they say they can trace the individual ions going across. Another explanation is through some sort of metabolic process that keeps concentrations on a level different from what they would be in an ordinary equilibrium concentration.

The question then arises: Do the two processes, even though physically different, have the same mathematical form? In other words, perhaps it is as *if* there were a physical barrier, even if there is none. Then you simply choose the simpler picture, keeping in mind that you are not describing what is going on but that you are describing a language to describe what is going on, and then investigate the implications of what you say.

HENRY: *Could we make this analogy to psychiatry, in this sense? The level of anxiety in a person, the permeability of his personality structure and the different kinds of impressions all change, so that under one state of anxiety he might become aware of several kinds of impressions that under another state might be completely shut out. As his anxiety mounts, the series of impressions that enter his mind at one point again would be shut out.*

GRINKER: *You can prove that as far as the individual is concerned, because in tests for perception you see variations in efficiency with the degree of anxiety related to specific situations, so that less of the outer impressions are accepted.*

RAPOPORT: This whole picture can be generally described as a phenomenon involving a positive feedback, in the sense that depolarization of the membrane enhances its permeability, and vice versa. A panic is another example. Some banks fail, and people rush to draw out their money from the banks. This causes more banks to fail, which induces more people to make withdrawals, and so on. With anxieties, too, I would be willing to accept the hypothesis that in anxiety the permeability of certain types of stimuli becomes greater, which in turn increases anxiety. There is a general tendency to emphasize process, rather than geography or structure. Geography used to be defined as the science that describes the outlines of continents and forests, and so on. Now more dynamic considerations have entered geography—for instance, ecological considerations. Anatomy described the structure of bodies and how they related to each other geographically; and now we stress physiology.

MORRIS: *It may be that some of the boundaries are changing, too. It may be that rather drastic changes are taking place in these structures.*

RUESCH: *When you come to that point, actually the whole thing amounts to the time scales of the observer, because what you call static and what you call flux is nothing else but relevant to the time studies.*

TOMAN: *Being sick or wounded is that state through which it is necessary to pass between being alive and being dead, even though it may be a very brief state. It is also that state in which one is least likely to find members of the population at a given moment. It is a good example of a necessary state between two relatively more probable states, and the important boundary question concerns the people who are moving between the two states.*

What we seem to be talking about in connection with boundaries is usually a distinction of at least a minimum of three states, in two of which it is probable that one will find any unit in the system. The third is necessary for the transition, but is the least probable state.

HENRY: *The difficulty I have in bridging the gap between your formulations and social science, particularly as stated by Ruesch, is that in the social science system there is always somebody making a decision. As you represent your system there is nobody making a decision.*

THOMPSON: *I would have trouble with both of your positions, because in some cultures there are actually not judges and generals and people of that sort. Again I will give my example of the Northern culture of Europe, and mention the Mesolithic core culture as it developed later in the Stone and Bronze and early Iron ages. The Nordic peoples did not have judges until a relatively late period.*

PARSONS: *There are a great many subject matters in social behavior about which, in the society concerned, decisions are ruled out. For example, we are not allowed to make a decision as to whether an anatomically male child should be brought up and socialized into a masculine or a feminine role. It is a perfectly possible decision. I would radically deny your proposition that all social phenomena are phenomena of decision.*

SPIEGEL: *I want to bring this back to a point that was made the last time we met, in relation to the properties of boundaries and of homeostasis, and that was the filter phenomenon. What this model does is to describe some statistical properties of the filtering process at that boundary.*

RAPOPORT: To make the analogy distinct, you would have to say that particles in a certain range of sizes go through. Those either too small or too large will not go through. Then you will have quite an analogy to the filter phenomenon.

SPIEGEL: *If you conceptualize it at that level as the filter process, then whether one speaks of openings or of judges in a social system, or commanding generals, or masculine and feminine roles, it is the same sort of filtering process. There is always a mechanism for what can go through and what can't go through.*

RAPOPORT: Nobody has ever seen a decision. What we see are certain states of events before and after, and it is a way of speaking when we say, "A decision has been made."

SHIMBEL: *In a sense, if you take "decision" in a most obvious sense, the more we use that word the more we negate the possibility of the science of psychology or social science. Is the process of selection an analyzable process? Therein lies the crux. If it is analyzable, then science is possible.*

PARSONS: *I don't think very many social scientists will consciously define it in such a way as to exclude its analyzability.*

RAPOPORT: No, but the analyzability is an extensible concept. Some people, upon seeing evidences of indeterminacy in any situation, will immediately say, "Here is a situation with which we cannot deal." By extending the notion of boundary to a statistical boundary, we thereby extend the range of analysis.

THOMPSON: *This is a very important point, because in all scientific work we have to think of the level of precision which is significant in the solution of the problem under consideration. The statistics need only be precise enough to be significant.*

HENRY: *What Parsons said about the ruling out of the possibility of making decisions in certain kinds of social situations might be demonstrated by Rene Spitz's moving pictures of passively rejecting and actively rejecting mothers. These were mothers who were making a decision, within certain limits, whether the baby would live or die. They also might be making other kinds of decisions; for example, as to whether the baby would grow up to be a full-fledged male or partially female.*

PARSONS: *By this you mean that the way we handle the situation will have certain probable consequences? You do not mean that there is an intention to bring about those consequences? There may not even be an unconscious intention to bring about all consequences which actually ensue.*

SHIMBEL: *Whenever you use the word "intention" or "purpose" or "decision," no matter how finely you try to define it, there still will be a very broad difference among any ten people as to what they think you mean by it.*

RAPOPORT: Nevertheless, there are clear-cut cases, and of course there is a boundary region, as in anything else. For example, a person describes some future state of affairs with reasonable accuracy, and then proceeds to act to bring about that future state of affairs—that is intention. If a future state of affairs is not determined in his actions, you say that his actions lead to that state of affairs without intention. There are intermediate stages, also.

DEUTSCH: *The problem of intention involves two things: First, is there an image of the future result? We know of many cases where such an image of the future is used, but the motive for the action is to get rid of another tension, and the entire supposed purpose may not be the actual purpose of the program at all.*

I would like to ask this: Are there analogies to the problem that occurs in politics between things which are routinely decidable in a community, in the sense that alternative decisions are made, and things that are decidable but are not in fact decided for a long time? When the Moslems conquered Kashmir some centuries ago, they put the men of Kashmir into women's dress in order to reduce the number of military men in the country. It could have been done at any time before, but in a particular situation the conqueror discovered that something was subject to decision, which in fact was a potentiality for a decision there that had not been used.

SPIEGEL: *Since we are trying to get at the general properties of boundaries from any examination of any particular one, and statistical approach is general, I wonder if there is any way of representing any interaction process or transaction process between the boundary itself and the process? With a certain amount of going through, something might happen to the spaces. They might change. If we are going to think of a boundary as a dynamic property of a system, then I should think we would have to be able to represent that statistically. Is that possible?*

RAPOPORT: That is exactly what is expected in the case of nerve excitation. As things become more permeable, things come through, and then the boundary changes.

SHAKOW: *In some ways the discussion seems to me to lead to a definition of "boundary" on an operational basis, as the area of relatively greater difficulty in assigning belongingness or class. It is that kind of thing which psychologically is a process from the point of view of the observer. Then, looked at from the inside, as it were, it is the area of contact, of the interaction between two distinguishing things.*

MORRIS: *This raises a whole host of interesting empirical problems, namely, what level of probabilities as mathematically defined do we find in various problems in an area that corresponds with the actual discrimination behavior?*

RAPOPORT: In a more complicated sense, recognition. An example is given, for instance, in information theory. Let's suppose you pull out letters at random, and you have a sample of language. It looks like gibberish. Then suppose you throw in the frequencies in which those letters actually appear in English. It still looks like gibberish, but somehow it begins to look more like English than it did before. Then you pull out the letters in pairs and triples, and it looks like jabberwocky, which is almost English. It becomes more and more recognizable.

A great many experiments like that suggest themselves, which would treat the notion of boundary in various contexts. I don't think any general statement can be made as to when there is a boundary and where a boundary would disappear.

PARSONS: *I think there ought to be a very careful discrimination between that which you might call logical boundaries, in the sense of discrimination of classes, and empirical boundaries, which are the difference between systems in an empirical sense. The boundary between a nerve cell and the muscle in which it is imbedded is a boundary between empirical systems. But the distinction between blue and grey is a definitional distinction which requires an operational definition, an empirical value.*

TOMAN: *In both cases, empirical and logical, there is a factor of self-perpetuation in a certain class, once the class has been decided on. Let us take the judge's decision. Regardless of whether it is true or not, it sets into operation a number of factors that will now perpetuate this classification, where the quality is still hanging in the balance. At one time the decision could have gone either way; but now perpetuating and self-exciting factors enter in, continuing the existence of one or the other class. This also would be true in any number of empirical systems as well.*

PARSONS: *For the social side, the judge's decision is part of the empirical system, so he uses the categories of the law.*

SHAKOW: *There are two senses of "empirical" that are being involved here: Is the person actually guilty, or is he not guilty? Second, what does the judge say about this situation? Toman was talking about whether he was actually guilty or not guilty. The judge's decision now tends to perpetuate the decision about guilt, and the question is not opened again except in extreme instances.*

GRINKER: *The question is considered settled, to perpetuate the judge's decision, his so-called inertia, his importance. Actually, uncertainty is one of the most anxiety-producing situations. Compulsive individuals, who can bear no uncertainty, see only polar opposites. Others who can see no boundaries are, for example, the schizophrenics who cannot comfortably distinguish self from not self. So there is a great individual problem. Most of us are satisfied with varying degrees of certainty in determining boundaries.*

FRANK: *That can be illustrated genetically and historically. The development of the individual as a personality involves just that process of increasing capacity for discrimination, or failure to do so. In the history of common law you can see how the merchant was established as the law, and then, as the common law gradually crystallized, it gave the judges the limits within which their decisions could vary. The cases then were: Did it come under one logical category or not? Law is, very largely, trying to bring your case into the category of a decision point of one boundary or the other so that you can win your case and can persuade the judge that you are on that side. You can develop that in English common law very easily.*

RAPOPORT: There are some things which are so just because people say they are so, without any possibility of verifying it. My name is Rapoport simply because people say my name is Rapoport, and it is so for no other logical reason.

PARSONS: *In social phenomena, things are as they are because the behavior of people make them that way. There are cases of boundary transition where it is decided by what they say. The honorary Aryans of Hitler, and of course other people may be put in certain categories by virtue of explicit acts of decision. For example, you certify this gentleman has fulfilled the requirements of the PhD degree and becomes a doctor, which he wasn't before.*

RAPOPORT: My point is that if you want to ascertain certain things, you don't take the sort of measurements that you would take if you were to ascertain what the chemical composition was of a substance.

PARSONS: *It is a question of how far the particular characteristics are those of generally organized systems. They may be just on the borderline of the system and can be extruded from it or included in it by a very trivial force, but the personality structure of an adult human being cannot be changed by just saying that it shall be changed.*

RAPOPORT: Take a better example. Suppose that the city passes an ordinance that from now on this particular street traffic will be one-way, but the city puts up no signs saying it is one-way. Nevertheless, sufficient publicity is given to it so that everybody understands it is now a one-way street, but only by virtue of people saying it is.

TOMAN: *Time after time the patient says, "I am sick; I hurt," and so on. This can be looked at in different ways. One thing admissible here is that you say it is so, so it is so. You may hurt and you may not hurt. What you are sure of is that in some contrast to some members of the population the person complains about hurting. Two things tend to happen: One is that his reiteration of the existence of the pain actually may have very real effect on his behavior, and he is bothered in such a way as to continue to bring about pain, and even, according to one theory, to determine eventually visible pathology. But also you work with him to the point where he eventually is all right. This is a situation where the mere saying that something is so, without proving whether it is so or is not so, brings all kinds of organic and empirical implications.*

Deutsch: *I was thinking that the question has been put to us in two forms. If we are dealing only with symbols, we can use symbols to set up distinctions between symbols and boundaries which are completely conventional, but actually we think implicitly that they may be relevant to something.*

We say two and two equal four because pebbles and eggs and other things behave roughly like integers. You can't say that two clouds and two clouds are four clouds. I wonder whether or not all boundaries which we set up are intended somewhere to have empirical relevance. If we say this is really different from something else, we mean that a boundary will be revealed not only by some discriminating operation number one about which we know now, but also by a future test operation. The more closely corresponding boundaries we get from mutually independent test operations, the more real we may consider them.

Can we usually say that empirically what we find is practically never a boundary, in a sense, but could we define it as a noticeable, recognizable differential in an interaction flow?

Morris: *I would agree with Deutsch, but also it seems to me that we tend to settle upon those boundaries for our symbols which are related to boundaries that we find elsewhere. This is a control over our symbol system. To have a language at all, you have to have a certain structure; do we have to have certain symbols whose boundaries are simply stipulated?*

I doubt if the control of the boundaries of symbols by other boundaries is complete. I think we must distinguish between the symbol boundaries which are simply stipulated (such as requirements that a yard contains three feet and each foot twelve inches), as opposed to those symbol boundaries which we have adopted because of their relation to other boundaries.

Parsons: *Morris points out something important. A boundary is not simply a reflection of experienced discrimination, but it organizes experience, and hence comes the capacity, both in the individual, in a limited way, and in the culture in a much less limited way because of the cumulation and the greater time and numbers, for discriminations that were never meant at all to be seen and symbolized. Generally the symbolization precedes the observation of the discrimination. Again and again, at the higher scientific levels, unless the way has been prepared by the development of conceptual schemes, the facts would never be observed; or, if observed, would never be interpreted and organized.*

TOMAN: *Here is something else about the development of conceptual schemes: First of all, the only raw material you have to work with at the beginning is experiential, and it is outside the boundary of what we call the body; ultimately, in an organic way, it has been built into the body. However, you have only partial experiences to work with.*

One important function of the brain, however, is that it is able to take partial experiences, reshuffle them, and eventually envision not only the more probable combinations but also to conceive those which are impossible. It may even treat them temporarily as possible, and find ways of exploring and testing whether they do in fact exist.

So we may envision more systems than actually exist. We temporarily consider them probable ones only because it is impossible to know the totality of the systems and the interactions in them. Our raw material is less than adequate so we are left with a boundary region where things that might conceivably exist are, but some of these are eventually going to have to be excluded.

MORRIS: *What you are saying is made possible by the genius of language. While language involves limitations on the possibility of types of combinations of signs, that is, they can be combined in certain ways and not in others, it sets no limitations on the number of combinations possible. So, always, by combining signs, you can get complex symbols (also complex concepts) which had no experiential origin and which may not denote.*

EDITOR: *The conference subject assignment of boundaries was opened by a discussion of statistical boundaries, transcending the physical demarcations. Abstract and ambiguous transitions from one region or notion to another may be dealt with statistically, resulting in more precise probability estimates. The question was raised whether statistical boundaries are real or part of continuities. The processes involving the structure-function of biological membranes were used as prototypes of boundary concepts in psychology and social science. Boundaries have the properties of a filter and the size of the openings become analogous to decision-making in social situations. It was stressed that boundaries are never static but are involved in and change through movement or transactions through them. Boundaries may not represent experiences but may be symbols which organize experience.*

CHAPTER TWENTY-THREE

BOUNDARY RELATIONS BETWEEN SOCIOCULTURAL AND PERSONALITY SYSTEMS

Presentation by Talcott Parsons

I WANT to stress the rather special relation that I believe exists between sociocultural systems and personality systems. I will first say a few things about two classes of background problems.

The relation between social systems and culture is the subject of unresolved controversy both within the anthropological profession and between anthropologists and sociologists. A rather heavy majority of American anthropologists hold that culture was the primary focus of their professional field; but, according to some, the British anthropologists aren't anthropologists at all; they are sociologists. In other words, there are not settled questions, and there is not any orthodoxy.

My view is that culture is keynoted by the concepts of transmission of the social heritage and of its relation to learning as over against the genetic determination. An inference which would not be universally accepted is that the focus of culture lies in its relation to symbolic process, and to the meaning which patterns of symbols in human (therefore social) interaction would help to define and stabilize. Culture there has a very intimate connection indeed with communication. This way of looking at it puts culture in a rather special position relative to the concept of action system or behavior system; for a system of culture is not a behavior system at all from this point of view, but is a set of components that are essential to behavior systems at a certain level.

Culture does not act—only human beings act as individuals. Culture is transmitted; it is shared; it is internalized in the personalities, institutionalized in the social systems. It is a set of meaning patterns of symbols. But it is important to point out that the discrete, completely isolated symbol is not a very good model because of the extreme importance of patterning and the relationships of many symbols and many meanings.

Now this view connects very nicely with Emerson's analogy of the gene and the symbol.[1] The cultural complex in this sense has functions in behavior systems that are analogous with those of the gene in individual organism systems. It has its evolutionary predecessors; a full-blown cultural level develops when certain evolutionary stages in the organization of behavior have been reached that have to do with such things as generalization, abstraction, and so on.

Beyond that there are two very important things about culture that are relevant to the boundary problem. One is that the distinction beween norms or values and other aspects of culture is a relative distinction. You do not talk about culture at all unless it has normative significance; that is, there is always an expectation and in some sense obligation to conformity with conventions.

You cannot invent your own symbols and your own meanings at will and arbitrarily. There has to be some kind of agreement. It does not have to be arrived at by discussion, but there has to be common understanding of common meaning. If you are going to be understood, you have to observe the conventions of the language. This goes for all kinds of symbolic communication, and therefore there is always a normative element: Are you doing it properly from some point of view? From that viewpoint, social norms, let us say, having to do with the definition of the major expectation patterns of social relationships, are special cases of this much more general normative emphasis.

The second item is the extreme complexity of culture with its many different systems and subsystems of meaning, and with differing levels of generality and specificity as well as of meaning context. On both the cultural level and the social system level our current trend of thinking is that it is dangerous to talk globally and analytically about A culture, A society, as if it were for most purposes a completely undifferentiated and definite entity.

That is not to say that for certain comparative purposes these have no place. But precisely in the social system field, the conception of a

[1] See Chapter Twelve.

society (which would be the term I would use to refer to the most inclusive system type) is that of a very complicated network of interlocking subsystems, and the analysis of those subsystems and their interrelationships are much more the focus of current scientific interest than the characterization of the over-all features of the society as a whole. This is different from what it was a generation ago.

This is particularly important in relating culture to social system as distinguished from society. To some extent and in some sense the same culture may be shared by more than one society or more than one social system, particularly the same cultural elements. The Boston Irish and certain elements of the French do not constitute the same social system in every respect, but that they share the culture of Catholicism is undoubtedly an important fact about them, and one which differentiates them from Yankee Protestants or from French Jews.

While on a certain level we can speak of cultural commonness as transcending the plurality and differentiation of social systems, on a more concrete level every social system must have a common culture, which may be a differentiated variant of a wider culture; but there are aspects of it that are specific to this particular culture in the social system. And in treating the concept of social system as a boundary on the cultural-symbolic level of system organization, then this criterion of the common culture is a focal one.

From this point of view, a society is simply the most inclusive general type of social system, which for most analytical purposes is capable of independence of existence as a system. Thus, by definition, a family is incapable of independent existence. If it were not part of a larger social system, it would not be a family in our sense. It might include certain characteristics but, for example, it could not possibly have an incest taboo, which is one of the fundamental characteristics.

There is a more difficult problem of boundaries in the case of society, than with reference to the individual organism, because, short of humanity as a whole, only in empirically secondary cases do there exist social systems which are completely independent of the rest of humanity.

For practical purposes we speak of the United States as a society; but very clearly we have international unions, corporations, associations, and many subsystems cross the boundary between American society and other societies. However, as a broad focus of integration and organization, this is close enough to be useful for many purposes, and it is qualitatively, of course, very different from a single occupational group or a single family, or a single city.

The important point here is social system as organized about a common culture of its own (a subculture of a society) which has a normative aspect. Those who do not recognize the same norms are outside the boundary.

HENRY: *It seems to me you are using the term "a society" in the same way in which anthropologists might use the term "a culture."*

PARSONS: They often do, but you see the difference. The English language would be part of American culture from the anthropological point of view, but the language isn't part of the society in the usual sense. It isn't part of it because a society would have actors as units, and a language is not an actor.

RUESCH: *Previously I defined* culture *as the cumulative body of knowledge of the past, contained in memories and assumptions of people who express this knowledge in definite ways. The* social system *is the actual habitual network of communication between people. If you use the analogy of the telephone line, it corresponds to actual calls made. The* society *is the network—the whole telephone network. Do you agree with these definitions?*

PARSONS: No, not quite. In the limiting conception a society is composed of human individuals, organisms; but a social system is not, and for a very important reason, namely, that the unit of a partial social system is a role and not the individual.

RAPOPORT: *The monarch is not an individual, but is a site into which different individuals step. Is that your unit of the social system?*

PARSONS: Yes. A social system is a behavioral system. It is an organized set of behaviors of persons interacting with each other: a pattern of roles. The roles are the units of a social system. We say, "John Jones is Mary Jones' husband." He is the same person who is the mail carrier, but when we are talking about the mail carrier we are abstracting from his marriage relationship. So the mail carrier is not a person, just a role. On the other hand, the society is an aggregate of social subsystems, and as a limiting case it is that social system which comprises all the roles of all the individuals who participate.

RUESCH: *I am still not clear. Could you give us a complete example? The Department of Social Relations at Harvard is a social system. The United States is a society?*

PARSONS: No. I would say the United States, for most practical purposes, is a society. But theoretically, to be a society it should include all the roles of all the participating individuals; but that is a limiting case which is seldom very closely touched upon. It is like a perfectly integrated social system which does not exist but is a very convenient heuristic device.

RAPOPORT: *What is the largest social system contained in the society of the United States?*

PARSONS: It is the limiting integral of all the role systems, where every role of every individual is included in the system. There are millions of social systems within the United States. A social system can reach beyond the society, but in the theoretical limiting case, it should not. Most of you have read about Tikopia. That comes about as close to a society in this sense. It is an island 400 miles from the nearest land. One little merchant ship a year normally calls there. It is about as completely independent of any outside participation and influence as it could possibly be.

DEUTSCH: *You say society is limited by self-sufficiency. Now, the private enterprise system, which is a system of roles, is clearly larger than the United States. In that sense, geographical terms of systems could be much larger than society.*

PARSONS: This is analogous to the interpenetration of species in ecological systems.

EMERSON: *Our definition of an ecological community that is likewise an interspecies system is an independent, self-sufficient system. But it is a relatively independent self-sufficiency rather than an absolute one, so that, as with your own case, it is self-sufficient in certain definable respects only.*

PARSONS: That is exactly the dilemma we are in. If I could concentrate on the subsystem, which is a system of roles, I would like first to speak about its boundaries vis-a-vis the three classes of other social systems. First, any such subsidiary social system is always, to some degree, a differentiated part of a superordinate system. An example would be a university faculty, or an urban community, which obviously has to be part of a division of labor, with a good producing area, and things of that sort. So its relation to and its functions and structural relations to the rest of the system are always important.

Now in a strict sense one would speak of its boundaries vis-a-vis the complementary systems, such as the university faculty vis-a-vis students, who also constitute a subsystem, and the two in turn are part of a larger subsystem, vis-a-vis cognate subsystems of a superordinate system, that have essentially the same function. We will say the Harvard faculty is distinguished from the University of Chicago faculty.

And, of course, mobility across those boundaries is possible in both cases in the case of memberships. A student can eventually become a member of the faculty, and a man may change his job from one faculty to another, but they still retain their identity as distinct systems.

Then, of course, there are boundaries vis-a-vis nonsocial systems, notably the physical environment. The problem of the organism of the individual and the personality, I think, needs to be treated a little distinctly; but I would speak of human relations to animals as often constituting social systems but not on the cultural level. A man's relation to his dog, for instance, is definitely a social interaction relationship.

DEUTSCH: *Does self-sufficiency imply that if you cut off your unit from something it will change its behavior in some respect, or is it limited to anything as serious as an impairment of its self-steering or its self-preservation? If I am cut off from strawberries, that is one thing; but if I am cut off from light, that is much more serious.*

PARSONS: I would essentially use maintenance of homeostasis, maintenance of its major patterns. There are all sorts of possibilities of new mechanisms and substitution, and so on; but it was not self-sufficient if it either had to become incorporated in a new society, or if it had to change its pattern fundamentally.

Now I am coming to the implication of the conception of a social system as consisting of roles and not of individuals, and the fact that both social systems and personality systems are treated as behavioral systems. If you take those two together you get a very important boundary problem. Social systems and personality systems are not merely interdependent, but they interpenetrate. That is, the role as a unit and a part of the social system is, in fact, part of the personality. It is not simply what the personality does—it is part of the personality, because the personality is what the person does. The condition of optimum integration is that the same cultural patterns, with special reference to the normative aspect, which are institutionalized in the social system, are internalized in the personality system.

But integration may not be optimal; there are degrees of institutionalization and of internalization, and it is perfectly possible to play a role overtly, with it only very partially institutionalized in the social system. The best case is the socialization of the child, which we know takes many years.

DEUTSCH: *The period required for such internalization may depend very much on the personality the individuals bring to it. A person who could get thoroughly indoctrinated in two years would make a suitable type of traditional German recruit, but would not make the same kind of soldier in another kind of group.*

FRANK: *Parsons, if you put the emphasis upon the roles being institutionalized, then what is the importance of their being internalized?*

PARSONS: Because it is a critical fact that social systems and personality systems are interpenetrating and also interdependent, so there cannot be a completely uniform degree of internalization in all the personalities participating in the system of social interaction. You have to make that distinction. Vice versa, there can't be a uniform degree of internalization of all of the patterns involved in all the roles that the same individual is involved in. So the unevenness, the lack of complete correspondence, operates both ways.

FRANK: *Do you define the institutionalized in terms of recurrent regularities of behavior?*

PARSONS: Yes. And internalization is seen as the uniformities of certain attitude patterns in a personality toward certain types of situations.

FRANK: *Institutional patterns or prescribed roles can be more or less successfully predicted because we know that a certain number of individuals are going to exhibit these roles and use these institutional patterns with certain recurrent regularities. But these predictions about the frequency of occurrence in a group do not necessarily apply to any single individual personality within that group. The situation here is like that in tables of life expectancy or predicted mortality. We can predict with considerable accuracy how many individuals in each age group will probably die within a given period, but these predictions do not give any clue to the survival or death of any identified individual. We can, however, make predictions about specific individuals on the basis of prolonged observation of their previous experience and activities from which we may derive certain probabilities of what they will or will not do.*

PARSONS: But that is because you assume the population involved is one of which the units are human individuals. But in the personality, the population would be acts. If a man has done the same thing thousands of times, this is a very big population, subject to statistical analysis.

There are many, many different degrees and levels of internalization and complications of roles and subroles. An actor is a relatively generalized role. Playing Othello is a much more specific role. I would say that Othello is probably slightly internalized, but much less so than the role of being a professional actor.

Might I now come to the point that, with respect to social systems, defined as having a common culture, there are two fundamentally different kinds of boundary relations. One is vis-a-vis the rest of the participating personalities; that is to say, the boundary of this social system vis-a-vis our family commitments, and its boundaries vis-a-vis other social systems that do not involve the common different segments of the same personality.

Now with respect to the common personality, it seems to me there is one extremely fundamental consideration; a behavior system is in certain respects parasitic on the physiology of organisms. It is always the behavior of organisms. And with respect to capacities, but particularly with respect to energy, there is no energy—there is in a psychological sense no motivation—which is not in some sense derived from the organism. Behavior systems are organic energy-consuming systems; they are not energy-producing systems. The inference is that we must treat apparent motivation as nontransferable between personalities. I know this is unorthodox, so I will explain further: You can transfer motivation from the search for better food to the solution of a scientific problem, or something like that. But what I call expressive communication seems to me to be the primary direct mechanism of the allocation of motivation.

However, when such communication is interpersonal, what it does is to operate on the balance of the other person, tending to encourage him to withdraw somewhat from one line or one set of goals and shift it to another set of goals.

When I encourage a student to do something, I don't give him more energy. I influence him to reallocate his energy in certain directions, in preference to other directions. It is analogous to a radio communication system; there is some sort of energizing of the sending set, and maybe a much smaller energizing of the receiving set, but the radio wave does not energize the receiving set.

GRINKER: *This is extremely important, because at the present time we are still using the assumption that there is such a thing as psychic energy that is communicated. Just as there is no social energy that is communicated, there is, however, energy transformed in the sender and the receiver. The transmission across the space is the communication which is not energy-consuming. We cannot conceive (although it is part of the*

Freudian theory), that there is such a thing as psychic energy, for the energy utilized by my speaking to you is part of my organism. The energy that you use in receiving my communication is part of your organism. I do not communicate any energy to you.

RAPOPORT: *It is questionable whether in many of our efforts the thing that we use can be properly called energy. What energy is used in intellectual work when we sit down and think? What is it we are relocating in our own organism?*

HENRY: *How do people get their social motivations? From where do they get them, if not from communication with other people?*

PARSONS: They have them because they are living organisms. The trouble is you are treating the motivation as a given, organized entity. But you should look at the energy component as not entering in as a prior organization primarily. The function of the earliest socialization is to destroy in the child the prior organization, such as it is, and to approximate, as nearly as possible, an undifferentiated state, which can then become differentiated and organized, first by oral dependency, then by further human attachments, in ways appropriate to the cultural level of interaction.

An important thing that perhaps is hard to understand if you have not been through a long analysis is this: This interpenetration of personality in the social system imposes certain conditions on the nature of personality. In other words, you cannot have a personality which is in fact part of the same system or that interpenetrates with an interaction system unless its organization is congruent with that of the social system.

This is the basic thing that Freud discovered with his concept of the superego, and the internalization of culture, and it is very interesting, although not nearly as widely recognized by psychiatrists and others as it should be. It was independently discovered by Durkheim from a sociological point of view.

It means that either some anthropologists are right and culture is independent of genetic constitution of the organism, or a certain psychological tradition is right, namely, society or social systems are essentially organized on the basis of genetic individual differences. I maintain that there are always organic prerequisites of behavior systems, but that in the human being much of the genetic specificity of behavior pattern has dropped out and, as it were, has been replaced by cultural and symbolic mechanisms.

EMERSON: *Behavior, of course, can be genetic. Most of the behavior with which I am dealing in social insects is strictly genetic, including their form of architecture and their form of agriculture as well as most of the interindividual behavior systems. It is initiated by genes.*

Now learning comes in, which is a liability of this system not dependent upon specific genes. The behavior after an experience is unlike that before an experience. There has been no change in the genetic components of these two behaviors; but the capacity or potentiality of learning may rest upon certain genetic bases. So the genetics is related to the labile learning in this way, without making a complete dichotomy between them. Then, when you come to the symbolic system, of course, that is learned, and it becomes divorced from the genetic system because the differences in learned behavior are not based upon genes.

GRINKER: *These two points of view demonstrate that society cannot evoke from the organism any more than it is capable of genetically. We do not "destroy," but we constantly change the pattern in, for example, the way in which we feed a child. We can almost completely repress the sense of smell. We can almost completely inhibit the formation of active immunity as we inject every child who has a slight fever with penicillin.*

RUESCH: *We have discussed homeostasis in the individual and in the larger social system, and the difficulty of linking the inner with the outer organization. The same dilemma faces us now. You mentioned concepts of motivation, energy, and so on. The model is based on certain assumptions which bear upon the internal structure of an individual, neglecting his social surroundings. You do not care how motivation, impulses, energy came to exist, but once they were there in the individual you wonder how they got organized.*

You have connected society or social system with the individual, linking the smaller system with the larger system. One of our tasks is to amplify this linkage of the smaller system with the larger system, because our greatest theoretical mistakes have been at that point. We can avoid these errors when we use the analytic system, or when we use the social system, or when we use homeostasis in the individual, or when we talk about death in one individual; but when we link the individual to the species, there our theoretical mistakes occur. We make some unpermissible generalizations at that moment for the sake of making the smaller system and the larger system fit each other.

PARSONS: But it is the nature of behavior to be a process and set of mechanisms of such linkage, and the linkage is the key to it. It is a relational system. So you are in trouble if you try to generalize from either system without explicitly dealing with the relationships as a system, whether you begin with the structure of the personality or with what the personality does.

RUESCH: *Granted. But there the question of language comes in. As soon as we use terms like motivation, energy, and so on, a pre-set mechanism in our mind begins to work. We need a new, separate term for those linkage phenomena.*

MORRIS: *It is essential, as Parsons would recognize, to see that the notion of role is really itself a symbolic concept. For him a role consists in sets of expectations—systems of expectations—so that the role, say of policeman, is symbolically defined and maintained. A policeman is meant to act in certain ways, and certain people are meant to act toward him in certain ways. Role behavior seems to me to be symbol-controlled behavior, and therefore role boundaries to be symbol boundaries.*

PARSONS: That is what I mean by the common culture element as defining boundaries. It is the symbol system that defines the location of boundaries, not the mechanisms.

MORRIS: *Now take the organism in its process of growth—and here I am thinking in somewhat Meadean terms: It does not become in a strict sense a personality until certain symbols are operative in the organization and steering processes of the individual.*

To the extent to which the symbols by which we define the social system become also the key integrating symbols of the personality system, there is a process of internalization of the social system.

The fact that the same symbols operate and constitute the social system that become dominant symbols in the personality system gives the linkage—the common element—between the social system and the personality system.

RUESCH: *When you use the word "role" as describing behavior, it is not the same as when you use it to describe expectancy in the head of an individual.*

PARSONS: No, it is not the same thing, but it is part of the same system.

RUESCH: *Yes, but then you use terms like these alternatively, as if they were one and the same. My expectancy about something, and the actual transaction, are two totally different things.*

MORRIS: *Insofar as the internalized role symbol becomes a dominant organizing element in an individual's personality structure, to that extent you have approximated a convergence of personality and social systems.*

This is a matter of degree, as Parsons pointed out, and it seems to me that it is a question of how basic the role symbol is in the organization of the personality.

A man may very well be a policeman in the sense of performing certain behavior conforming to the role symbol "policeman," without this symbol being a basic organizing component in his symbolic process—and to that extent the personality system and the social system diverge.

GRINKER: *I think it depends on the closeness to the reception of energy-giving substance; that is, the closer the symbol is to the source of energy, the more internalized it is. The mother role, when feeding is by bottle or breast, becomes internalized much more than the role of breadwinner, which furnishes the money to buy food in later life. In other words, there is a gradation, a continuum, which is more powerful the closer it is attached to an energy-giving substance directed by the symbol.*

PARSONS: There are many, many levels of internalization and symbolization. The more complex the organization, in some respects, the more unstable its structuring, and subject to certain kinds of influences. I think this underlies the phenomenon of regression—that regression is to more stable substrata which go back to more elementary motivational associations, and so on. All of this fits in with the idea that personality development should be treated as very closely analogous to the embryological development of the organism, with certain roots from which a branching process develops.

DEUTSCH: *Would it be useful to distinguish energy-linked systems from trigger-linked systems? In an energy-linked system to some extent the scale of magnitude of the event that goes on from one subassembly to the other, from one individual or group to the next individual or next group, is proportional in some way to the energy transmitted. In trigger-linked systems it is not at all proportional to the energy transmitted.*

Within the trigger-linked systems, then, it would make sense to distinguish, shall we say, between gene-linked systems, where what is transferred is largely genetic, and message-linked systems, where what triggers the reaction in the next subassembly is a very small energy input which actuates something from the memory.

The critical point would be this: Does the input go through a memory stage in the receiver? If one uses this, one can try to measure autonomy in a very crude way, and I think Rapoport might have a more precise way of putting it.

You could measure autonomy by the amplification ratio or the trigger ratio. In other words, what is the proportion of output into input, or of the scale of magnitude of output to the scale of magnitude of input?

In addition to this amplification ratio, you could measure autonomy in terms of the unpredictability ratio. In other words, if the input implies a certain probable subsequent development, with a certain number of degrees of freedom, what are the number of degrees of freedom in the output? If the output is much more improbable, so that it can be predicted that much less from the input, then you have more autonomy. The unpredictability ratio would thus denote the eon of predictability—and conversely, the gain in autonomy—from one stage to another.

These two numbers together could give you certain numerical measures for autonomy, and I suspect that in cells within a biological organism both of these ratios should in most cases be quite significantly lower than they are in societies. In other words, this might give us an impersonal measure which would distinguish sharply societies and social organizations from cells and organisms.

As regards the problem of triggering, can you predict the extent of the response, which is the amplification ratio, from the instability and internal imbalance already existing at the receiver? That is, the more unstable the receiver is, the more closely it is balanced so that a very small input might touch it off, and the greater the imbalance after it has been triggered off, the greater the response, and the greater the amplification.

If this is so, a system of internal imbalances or tensions might be essential to responsiveness. In that case it might be difficult to teach children very much by destroying completely their previous system, and it might be easier to teach them in those terms in which instabilities or imbalances or needs already exist within them.

PARSONS: I hope Shakow will agree that learning without frustration is not likely to be successful. There has to be a combination of frustration and timed reward. This gets into a complicated set of considerations, but there is a sense in which too stable a balance of the organism is unfavorable to learning.

I think the basic kind of organization we are talking about applies on the very elementary behavioral levels of learned behavior patterns. The stimulus-response sequence, which really is an action system of a very elementary character, and the socially structured system, I think, should be regarded as superordinate organizations of more elementary behavioral systems. They are clusters of organization of the more elementary system components.

I might try to sum up a few considerations about how all this seems to apply to boundaries.

If you conceive a social system as a behavioral system, I would say its boundaries are defined by the relevance of a subculture—defined, not governed nor regulated. I would say that there are two sorts of boundaries —the boundaries vis-a-vis the rest of the personality of the participants, and the boundaries vis-a-vis the activities of nonparticipants.

From this point of view an individual personality has several subcultures (it is not just a single unified culture) which have to be organized in a system. Boundary processes are input and output processes, and I think you must distinguish those which go on within the same personality.

Intrapersonal communication as well as interpersonal communication is a fundamental process, but trans-system communication has to be different from intrasystem communication. There is always a problem of translating meaning from intrasystem uses to intersystem uses, and that is a major aspect of boundary process.

In social systems a most useful concept is the concept of representative role; that is, the role which acts on behalf of a social system vis-a-vis other systems. The special communication skills necessary for that as an interpreter in one set of respects are very important.

I would distinguish communication process as one of three fundamental types of boundary process going on between social systems.

A second type of boundary process is interchange of members, which I think is another qualitative difference from personality system, because it cannot be the same order of process. It is like recruitment of personnel into an organization.

The third is the interchange of possessions. I distinguish communication from possession. If, for example, information is transmitted from A to B, A still knows it, although B has learned it. However, a possession is transferred. B has it and A no longer has it. That is a critically important aspect of intersystem process. It goes on within a system, but when you look at it that way it is between the subsystems of the system; that exchange of emphasis I would use as a technical term for the transmission of possessions.

◇◇◇

EDITOR: *Parsons differentiated social systems from culture, defining the latter as a shared and transmitted set of meaning patterns of symbols which are internalized in personalities and institutionalized in social systems. In behavior systems culture is analogous to the gene. Culture has many differing levels of generality and specificity, yet within each there is always a normative element. A social system is organized about a common culture of its own; those who do not recognize these norms are outside a boundary. The unit of society is a human individual, of a social system it is a role in a particular behavioral system. Boundaries may be said to exist between differentiated social systems in a society, characterized by mobility across and interpenetrability. Boundaries exist between social systems and personality systems which are not only interdependent but also interpenetrate. The role is the unit of a social system but only part of the personality.*

Discussion ensued on the boundaries between the behavior system and personality, and included the question of what is transmitted in interpersonal communication: energy? motivation? Parsons maintained that although there are always organic prerequisites of behavior systems, in the human the genetic specificity of behavior patterns has been replaced by cultural and symbolic mechanisms. Role behavior is symbol-controlled and therefore role boundaries are symbol boundaries and personality comes into being when certain integrating symbols become operative, thus establishing linkage between personality and social system.

CHAPTER TWENTY-FOUR

ANALYSIS OF VARIOUS TYPES OF BOUNDARIES

Presentation by Jurgen Ruesch

LET us now consider the boundaries that delineate the individual. *First*, we encounter the physical boundaries: the skin; meninges; periosteum of the bone; fasciae of the muscles; capsule of liver, spleen and kidney. These structures function as organ boundaries. *Second*, we have the system boundaries. Obviously, the vascular system interpenetrates every other tissue and is found in all organs of the body. The respiratory, intestinal and genito-urinary systems likewise interpenetrate. Although found everywhere in the body, these systems also have boundaries. There exists a *third* type—the biochemical boundaries. Selective absorption from the intestinal tract, selective passage from blood to spinal fluid constitute such boundaries. The *fourth* type is the psychological boundary. When psychologists talk about "identity," they mean the sense of boundary that mature people possess about their limitations, social functions, and roles.

Although the terms I have mentioned often infer natural systems such as a capsule of the liver or the glucose content of the blood, there must be an observer, and the observer does two things:

First, he observes the naturally existing boundary, calls it by a name, and has a concept of it in his head which he maintains until a revision of his view becomes necessary because the situation has changed. If you view a road which is divided into three lanes, you would say that the middle lane is the boundary between the two outer lanes. Why? It is an interesting

Gestalt problem, because it depends on the relative sizes of the lanes. If you plant trees in the middle lane and make it narrower, you still call it a dividing lane. However, if you made the dividing lane a mile wide, you would not call it a boundary. Actually, then, in perception, boundaries are dependent upon size, situation, density, proportions and all sorts of other factors which are functions of the observer's perception and evaluation system, and not functions of the naturally existing boundary.

Take another example. If you sit at a bar with two other people to your right and you want to talk to the third person, you find that the second person is in your way. For practical purposes, he becomes a boundary. Or if one person is sitting behind a desk and the other two are in front of it, you would probably say there is a boundary between them. Why? Because of special configurations! Or if two people live together but are separated in a Japanese paper house by a piece of paper hanging down, you would say that the paper is a boundary. Or if someone in a log cabin makes tracks in the snow around the cabin, you would say that the boundary is somewhere where the tracks end and the untrodden snow begins. That also is a boundary. These few examples might indicate that the problem of boundary is essentially a very complicated one, depending both on the natural systems on the one hand and on perceptual configurations on the other.

THOMPSON: *In Polynesia and many of the Pacific Islands the ground plan of a house is divided into sections for each class. There is no line or marking of any sort—the division is invisible, just in people's minds. If you belong to one class, the upper class, you go to one end of the house; if the middle class, you stay in the middle; and if you are in the lower class, you stay toward the door.*

RUESCH: *Second,* there are the type of boundaries that the psychiatrist meets empirically. Many terms in psychiatric practice essentially refer to boundaries. The term "dependent," which is used psychiatrically in many different ways, refers to people who eliminate certain boundaries. If you have two people who are mutually interdependent, both have formed a symbiotic system in which they function as a unit. Consider the case of "compulsive" people who stick to rules and rituals and do things just so. They seem to classify, order and divide, and they see boundaries where others do not see them. Informal people, in contrast, by mutual consent omit formalities and temporarily discard existing boundaries. The typical example is the yearly office party. When psychiatrists use the word "hostile," they mean essentially a penetration of boundaries to which one person does not consent.

There are boundaries in human behavior which are legally defined.

Such are the laws that pertain to property, civil rights and crime. Rules define boundaries of individuals against other individuals and list the sanctions involved in case of violation.

Then there are boundaries defined by tradition. There is no lawful definition of what a mother is supposed to do, but if the mother does not do it then the juvenile court intervenes. She may have violated nothing legally, but the neighbors think she is a bad mother and denounce her.

There is a third type of boundary, which is neither legally nor traditionally defined, but the participants make up the boundaries as they go along. It is something like detecting hidden land mines. One does not know where they are. A pertinent example is that of two lovers who accuse each other of inconsiderate behavior. Of course, this aspect of love-making is not regulated by law, and they cannot fall back upon precedent or tradition. How this boundary is detected depends upon the culture in which it occurs. One of the frequent methods is to push one's boundary until the other person says, "Stop!" And then the other person pushes back, and there will be an area where both agree the boundary should fall. This kind of boundary thus is experientially determined.

In daily life, we constantly cope with boundaries. I might remind you of a few of these instances. Someone says to you, "I took three of your cigarettes. I forgot mine. I suppose you don't mind." He means, "I transgressed a boundary, but I suppose you will permit me to because I am your friend."

Three people are at a bar, and in walks a fourth person known to them. "Won't you join us?" There is an existing imaginary boundary among the three people, and the fourth one stands a little hesitatingly until the invitation is extended. Or someone says, "Give me a ring before you come out," which means, "Warn me before you call. I don't want you to penetrate my boundaries without my knowledge." Or in a meeting someone says, "You never talk. Can't you say something so we know where you stand?" He means, "We don't know where your boundary is, so please define it."

THOMPSON: *If we really believe that through a few words a person can express enough for the boundaries of his point of view to be apparent, we are heading toward tremendous misunderstanding. I have no quarrel with your use of the term in simple situations. But when you deal with complex symbol systems I think we should be careful.*

TOMAN: *In human affairs the important boundaries are not those taken for granted, but are certain crucial areas over which there is conflict. We have litigation and wars over boundaries. Usually it is not the entire boundary of something, but a particular area that lies in doubt.*

GRINKER: *We have a habit of taking the natural significance of a boundary and extending it to infinity. The psychiatrist takes a particular small boundary and generalizes it, which means he extends it. If I know Toman's point of view about a particular situation, I extend that into many other situations. We make a lot of errors that way, of course, but that is our natural tendency.*

DEUTSCH: *To go back to the description of boundaries: If you have told a child it should not play with a certain toy it wants, it will hover just about six inches away from the toy for about one more minute, and sometimes you can actually see in his bodily movements where the boundary is between the toy and himself. You can almost photograph it.*

RUESCH: Perceptual boundaries exist where the stimulation changes. If there is continuous stimulation, there is no boundary. If it stops, or becomes more intensive, or decreases, or changes in nature, there we detect a boundary.

The same notion applies to action. We may do something that we are not aware of, and someone else may perceive it. Whenever action becomes discontinuous, a boundary exists.

The greatest probability of finding boundaries occurs where signals are transformed or recoded. Where light rays are transformed into nervous impulses, or where sound waves are transformed into nerve impulses, the human being tends to place a boundary. Next, boundaries are likely to exist where signals meet barriers: for instance, an insulation for sound, or the insulation of a telephone wire. Wherever a signal cannot spread but has to go along a prearranged channel, where signals join or split, where time relations and quantitative relations change, where the magnitude changes in the amplitude of waves, where the directions change, there we place a boundary. In other words, whenever there is a change or discontinuity, the chances of finding boundaries increase.

I would like to come back to the human being for a moment. Perhaps we have been talking about the interrelationship of the physical and psychological boundary. Distinct physical boundaries exist in the ovum as a boundary; the neonate has a boundary. After birth there still exists interphysical penetration in breast feeding. As the age of the child increases, there is less and less of skin-to-skin touch and physical interpenetration. At birth it needs the physical protection of another person. First the child is breast fed; later it is spoon fed. As the information about things increases, the reliance upon physical help decreases, and there seems to exist an inverse relationship between the two. At maturity, we have lots of information and we put little reliance upon the actual help of others at that moment. But as we get older we again eventually need the physical assistance of others. Maturation consists of acquiring information and giving up reliance upon the physical support of others. If that does not occur, then we deal with arrested development. Such is one aspect of the interrelationship between the psychological and the physical universe.

EMERSON: *Even with food, in a mature civilization we don't go out independently and get our own food. We expect someone else to deliver it to us. In our own civilization we are much more dependent upon other people feeding us than we would be if we were living in a pioneer or primitive civilization. Advancing civilization modifies the pattern of interdependence.*

GRINKER: *The point is that an actual temporary contact like feeding through the orifices develops into communication or contact with words through space. Therefore information must be the thing that the child relies on, whereas in the infantile stages it is actually physical touch. This corresponds with the development of the perceptive systems as well as the capacity of the child to store. The child can store and exist over a period of time without physical contact, and when its distant perceptors are developed it can rely on information.*

PARSONS: *It amounts to the proposition that organization makes possible, and in one sense has the function of making possible, the freeing of certain parts of a system for other functions. People would not be discussing scientific theory if they had to be in the fields planting their crops.*

RAPOPORT: *In a more primitive society I depend for the satisfaction of my needs on certain persons. In an advanced society, I depend for the satisfaction of my needs not on certain persons, but on the existence of certain roles. I do not care who the mailman is—there has to be a mailman. Is there any connection between your progressive scheme of perception and the depersonalization of the dependence relation? There is still a great degree of interdependence—it is not personal, but functional.*

RUESCH: Unless you have information about institutionalized roles, you cannot use them.

When you have an external boundary you necessarily have an internal boundary. Within the organism is located a communication center. There must be a boundary somewhere between the soma and the communication center; otherwise there would be no information about the self. The existence of information presupposes an internal and an external surface, meaning that the center in an organism is set off against its machine, its body, by some sort of boundary. Transactions are carried out along prescribed pathways which are openings in these boundaries. There are officials and unofficial gateways. Spies don't use the official pathways, nor do bootleggers.

I have outlined a number of features which represent an analytical breakdown of structure and function of boundaries. These have been treated from an individual and a social viewpoint. An individual may be treated either as a physical or as a psychological entity.

From a social standpoint, one can treat the boundary problem as related to cultural and social institutions and to communication processes. Thus anatomical and physiological considerations in the individual correspond to cultural and social institutions, and psychological considerations in the individual correspond to communication between two or more people. The rest of the outline seems to be self-explanatory.

TABLE 6

ANALYSIS OF VARIOUS BOUNDARIES

Individual Viewpoint

Analysis of Boundaries	Physiological-Anatomical Universe	Psychological Universe
a) Delineation of boundary.	Membranes delineate organs.	Me and not me—mine or not mine, delineated by feelings and thoughts.
b) External boundaries.	Skin, hair, horn.	Intellect is external facet; acknowledges rules that regulate boundaries.
c) Internal boundaries.	Mucosa, endothelium.	Affect and emotions are internal facet.
d) Structure of boundaries.	Stretchable, flexible tissue, semi-permeable.	Imaginary—only present in terms of feelings and beliefs.
e) Openings in boundaries.	Mouth, anus, urethra, vagina, sense organs, skin pores.	Adaptable person with ability to correct performance; receptivity.
f) Filters and selective exchange.	Sense organs, organs of secretion and excretion.	Repression, maximization, minimization, personal bias.
g) Transactions at places other than openings.	Bleeding.	Corruptible ego; mental reservations.
h) Changes in location of boundaries.	Little, if any.	Image of self may change; ideas of grandeur or depression change psychological boundaries.

TABLE 6 (*continued*)

ANALYSIS OF VARIOUS BOUNDARIES

Individual Viewpoint

Analysis of Boundaries	Physiological-Anatomical Universe	Psychological Universe
i) Interpenetration of boundaries.	Adjoining tissues; vascular supply of organs; carcinoma.	Conflicts between ego and superego or ego and id. Ambivalence.
j) Maintenance of boundary.	Metabolism; regeneration.	Mechanisms of defense.
k) Growth of boundary.	From time of conception until about 6th month; thereafter only proportionate expansion.	Identification and internalization lead to delineation of self.
l) Function of boundary.	To hold organs together; to maintain temperature; to act as dust cover and protective cover.	Maintenance of self-respect.
m) Irreversible change and destruction of the boundary.	Burning or skinning of ⅓ of surface or more leads to death.	Broken self-esteem; psychoses with defect; brain-wash.

Social Viewpoint

Analysis of Boundaries	Social Universe and Cultural Institutions	Communication Universe
a) Delineation of boundary.	Identification of person, family, or organization by role, function and purpose.	The actual communication network.
b) External boundaries.	Duties, responsibilities and spheres of activity.	Functions of reception and transmission.
c) Internal boundaries.	Specialization of functions within an organization.	Function of evaluation.
d) Structure of boundaries.	Demarcations defined by rights, laws and rules.	Fictitious line somewhere in the paths between receiver and transmitter on the one hand and evaluator on the other.
e) Openings in boundaries.	Birth, marriage, death, initiation rights.	Stations where information is put in or put out from receiver, evaluator or transmitter.
f) Filters and selective exchange.	Choice of associations; specialized trade; social discrimination.	Selection of language, topics and channels of communication.

Social Viewpoint

Analysis of Boundaries	Social Universe and Cultural Institutions	Communication Universe
g) Transactions at places other than openings.	Illegal transactions; adultery, corruption.	Non-intentional, often non-verbal communication.
h) Changes in location of boundaries.	Birth, marriage, death, adoption denote the formation of new boundaries.	Changes in the location of perceiver, transmitter and evaluator.
i) Interpenetration of boundaries.	Intercourse — pregnancy. Community property.	Overlapping functions: one person changing from receiver to transmitter or evaluator.
j) Maintenance of boundary.	Public servants; governmental agencies; armed forces.	Metabolic upkeep as well as upkeep through exchange of information.
k) Growth of boundary.	Empire building; sales campaigns.	Increase in network and load.
l) Function of boundary.	To hold together families, groups, and nations; to preserve tradition.	To hold together the overall communication systems as well as the constituent parts.
m) Irreversible change and destruction of the boundary.	War, fire, floods, abandonment, migration.	Voluntary or forced disruption of communication systems through death, war or age.

EMERSON: *Why can't you find structural relations in personality?*

RUESCH: You can psychologically define personality structure and we have ways of inferring what the structure inside a person looks like. But don't forget that it always occurs in an interpersonal context. There must be a human observer who looks at this other person. In order to form an opinion about another person, we have to rely on that individual's expressions in terms of words or gestures or actions. Based upon this behavior, we make a lot of inferences about the internal structure. On occasion, we may learn that a person feels that something is due him; we then can postulate a boundary; but this boundary may be an imaginary one, and others may not agree. So where do we put the psychological boundary? No anatomical or physiological function seems to relate in a one-to-one way to psychological function. This is one of the great obstacles to progress of psychology.

SPIEGEL: *The psychological property is always being created in any particular interpersonal situation, and if there is no interpersonal situation you don't know anything about it at all. But in an interpersonal situation the psychological property is created by the very act of communication. For example, when one person says to another, "You are angry with me," and the second person replies, "No, I'm not; you may think I am, but I'm not," thereby they are defining by their operations where the boundary is—but they have to create it.*

RUESCH: You define what it is and what it is not, but you never define the boundary. That is one of the peculiarities of the psychological boundary. It is a zone. Whether it has any physical counterpart, I don't know.

GRINKER: *We use the concept of structure psychologically in a very vague sense: when we have so many examples of behavior under a variety of circumstances that we can say that this personality will repeatedly do the same thing. Prediction with a high degree of error on numerous repetitive situations can be called the structure.*

RAPOPORT: *Failures to find localized functional areas in the brain were due, in the first place, to the experiments being performed on rats only. Moreover, localization of function depends a great deal on how you define function. What is it you abstract from the human behavior and call, "This is a function"? The trouble with the attempts to localize brain function is in the way we organize the concepts. If, for example, you don't talk about aggressiveness or piousness or ability to speak Greek, but talk about such things as vision or speech, then you have a great deal more success in localization. This raises the question: Where is the boundary between physiological and psychological functions?*

RUESCH: I cannot say where the boundary is or what it is made of. I can only describe its effect. When you say, "This is I, and this is not I," where is the boundary? In the head? If I imagined what such a boundary would look like, it would be a special configuration of nervous impulses that are fired in certain ways which are juxtaposed to others that are fired in other ways. But we have no evidence for that.

SPIEGEL: *Could you define it, though, in terms of information units? When I say, "This is not I," am I not saying that "As far as my information goes, this is nothing that I put inside the boundary?"*

RUESCH: Right you are. The whole advantage of using communication theory is just at this point.

DEUTSCH: *When you say "This is I and this is not I," what you call the "I" in this case is that it is a very rapid and very rich type of feedback that you call "not I." The boundary might be in the rate and the richness of feedback.*

PARSONS: *Putting it a little differently, you have to define the boundary of the self in terms of probabilities of behavior. This is "I" if it is something which as an organized system over time I am likely to do.*

RUESCH: It is a sort of extension of you. One of the most interesting features of people is related to their notion of self. One type of individual will tell you the self stops below the skin. Some believe it stops at the skin. Some include their clothing; some include all their possessions; and some include the possessions of others—some even the lives of others.

PARSONS: *This is a very important point. You can say, "I am an automobile owner," or "I am an automobile driver." The specific automobile may change, and yet there persists this characteristic of the person, that he drives an automobile.*

Coming back to the problem of interpenetration of boundaries, the question arises: Need conflict involve interpenetration? Sometimes it does and sometimes it does not. I make a very careful distinction between conflicts where there is no common segment. Interpenetration means a common segment belonging to both systems. There can be integration without interpenetration in a common segment, and a conflict would be a breakdown or lack of integration.

RUESCH: In the Social Universe, intercourse is a good example of interpenetration. In the Communication Universe, we have the example of interpenetration of such phenomena as two people being married for a long time, one of whom begins a sentence while the other finishes it.

DEUTSCH: *Does marginality come in here? A person who comes from one group and joins another and takes over the second group's attitudes, but keeps some of his own?*

PARSONS: *I think marginality could be defined, in this sense, as a case of interpenetration between imperfectly integrated groups. The fact of playing a role in both is not a source of conflict, but if you have to be both a Jew and an American, to take one of the classic examples, especially a recently emigrated person, since there are elements of the one culture pattern and social organization which do not match very well with the other, then the fact of belonging to both may be a source of conflict.*

THOMPSON: *By "growth," in the next category, do you also mean "extension?"*

RUESCH: Yes, during the life cycle of a phenomenon. Growth always includes also the dissolution of that particular unit. Individuals dissolve, as do value systems.

PARSONS: *Even in the physiological case, I think you must be a little careful about too simple a physical location of the boundary. Food in the stomach is really not a part of the organism; it is only when it has been processed that it becomes part of the organism. It is in the boundary zone, as it were.*

MORRIS: *I think the richness of Ruesch's tabulation is in the details in the rows; but before we get further into that I would like to say something about the problem of relation of the columns in his table. You will remember that Parsons distinguishes the personality system, the social system and the cultural system. The personality system intersects with the social system, and the social system intersects with the biological system. The question is, what makes them all "a" system?*

Now there are certain symbols, which we may call common symbols, which are common features of the cultural system, the personality system and the social system. It seems to me that these symbols which are common to the discriminable subsystems make of them a human action system.

If you hold a theory of signs in which a sign or symbol always involves some change in the organic state of the person for whom something is a sign, then these common symbols would also involve changes in the biological system. Therefore, whether you want to consider the total human action systems formed from just the three subsystems so far mentioned, or whether you also bring in the biological system, is largely a terminological matter. In any case, it is these common symbols that make human action "a" system, and which anchor the human system upon the biological system (Figure 20, below).

I think this position fits in with Parsons' scheme. It is clear that for him a culture system is a shared symbol system. This would be analogous to Ruesch's communication universe.

The social system is a role system in Parsons' analysis, and roles are ultimately symbol-controlled behavior; so this matches the social action universe in Ruesch's scheme. The personality system, as distinct from the biological, involves some sort of self-reference or some sort of "I," and hence symbols. The personality is more than the organism, by virtue of the fact that symbols play a certain key role in the orientation and direction of the biological system.

It seems to me that the psychological, social action and communication systems in Ruesch's chart all involve the operation of symbolic be-

havior, and that they are linked with the physiological universe in his scheme through the fact that these symbols modify the organism and hence its responses.

HENRY: *What would be an example of such a common symbol that unites the three systems?*

MORRIS: *Well, "policeman" is the example we used before. It pertains to all of them. It has a meaning in the communication system, and it has a meaning in the social system in that it defines a role; it also has a*

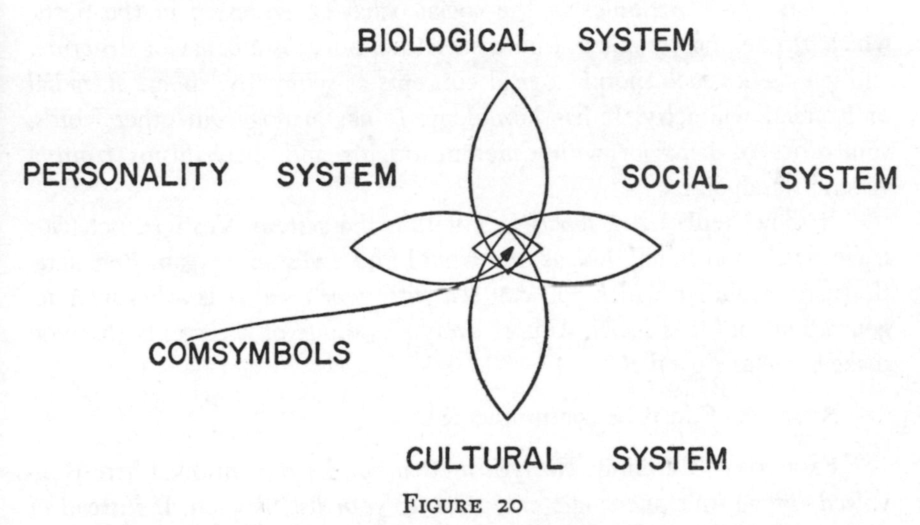

FIGURE 20

RELATIONSHIP OF SYMBOL SYSTEMS

meaning in the personality system in that if a person becomes a policeman and now symbolizes himself as a policeman, he has become a policeman. He is then not merely performing that role in the social system but has become a changed person.

PARSONS: *I like that very much. There is an aspect of the definition of "culture" that eliminates one way of looking at this matter. This gives us a very nice criterion for the interpenetration with the physiological system in that you can say that insofar as physiological process is symbol-controlled (and that surely has very definite meaning), it interpenetrates with the personality and social systems.*

MORRIS: *I think the problem about the psychological is to clear up what we mean by "psychological." The "psychological" might be regarded as the field of sign processes. This is perhaps the "psycho" in "psychosomatic."*

EMERSON: You had some question about the inclusion of your biological system. If you will grant that there is some relationship between behavior of insects and your concept of psychology (and we do not know the subjective aspects for these remote organisms, so I have to leave out of my consideration, at least, the subjective aspect of psychology and concentrate wholly upon its external action for my understanding or awareness of what is going on), I can fit this scheme into the action of the social insects. A parallelism and even very striking structural similarities are to be found in the nest-building behavior of the social insects.

I have such attributes in the social behavior expressed in the nests, which can be photographed. I have structure, but it is a behavior structure, and it matches such morphological concepts as symmetry: spherical, radial or bilateral symmetry. It has homology. It has analogy—in other words, similarities of behavior with different origins and mechanisms from a genetic standpoint.

It shows replication, repetitions within the system. Vestigial behavior is clearly demonstrated, just as one would find a vestigial organ. Regenerations are exhibited, which you can see with your eyes. It is a behavior regeneration, and it is social. Almost every single one of the points that you make here has a parallel.

RUESCH: Can it be communicated?

EMERSON: Certainly. Everything that you have mentioned here is involved. There isn't one single exception to your list, Ruesch. If instead of "psychological" I said "behavior," I would not have a question mark where you put it. It matches completely all the way through.

FRANK: Would we agree that the development of every one of those boundaries has to be seen in the time perspective? There is growth, development, maturation and learning. Boundaries have to grow and develop and change with learning, for example earlier I asked how we are going to conceptualize this process of boundary change. In the physical spheres, if you have an electrical conductor that has certain boundaries, then you put a current through it and you have what is known as hysteresis, and the boundaries change. In the same way the receptivity of the organism and personality will change with learning. So the time dimension in every aspect of boundaries is a way of showing the genesis of the boundaries and their modification.

SPIEGEL: I want to say something about this theory of theories that Ruesch has shown on the diagram. He did not show "system" at the top of his column; instead, he wrote "universe." In other words, he hedged as *to whether those columns would represent organized entities or ways of just looking at one sort of phenomenon. But it is crucial for us to reach some kind of decision, whether we are just talking about ways of talking or whether we are talking about systems that have qualities of system.*

RUESCH: I presented analogies of four different universes because we discussed the physiological, psychological, social action and communication universes. This is not to imply that those are the only possible approaches, but they are the principal universes which we have discussed.

SPIEGEL: *If, then, this is a sufficiently rich way of looking at the boundaries, and if it gives us a sufficient number of methods for getting at them, then we can apply them to the system-finding process, and can avoid the problem that arises in naming all the systems and trying to put them together in advance of any consensus as to what they are.*

SHIMBEL: *An important distinction is to be made between three different concepts we have been using more or less interchangeably. I would choose to call them by three different names. The boundary is a set of rules which tell us how to distinguish two classes. Any other possible set of rules, or the collection of all other possible sets of rules that would give us the same result, I would call the* border *or* margin. *Any agency which tends to maintain this state of affairs I would call the* barrier: *it might, for example, be a wall.*

You would point out that the meninges are a boundary between the soma and the brain, but I would say they are a barrier between the soma and the brain. The boundary is the way in which you describe the brain and the way in which you describe the soma. The border is the space in between. Or, putting it another way, the border is the collection of alternative distinctions, alternative ways of telling the difference.

RUESCH: Whenever you deal with the boundary between the contents of a blood vessel and the surrounding tissue, you deal with the natural boundary called blood vessel wall. The naturally occurring boundary, which has a certain physiological structure, has determined our way of looking at it. But when I talk about the definition of "self," it is more a dialectic problem than a naturally existing problem. The relationship of this problem can be stated as follows: "Statements referring to the observer stand in a complementary relationship to the statements referring to the system. The more we know about the first, the less we know about the second, and vice versa."

RAPOPORT: *I think both concepts, boundary and barrier, could be subsumed under one. When we have a physiological boundary we can* speak of a barrier being a physical boundary. The classification of the brain cells and somatic cells is made easy because we can define the brain cells, which are those on this side; the somatic cells are those which are on that side. Being on this or that side is another way of saying they have certain characteristics.

If we say, for example, that some circles are green and some circles are white, we don't have to speak of any physical boundary; nevertheless, we are defining them as certain characteristics, and therefore they are distinguishable. A physiological boundary is a special case or a more general constant boundary, and I think the word "barrier" is a useful one to apply in this case.

FRANK: We find, however, considerable effort being made to break down these conceptual boundaries and barriers which have served a very useful purpose in the advancement of knowledge, as we know, but which today may operate to impede our efforts to understand organized complexities, such as organisms, and especially the human personality. To develop a field theory, we must apparently give up the concept of specific entities with rigidly defined boundaries, and recognize that we are dealing with a total field in which we can distinguish continually fluctuating components. If I understand correctly, this is what has happened in physics where an earlier conception of an electron as a specific entity has been replaced by the idea of an electron as indicating only a high probability that certain kinds of electrical charges will be present in a given location. Indeed, one gets the impression that the physicist is inclined to designate an electron by the symbol of a crosshatching, with an indication that somewhere within that gird what he calls an electron is probably present.

DEUTSCH: Frank brought up the problem of a field theory in the social sciences, and I should like to tell about four months of work which we have done at Princeton that may have some bearing on this point.

Our problem was to find out whether, and to what extent, a nonarbitrary boundary between political systems exists. We began with the assumption that you cannot take for granted the politically established boundaries of the day because they are exactly the ones that often are called into question, and you cannot take for granted even boundaries established by plebiscite, merely because the participants say so, or said so at some date in the past.

Rather, we tried this: Take a large number of human beings on a map. Try to find out as far as possible, empirically, what their field relations are, and see whether we get the boundaries from the differential flow of transactions between them. To determine the boundaries in the direction flow, we made a tentative list of twelve dimensions. The first five dimensions all *deal with a single range of interaction. This may be, for instance, market fluctuations in economic life, or it might be cultural diffusion, or some kind of political behavior, or it might be communication.*

First, the frequency of transaction is measured by counting. If I want to know whether Montreal and New York are in one system or not, one of the things to count would be the frequency between them of the kind of transactions chosen for our study. The second would be their speed. The third would be their fidelity. If an event happens in New York which has a certain pattern, how much of that pattern reappears in Montreal? The economists do this for fluctuations, for example; or, vice versa, if I want to reproduce a given Montreal pattern in New York, how far can I go in the economy of coding?

The fourth is effectiveness: A change in the coffee price at New York could affect the coffee price somewhere else.

Finally, what is their temporal stability or probability, and what is the relation over time? Does the boundary or the sharp step in the distribution stay stable over 50 or 100 years?

One point we ran into immediately was that we should not count frequencies, but critical frequencies. The crude opportunities for this, it was argued by Steward and others, are measured by the population potential, $\frac{P}{D}$*, that is, by the product of the two populations divided by their distance. I wonder whether there are biological parallels to this—that is, if a lot of units are reasonably close together, the development of transactions might go up because there are more of them and they are nearer. You could count their frequency, not the crude frequency but the differential, between the crude frequency indicated by* $\frac{PQ}{D}$ *and the actual frequency found.*

Similarly, we should not count speed, but critical speed—speed above the average with which an impulse of transaction goes on. We thus tried to find and use the differentials rather than the crude dimensions in all these five dimensions.

The second thing to be put on the map would be the distribution of different interaction ranges above some threshold of significance. Draw a line around all those points between which you thus find at least five ranges of transactions. Draw a heavier line around all those points with at least ten such ranges in common, and those with fifteen or twenty. Related to this multiplicity of ranges would be the seventh dimension, the mutual reenforcement of interactional transaction processes. This is the coincidence of critical ranges.

The outstanding notion we had was that if you have a high level of interdependence with a low level of communication, you are apt to get conflict. It is the story of two persons chained together. A map of the population potential of Europe shows the biggest peak in the Low Countries, which have been the theater of most of the wars in the last 300 years.

RAPOPORT: *Which variable shows the greatest peak?*

DEUTSCH: *Population potential! The critical point is, do the ranges reenforce each other? In other words, you could argue that it is not lack of integration that makes conflicts, but it is the presence of interdependence with lack of communication that causes them.*

The eighth point is the balance of flows of assets or benefits. That is, large transaction flows are likely to remain stable over time only if there is no destructive net transfer from one transaction system to the other. This is a problem of the drain of wealth from one region to the other, such as may occur sometimes through free trade, or destructive taxation, or even conditions conducive to soil erosion. There must be either compensation or interchange of roles, but in any case there must be some balance of the flow so that there is no destructive outflow, if the flow pattern is to be expected to continue for a longer time.

The last four dimensions deal with the point that we were not dealing with cells but rather with highly autonomous subassemblies, human beings in social groups. We thought of four characteristics for the behavior of autonomous groups which we might use for finding boundaries between larger political communities in which some but not all of these smaller autonomous groups might be united.

The ninth dimension is compatibility. It is found in autonomous systems which have no very sharp limit sanctions against each other, which are not incompatible in their behavior, which do not destroy each other, or inhibit each other in a destructive way. (You can be inhibited by your neighbor, but if the inhibition is within your own capacity for adjustment, the inhibition can be borne.) You draw a line again on a field map around all these points which are not mutually incompatible in this sense.

The tenth dimension is interchange of group roles. How often and in what respects is it apt to occur between two groups, and what are its effects on the probability of mutual understanding and mutual predictability of behavior between them? Our map would include all groups between whom such role change and/or mutual predictability of behavior was found to a more than average extent.

Joint rewards is dimension eleven. An autonomous organization is steered to some extent by rewards of some sort. We make a line around all those points where a reward for A is accompanied by or associated with a reward for B, or a reward for A is contingent upon a reward for B. These are joint payoffs.

Dimension twelve is responsiveness. If group A sends limit signals to B, does B receive the limit signals quickly and respond to them efficiently? Or if A sends need signals to B, is B able to respond quickly? Therefore, you draw lines around all the points connected by efficient mechanisms for the reception and response to limit signals or need signals.

Within the British economic system, Ireland experienced a devastating potato famine in the 1840s. The British economy and policy proved to be incapable of producing quick and substantial aid, and the experience had a shattering effect on the Irish attitude toward staying in the British Empire. It seems that these memories were more decisive and vital than their earlier memories of Cromwell and of religious conflicts.

Responsiveness means the ability to help, to move in and take over; it implies material and intellectual resourcefulness as well as ability to make an emotional response.

The point in this scheme of analysis is that every one of these dimensions is entirely empirical. It could be mapped on a field map and could then be correlated with the morphological criteria, memories, boundaries, gaps and the like.

FRANK: In the field theory, as I understand it, we are attempting to get away from fixed boundaries since they create a difficult problem of how to get across those boundaries. Thus, if we are faced by boundaries which are created by our own conceptual formulations, we then have to create another set of entities or processes to transcend the boundaries which we have imposed on the situation. If, however, we are faced with boundaries, barriers, borders, whatever we may call them, which are self-maintaining in the sense that they arise from the very processes we are studying, then we must try to develop a conceptual apparatus that will enable us to deal with such situations. For example, Pauling's conception of resonance suggests that instead of the idea of specific bonds or valence holding together two separately bounded atoms, we may think of those two atoms as sharing electrons which, so to speak, do not know whether they belong to one atom or the other.[1] In a similar way we may say that our effort to develop a unified theory meets with difficulty because we are confronted with so many separately bounded parts, entities and functions, as assumed by the different disciplines studying the organism-personality in its varied activities and relations. If we can develop some kind of a field theory in terms

[1] Linus C. Pauling, The Nature of the Chemical Bond and the Structure of Molecules and Crystals: An Introduction to Modern Structural Chemistry (Ithaca: Cornell University Press, 1940).

of on-going processes which may be located and identified in terms of different organ systems and cultural, social systems, if we wish, we may be able to unify these various processes which have always been related in and through the individual except as we have insisted upon treating them conceptually as distinct and separate.

THOMPSON: *I think the use of the term "transaction," as Dewey and Bentley use it, is an attempt to help us over this transition period when boundaries are changing. The word "interaction" introduces the notion of relationships between systems that are bounded in a traditional way. But if we use the word "transaction" we do not have to define the boundaries, but can suspend judgment until we have arrived at our new boundaries.*

MORRIS: *The point is that we still do not expect to reach the state where we have no boundaries. As you say, we are trying to find out the new boundaries, and they would be statistical (Deutsch states them as certain types of relatedness, and greater and less, and so on), and thus obtained operationally.*

FRANK: *Now we come back to the point raised earlier. If we are faced with boundaries, barriers, borders, whatever you call them, which are self-maintaining by the very processes we study, that is one thing. If we are faced by boundaries which we have put into the system by our mode of formulation, that is another thing. In the first case we are challenging the validity of many of the traditional conceptual boundaries, in order to recognize the self-maintaining boundaries.*

THOMPSON: *Then the danger is that we will draw around our systems black lines standing for boundaries before we really have made the transition to functional systems.*

SPIEGEL: *That is exactly the danger in prematurely closing up a series of systems together. I do not believe the decision we can arrive at about boundaries is putting the cart before the horse, as Thompson said. It is a method, and we can determine upon our method for finding the distinctions of existence.*

MORRIS: *It seems to me it is rather important, too, to make clear what we mean by "theory." This is a term that is the source of much ambiguity. Some people think that a diagram on the board is a theory, but that is not so. The Newtonian terms in their interrelation do not constitute a physical theory. You have to add something like Newton's laws in addition, and that I did not do.*

RUESCH: I think there are two things which perhaps Morris could speak about. One would be a theory of theories that encompasses all the universes represented in this group. I think, however, that this is out of the question at the present stage. Instead, we need a first approximation; for example, let us consider all the existing scientific systems represented around this table, and try to identify the operations they have in common. Next, let us search for bridges or transformation hypotheses which translate language A into language B. Freud attempted to bridge the gap between the psychological and the physical universes by means of his conversion theory. That is possible when the operations are similar. We cannot translate it when the operations are dissimilar.

MORRIS: *In this first stage we are engaged, in a certain sense, in the theory of theories; that is, we are taking the different theories and are asking for translation and the operations by which we can do it. That is a necessary part of the job.*

But the name of our group shows that we are concerned in principle with the possibility of a further stage, in which we are attempting to get a theory. In that case we are attempting to get laws that will connect these various variables in the various systems in which, rather piecemeal, we have studied them. We want to do that in a great variety and number of ways.

THOMPSON: *There are two different types of approach—the approach outlined by Ruesch, whereby you start with the existing disciplines, and that of interdisciplinary research where you start with a problem. In the latter type of approach it depends on the unit of research—it might be a single individual, or a natural ecological-cultural community—whichever you consider significant in solving your problem.*

Then you bring in the individuals, regardless of what discipline they belong to, who control the methods and operations you have found necessary to solve the problem. Then you continue working on the problem, and perhaps you have to reformulate it as your knowledge of it grows through this interdisciplinary research; and perhaps you have to bring in more individuals who have other skills not represented in the group, until finally, by this method, it is theoretically possible to solve the problem.

GRINKER: *But when you set up your multidisciplinary research—for example, when you take an individual in whom you want to study anxiety —in your design you immediately get a daisy, a series of joined circles, like that which Morris demonstrated. It is inevitable that the "daisy" of cycles, which have a central point and "petals," represent systems or disciplines,* either one or the other. You can choose a system or you can choose a discipline, but you end with a daisy, no matter which way you start.

THOMPSON: But if you use the interdisciplinary method, you do not talk on a high level of abstraction; you talk about the individual you are studying.

GRINKER: You cannot talk about "him" unless you have the abstraction possible to indicate the cyclic processes that you are using to determine the central point of confluence. That is your design before you begin.

TOMAN: We have accepted the idea of continuity of everything in the universe. It is impossible to separate the idea of a mass from its gravitational field. You can't say where one ends and the other begins. Furthermore, the mass can disappear and can be replaced by an equivalent amount of energy. We can understand mass only in relation to another mass. The boundaries here are obviously interactions of some kind. As far as I am concerned, in one way or another all of these boundaries—whether we are dealing with symbolic rules or with actual physical operations—are still problems in energy transformation or energy transduction or the possession of energy.

The problem of communications is not an energyless problem. There is still the necessity of energy exchange, but the emphasis is on the pattern and not on the intensity or the quantity. The communication is between systems that have energy relationships within themselves, and the pattern corresponds or can induce some kind of patterning between the two interacting bodies or systems.

It seems to be implied in some discussion today that in human interrelationships the main and possibly the only type of interaction is an energyless communication. But communication is not necessarily the only type of interaction. A large part of human interrelations involve energy transfer in a very real sense—in economic relations, for example, or in physical contacts.

On the question of the reality versus the symbol, at one time we seem to be talking about rules of operation with symbols, and at other times the actual rules of operation of the universe external to symbols. As far as I can see, the symbols themselves have as much a real physical meaning as anything going on outside of them, and they make sense only insofar as they refer to things going on externally. They are representative, not identical with things going on elsewhere, nor are they usually complete. Furthermore, they do have a time element which enters constantly into our thinking. Our symbols always lag behind what is actually going on. The universe is always changing. Our symbols take time to catch up. On the other hand, they have the persistent quality that they outlast a particular event, and their utility is that they are relevant to something which might happen again.

Our problem, as I see it, is limitless if we do not settle down to a theory for something. Our working with symbols and our attempt to work with some systems rather than others seems to be determined in part by what it is convenient to work with. It seems to me that in the course of this conference we have never really asked ourselves what the use of the unified theory will be.

To the extent that we select enough kinds of interaction, enough components for study, following our best hunches as to their crucial character, to that extent our operations will not simply be rhetorical or linguistic, but will have some actual relevance and some predictive value.

Editor: Ruesch discussed physical, system, biochemical and psychological boundaries. He pointed out that even so-called natural boundaries are modified by the observer's perceptive and evaluative systems. Empirical relational boundaries may be affective, legal, traditional or made up as one goes along. Such boundaries usually exist where change or discontinuity of action or perception occur. The child's boundaries change in maturation from that of physical contact to information through space. Its knowledge about self occurs when an internal boundary develops between the soma and a communication center (the development of a self-reflective consciousness). Ruesch then presented a table comparing various boundaries of universes (not systems) from the individual and social viewpoints.

In the discussion the difficulty of attributing boundaries to the psychological universe was emphasized since it has no anatomical or physiological functional correlation or localization. It is always an interpersonal process for which communication is necessary. However, there are symbols common to cultural, social, personality and somatic systems. Boundaries change with time in growth, maturation and learning.

SUMMARY

CHAPTER TWENTY-FIVE

SUMMARY

By Roy R. Grinker

ALTHOUGH a brief summarizing statement has been added to each chapter, the reader's fare nevertheless has been extremely rich and probably difficult to digest. It, therefore, seems advisable to attempt making a generalized statement of what has been accomplished, indicating some of the difficulties that we encountered and how the future looks to us after our first preparations toward formulating a unified theory.

It should be re-emphasized that the transcriptions of our conferences have been greatly condensed. Some discussions and questions that also add to the substance of the proceedings were included to give a taste of the spontaneous excitement and flow of ideas between participants. Although we do not stress the role of communication processes within our conferences and no trained person familiar with group dynamics was present, there has been much to learn about these subjects from our discussions.

In my introduction to the second conference in Chapter Ten, I remarked that individuals emphasized different aspects of the material under discussion. Some were more interested in the location of the identified human observer, others with the precise definition and description of the various organized systems or levels. Still others were more concerned with establishing a conceptual model and finally, there was considerable attention paid by some to the formulation of hypotheses which could serve as bridges from one system to another.

The position of each individual member of the conferences within these categories was not stable, but varied from time to time under different circumstances. Variability of individuals could be noted in change from emphasis on theory or hypotheses to an interest in a detailed discussion of empirical data, particularly in those fields with which the person had least experience. Theoretical considerations were frequently interrupted, by some fatigued member of the conference by more trivial practical discussion. Finally, in later loosely structured conferences we could observe that individuals grouped themselves less according to emphasis on particular aspects of observation, or on theory versus empiricism, but more in terms of their personal, habitual ways of viewing the world. Break-throughs sometimes occurred indicating that anxiety changed a discussant's frame of reference and his usual mode of dealing with the subject matter.

The members of the conference were committed with great zeal and seriousness of purpose toward a program of developing a unified theory of human behavior. Yet all of us implicitly knew that this could in reality not be attained by us in our time and that we would be satisfied with a little progress toward the ultimate goal. It was amazing that through the years the group continued to be overtly optimistic, each member continually striving to understand various aspects of human behavior discussed by the others.

We were sensitized from the beginning to define our positions in viewing any system or system relationships. It seems, therefore, appropriate to make explicit my position as the summarizer. I stand in the present, attempting to put the enormous details of several years' work into a few general principles. Yet at the same time as the summarizer, I have participated in the five subsequent conferences that are not included in this book, thereby knowing both the past (the first four conferences) and the future (second five conferences). It is not likely that succeeding conferences will be abstracted and published together in book form. It is more probable that the subsequent conference discussions will be fractionated according to topics and each published in monograph form. Therefore, in this summarization some of the material that was presented at the last four conferences will be mentioned briefly.

The first conference was opened by a presentation of the basic concepts of the interpersonal or intraorganismic organization which could be called the biological universe. There was an attempt to show that many of the laws of its structures and functions could be applied to the psychological system without reference to any specific organic substrate. The relationship among parts to the whole and the involvement of each part under stress within a total field were considered. Many topics, later discussed in detail during the work of an entire meeting, were introduced in brief form.

In retrospect such an introduction had value because it defined certain basic principles which have long been recognized as characteristic of biological activity including that of the human organism. It was indicated clearly that many homologies and analogies could be made between biological systems and those that we call psychological and social. It was not explicitly stated at that time, but later made quite clear, that these principles were applicable to the participation of somatic processes in psychological and social behavior. It was explicitly stated, however, that these biological structure-functions were not limiting factors, since the evolution and ontogenesis of psychological and social systems add new processes which must be considered in their own right and dealt with as if they had their own laws and regulations. We had no intention of reducing all of human behavior to the biological level.

Following this Spiegel made a huge jump into consideration of an extended field, including all of nature, in which each system comprises a focus without concern with hierarchies, levels and derivations. Each focus in some manner is in transactional relationship with each other and any disturbance of one of necessity affects all. An attempt was made to consider certain functional components of each focus. These include the constitutional, that is the specific inherent function of a particular system; the integrative, which maintains the pattern of organization; and finally, the system determinants which include the functions of the system in relation to others.

At this point the conference considered a theme that was repeated over and over again for it was often forgotten: The fact that observations in all sciences are made by an individual who has a position relative to his object. He can only have one frame of reference at a time, although several may be put together through a mental operation. Natural events are viewed not in terms of the reality of the matter but through the eyes of an observer who is part of a specific communication system. Much was said about communication processes and how they differ with the type of system under observation.

The social system was viewed from an action frame of reference and four specific laws were derived theoretically by Parsons from several dimensions which he explicitly defines and summarizes in Chapter Five. In social interaction are embedded symbol meaning systems which may be transmitted between various systems of action. It was interesting that Parson's theoretical concepts of social structure drew a discussion from the biological point of view to the effect that whatever new entities that we could postulate should be considered in terms of their relationships and not necessarily as some irreducible quantities. Furthermore, any theory should contain implications for its own refutation.

The concept of core values was introduced by Thompson who developed seven minimal conditions to be met by an adequate theory of the formal and informal aspects of intrapersonal relations. She contended that societal systems must be viewed as a multi-dimensional pattern in the space-time of which it is a part. Kluckhohn's value orientations were then presented and are related to five common human problems of key importance. These included the innate predispositions of man, the relation of man to nature, the significance of the time dimension, the modality of activity most valued and the dominant modality of man's relations to other men. Kluckhohn showed how she used these five orientations as a means of categorizing various societies.

Jules Henry returned to the relationship of individual to society by suggesting certain invariant equations applicable to intrapsychic as well as to social systems. His paired socio-psychological factors were presumed to exist in dialectical relationship to each other. The behavior of the individual is not understandable if detached from the culture of which he is a part and culture cannot be understood without considering the individuals in it.

Having dealt with statements regarding the basic concepts applicable to the disciplines operating within the somatic, psychological and social and cultural systems, we compared systems with special references to differences between them and the utilizability of concepts from discipline to discipline. Here for the first time the notions of analogy and homology were fully developed. It was stated that derived systems characterized by expanding organization and more complicated methods of integration may function quite differently than their antecedent systems. Differences may include those of quantity, type of organization, kind of communication, and degree of integration. It was stressed that similar functions expressed through different forms of communication may give rise to dissimilar effects.

We next entered into a discussion of homeostasis with regard to its manifestations in different systems and as a unifying principle. It was conceived by Emerson as being more than just a concept of stability of the internal milieu of the living organism, but as a principle encompassing growth, evolution, social organization, increasing complexity of organization, increased range of control, etc. It seemed that value judgments were attached to it and, in the minds of some, it was considered as an irreducible principle applicable to all systems and forms of life.

A comparison was made between the individual as a personality and as a member of the group. Role behavior of the personality within the group could be contrasted with personality as an individually developed somato-psychological structure-function. In comparing the psychological and the social systems the conference encountered its first difficulties with multiple terminology. There was considerable controversy as to whether the psychologists and the sociologists were referring to the same processes in their use of similar terms. Further discussion of the relationship of personality and social systems revealed how the individual's adjustments within large groups of diverse kinds were affected by various types of socialization in the family setting. The reader is referred to a very complete summary account of social systems and culture in Chapter Fifteen by Lawrence Frank.

The third conference returned to the subject of homeostasis. It was reconsidered from a mathematical point of view, exemplified by the analysis of random nets. Further details of the physiology involved were presented with reference to the most primitive systems of chemical memory. Homeostasis was then discussed in the life situation of mother and neonate in a lying-in hospital, bringing forth as a by-product evaluative affective terms such as happiness, progress and improvement.

Up to this point we had discussed internal structures of systems and dealt with the problems of organization, differentiations, specialization, etc. We had also discussed boundaries of systems and the maintenance of the bounded system including upkeep in the metabolic sense, maintenance in terms of reversible changes, homeostasis, etc. We had also discussed in some detail the relationship of one system to another. In all of this we were very careful to deal with the position of the observer, sharply differentiating things attributable to the system and things attributable to the observer. It became clear to Ruesch that we could best proceed in the future on the basis of an outline which he prepared for the group and which is attached to Chapter Twenty.

Correspondingly the fourth conference was devoted to a detailed discussion of boundaries. We went into considerable discussion of statistical boundaries, especially their filtering properties. Boundaries between the behavior system and personality evoked the question of what is transmitted in interpersonal communications. Boundaries may be said to exist between differentiated social systems in a society and between social systems and personality systems. In Chapter Twenty-three an analysis of various boundaries was outlined by Ruesch. In system processes, viewed from the frame of reference of communication theory, boundaries are in a constant state of flux and new forms of boundaries are constantly created.

The reader may be somewhat bewildered by the use of the term "system" applicable to the biological, psychological, cultural or social aspects of life-in-process. A "system" is considered to be some whole form in structure or operation, concepts or functions, composed of united and integrated parts. As such, it has an extent in time and space, and boundaries. A system has a past which is partly represented by its parts, for it develops or assembles from something preceding. It has a present, which is its existence as a relatively stable or what might be called its resting form, and it has a future, that is, its functional potentialities. In space form, structure and dimensions constitute a framework, which is relatively stable and timeless, yet only relatively so, for its constituents change during time but considerably slower than the novel or more active functions of the system. To view the change of these functions through time, the frame or background may be artificially considered as stable.

Although its parts are in continued activity in relation to each other and the whole, the function of a system in relation to other systems involves mostly its surface or boundaries and their openings. In other words, the function of parts of a system are projected to the whole surface. We questioned whether systems are defined and demarcated by the focus of the observer, which he may shift as he pleases, and, therefore, may use any number and sizes of systems. In other words, are systems real, something outside of us in nature, which do not depend upon the process of observation? According to Ashby, "The observer defines his system by selecting a definite number of variables. The experimenter can control any variable he pleases. He can make any variable take an arbitrary value at any arbitrary time. The state of a system in any given instance is the set of numerical values which its variables have at that instant, in the line of behavior specified by a succession of states and the intervals of time between them." [1]

The common-sense view, however, of a system, would include those aspects of behavior in which the variables have some naturalness of association. Experiments are possible to ascertain whether empirical data or naturalness of past experience can be verified by manipulating certain variables and determining whether changes in them have any effect on the system. If they have an effect, then they may be considered significant to certain degrees. If they do not have an effect, they may be neglected.

The dividing line between organism and environment becomes partly

[1] W. R. Ashby, *Design for a Brain* (New York: John Wiley, 1952).

conceptual and to that extent arbitrary. That is true of a blood vessel in living tissue as well as the relationship between people, their physical, social and cultural environment. Although anatomically and physically there may be some distinction between two parts of a system, if we view the system functionally we may ignore the purely anatomical parts as irrelevant and the division into organism and environment becomes vague. Thus, a system is the whole complex of the organism and environment. Environment is composed of those variables whose changes affect the organism and which are changed by the organism's behavior. Thus, both the organism and environment are two parts of one system. By adding an environmental parameter to the variables that are significant for a system, then the system always has an extended environment. Reversing this, passing to within the boundaries of a system, what are known as system functions become environment, and the parts of the system become in themselves focal systems under observation.

However, sociologists have a tendency to deal with current processes in time and to consider developmental transactions as less important, dealing, therefore, with non-hierarchical, non-gradient, current action. Parsons stated that there is a distinction between a frame of reference and a class of systems. Action is not concerned with the internal structure of processes of the organism, but is concerned with the organism as a unit in a set of relationships and the other terms of that relationship, which he calls situation. From this point of view the system is a system of relationship in action, it is neither a physical organism nor an object of physical perception. On the other hand, some of us consider that the foci or systems which are identified in a living field must be considered as being derived through evolution, differentiation and growth from earlier and simpler forms and functions and that within these systems there are capacities for specializations and gradients. Sets of relationships among dimensions constitute a high level of generalization that can be more easily understood if the physical properties of its component parts and their origins and ontogenic properties are known.

In general summary, we started out rather naively and decided to make all sorts of comparisons and contrasts among the various systems in which we were interested. We viewed them from outside and inside and at their boundaries. Sometimes we viewed them from a distant level of abstraction without knowing exactly where we were. However, I think as a result of these many observations of multiple systems, we extended our view of the total field of action in which the many systems seem to operate.

Sometimes overtly and explicitly we accepted the following general principles that could be dignified by the concept, "unified." There were only three in number:

Firstly, we recognized that within all systems and in all fields there is a principle of stability which we have considered under the term *homeostasis*. For some people this includes change, growth and evolution. For others it seems that the homeostatic principle applied only to stability and that additional theory is required to include change and growth. Whether or not this is necessary, such stability or homeostasis or trend toward stability, as the background of change or novelty, is best understood as being accomplished through transactional processes within ever extending fields. The limits to the fields are based on our positions and our powers of observation and also our theoretical point of view.

One can consider then the second principle as being *transactional*. We use the term transactional as meaning a reciprocal relationship among all parts of the field and not simply an interaction which is an effect of one system or focus on another. It is a philosophical or theoretical attitude and yet also a system of analysis. If one makes observations on multiple systems as nearly simultaneously as possible, one can see a sequence of change among several systems which involve adjustive processes across boundaries. There is not simply a response to a stimulus, but a process occurring in all parts within the whole field. Any transactional study, of course, can be broken down into the interactional if observations are focused on two systems in order to see the isolated effect of one on the other. For the purpose of developing a unified theory we have talked about transactional processes consistently considering that the types of relationships among systems could be left unspecified.

The third principle which we have discussed in many ways and at many levels is the process of *communication of information*, which varied from signals characteristic of biological systems to symbols characteristic of social systems.

Ruesch at a later conference indicated that it was possible that one could formulate an over-all theory that covers *several* universes and orders of complexity. Communication theory and homeostasis for example, might be such theories. However, these are not directly applicable to *all* concrete operations. There seems to be necessary, in addition, special theories applicable to particular fields and subject matters. It might be possible to formulate intersystem theories that cover at least two universes or orders of complexity but little headway has been made between them, as for example connecting the psychological and the physiological in the so-called psychosomatic approach. I might point out that an attempt is being made to create a bridge between personality and social systems by means of role theory. For an intersystem theory it would be necessary to observe both systems from the same relative position of the observer and at the same time. Since these criteria are not always possible, it is often necessary to develop new units of measurement and to observe intervening variables.

At the eighth conference Marion Levy [2] attempted to define the specific goals of construction of theory, applicable to our group. He stated that good concepts are precise, have empirical reference and are useful for the formulation of theories related to the problem under consideration. Good theories are precise, have empirical reference and are fruitful for the development of still further theories and are more nearly tenable or relatively well confirmed. If they are tenable, this would mean a breakthrough followed rapidly by other theories as elaborations at lower levels of generalization. If they are untenable, they close off blind alleys for future investigations, so that it is fruitful to determine whether a theory is tenable or untenable.

Levy further brought out the fact that a system of analysis may be defined as a generalized description of the class of phenomena concerned —a description that states the component parts or aspects of the phenomena and some of the interrelationships among those parts that would be considered relevant for the treatment to be attempted. A system of analysis defined in this way is equivalent to what is called a model in scientific circles. Systems of analysis are not concepts nor theories although they involve both.

There can be no theories without conceptual schemes, however, rudimentary or implicit the latter may be. Fruitfulness of theories cannot be obtained in the absence of what may be called good concepts. A system of analysis is made up of concepts and involves theories. The greatest difference between systems of analysis and systems of theories is that the primary interest in the system of analysis lies in its use as a tool for developing theories or systems of theories.

For systems of analysis the question of tenability is not germane for one throws out elements in a system of analysis when they are not fruitful for the development of theories regardless of whether they seem tenable or not at the moment. The concern over the tenability of systems of analysis rather than their fruitfulness can be a source of much delay and even misdirection of effort in the sciences. In essence, if one refuses to proceed with the system of analysis until he is sure of its tenability, one is refusing to set up tools for a task until the task itself is already accomplished.

Levy furthermore discussed the problem of approaching a unified

[2] Marion Levy joined the conference group at its fifth meeting. Dr. Levy is Professor of Economics and Social Institutions at Princeton University.

theory of human behavior. He stated that if great progress is ever made in this field we may some day be in possession of some kind of over-all generalization as put forward in physics by such men as Newton and Einstein. For the present at least we shall have to progress in somewhat more pedestrian fashion. In the absence of these geniuses, we shall undoubtedly have to proceed toward this goal by breaking up the problem into different stages.

These stages should be selected in terms of differences in levels of generalization about an empirical phenomenon rather than on any alternative, substantive basis of selection. Our most general level must deal with propositions that apply to any empirical phenomenon. Our less general levels must deal with propositions that refer to some specific portion of those empirical phenomena. For example, in a very crude fashion we could break our problem into four levels. One, any empirical phenomenon; two, any living empirical phenomena; three, any living empirical phenomena that are social and four, any social living phenomena that involve members of the species homo sapiens. In a rough sort of way these levels conform respectively to the level of operation of the fields of physics, biology, general social analysis and human social analysis.

In our conferences, as Levy stated, even the most fascinating materials have usually been presented without any initial or subsequent attempt to indicate their relevance for the general problem. As far as our general interests are concerned, virtually every special topic taken up has been left at the descriptive level. This has served a useful function in obtaining a broader knowledge of what is going on in the world of science. But if we are to make substantial progress, we have two alternatives. The first is to work on the most general level, the second is to take a much smaller specific problem and examine it in terms of different disciplines and tenets represented in the group and seek the implications of such examination for our general problem.

The first alternative is rather easily disposed of, for substantial progress toward our goal with such a method would involve performances of comparable magnitude to those of Newton and a few similar persons. This is usually the product of individual work rather than groups. It predicates a major breakthrough at highly generalized levels.

More specific problems as a practical alternative face us with less great odds. We may not progress toward our goal by any important steps but we could tell where we have been, what it showed for our goal and what we had learned from one another. This is obviously the subject matter of group work which we are embarking on for our ninth conference. The attempt to pick out a specific problem for attack by the various members of the group in common might be valuable in illuminating our obstacles. This sort of approach, even if our results are negative, might hold out hope for some progress on a given problem, considerable clarification of what is not known that needs to be known for these purposes, and the discovery of what can be brought into focus from different disciplines and techniques.